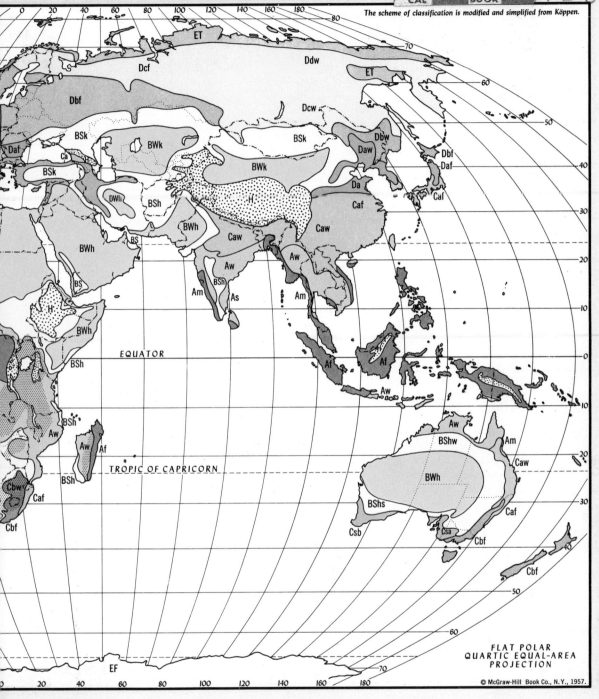

The scheme of classification is modified and simplified from Köppen.

FLAT POLAR
QUARTIC EQUAL-AREA
PROJECTION

© McGraw-Hill Book Co., N.Y., 1957.

Fundamentals
of physical
geography

Name *Sue McMills*
228-7317

McGRAW-HILL SERIES IN GEOGRAPHY

JOHN C. WEAVER, *Consulting Editor*

BENNETT *Soil Conservation*

CRESSY *Asia's Lands and Peoples*

CRESSY *Land of the 500 Million: A Geography of China*

FINCH, TREWARTHA, ROBINSON, AND HAMMOND *Elements of Geography: Physical and Cultural*

FINCH, TREWARTHA, ROBINSON, AND HAMMOND *Physical Elements of Geography* (a republication of Part I of the above)

POUNDS *Europe and the Mediterranean*

RAISZ *General Cartography*

TREWARTHA *An Introduction to Climate*

TREWARTHA, ROBINSON, AND HAMMOND *Fundamentals of Physical Geography*

WHITBECK AND FINCH *Economic Geography*

VERNOR C. FINCH *was Consulting Editor of this series from its inception in 1934 to 1951.*

GLENN T. TREWARTHA
Professor of Geography, University of Wisconsin

ARTHUR H. ROBINSON
Professor of Geography, University of Wisconsin

EDWIN H. HAMMOND
Associate Professor of Geography, University of Wisconsin

NEW YORK   TORONTO   LONDON

Fundamentals

of physical

geography

McGRAW-HILL BOOK COMPANY, INC.   1961

Introduction

The surface of the earth is a complicated combination of a great many things. Some of these are the natural features, such as the land, air, vegetation, soil, and water. Man lives within this complex natural environment, and, according to his interests and his knowledge, he takes it into account in planning and carrying out his activities.

If a person travels over the earth, he will observe that the various physical features change from place to place: it is warmer here; it rains more often there; the land surface is relatively smooth in one place, mountainous in another; and so on. To appreciate and understand the character of the differences and similarities of the earth's surface from place to place, he must turn to the study of physical geography, the body of knowledge that deals with the description and interpretation of the physical features of the surface zone of the earth.

In general, the description and interpretation of the myriad interrelationships among the physical elements of the earth is properly called earth science. Earth science includes many fields of systematic investigation. Physical geography is the segment which studies the elements that man finds significant in his use of the earth; in this respect, physical geography is the study of man's natural environment. In particular it concentrates upon the manner in which the environment differs from place to place and upon the reasons for the differences.

Man studying the earth has been likened to a curious ant upon a patterned rug. Because of the ant's diminutive size and limited range of vision it cannot easily comprehend the broad arrangements of the different colors. To develop a clear description and interpretation of the general pattern, the ant would need to employ several scientific techniques, such as careful observation, data reduction, the development of systematic classifications, and mapping. The physical earth is like a patterned rug, albeit a relatively large and complex one. But rather than being simply a uniform surface on which the only thing that changes from place to place is the color of the fibers, the earth's surface zone is made up of many different elements, ranging from air temperatures to the flatness of the land, each with its own more or less complex pattern.

Through the scientific study of physical geography the student will become aware that there are both striking similarities and fundamental differences in the physical environment from place to place. He will learn of the great and important variations in the surface forms of the land, from the broad patterns of the continents to the smaller irregularities that complicate the local scene. He will come to appreciate the general character and movements of the great mass of water that not only floods the great depressions of the earth but also exists on and beneath the surface of the land. He will become acquainted with the nature and behavior of the atmospheric film which envelops the earth and acts as a transporting and distributing agent for life-giving energy and water. He will find also that the materials and forms of the earth's solid crust and the behavior of the gaseous envelope are all interrelated, and that they, together with organic life, combine to produce yet other patterns such as those of soils and natural vegetation. In fact he will find that the pat-

terns of the several physical elements are all interrelated and that their spatial relationships are at once simple and complex.

To study scientifically the elements of the physical environment, one must consider the physical processes involved in their interaction in place; this is necessary background for an understanding of the place to place variation of each physical element. One of the purposes of this book is, however, to focus attention, as much as is possible in a survey treatment, on the areal distributions and functional interrelationships of the physical elements over the earth's surface. In this it strives to emphasize the basic locational aspects of these matters. Thus the broad earth patterns of variation and their interrelationships are stressed, with less emphasis placed upon the mechanics of process independent of place. It is hoped that this will enable the student to obtain in a direct manner that appreciation of the earth as a physical environment without which he cannot be considered properly informed as a tenant.

Although this briefer book has been organized and written afresh, much of its content is based upon materials in the more comprehensive *Physical Elements of Geography* by Finch, Trewartha, Robinson, and Hammond. The selection of materials has been made to fit a one-semester, one-quarter, or two-quarter introductory college survey course in the fundamentals of physical geography. In every case the degree of generalization has been kept at a high level, with the focus on general world patterns and their interrelationships. In some sections of this book a completely different approach has been taken from that in the earlier book, and recent materials have been included.

A number of new illustrations have been prepared and procured, but many are taken from the larger book.

The student and the instructor will note that there are no chapter outlines or review questions. It is the authors' opinion, and they feel it to be the judgment of many instructors, that to include such materials is to subvert an important part of the learning process. The good student finds them useless, and the mediocre student is likely to grasp them as straws without going through the essential learning process of formulating them for himself. For the student who wishes to range further, brief bibliographies are appended at appropriate places.

The authors acknowledge a debt to both their colleagues and their former students.

At the University of Wisconsin most of the physical science departments, among them the Department of Geography, offer one-semester survey courses as well as year-length courses. Each of the authors has taught the survey course in physical geography and by contact with the students has become familiar with the capabilities of those who take such a course with little or no background in the subject. Colleagues in the Department of Geography and in other departments of the earth sciences have been helpful in many ways.

Glenn T. Trewartha
Arthur H. Robinson
Edwin H. Hammond

Contents

Fundamentals
of physical
geography

CHAPTER 1

The earth: basic facts and mapping

SIZE AND FORM OF THE EARTH

The earth is almost a true sphere, with a radius of nearly 4,000 miles and a surface area of about 197 million square miles. The earth rotates steadily, and for some time the surface has maintained its position relative to the axis of rotation. The opposite, or antipodal, points on the surface that lie in the axis of rotation are called the earth *poles;* an imaginary line encircling the surface midway between the poles is called the *equator.*

The greatest departure of the earth from sphericity is a flattening in polar areas and a correspondent bulging in equatorial regions. The polar radius is about 13.5 miles shorter than an equatorial radius. Yet given the size of the earth, this spheroidal deformation is small: it would amount to less than $\frac{1}{10}$ in. on a ball 5 ft in diameter. None of the other departures from sphericity is even this great, for the highest mountain projects only about 5.5 miles above the general level of the sea, and the greatest ocean depth is less than

1

7 miles below sea level. The almost perfect smoothness of the earth's surface relative to its size may be illustrated this way: on a true reduction of it with a diameter of 1 ft, the size of an ordinary desk globe, one could hardly feel any roughness. On such a globe the peak of **Mount Everest**, approximately 29,000 ft above sea level, would be less than ¹⁄₁₀₀ in. above the general surface of the globe.

The exterior of the earth nonetheless consists of markedly different substances. Most of the solid surface is covered with water that has an average depth of more than 2 miles. Only a little more than 29 per cent of the solid material protrudes above the water surface, and this but slightly, since the average elevation of the land surface above the water is only about ½ mile (Fig. 1.1). Overlying both the solid and liquid surfaces is a mixture of gases, the atmosphere. The distribution of the land and water surfaces is not symmetrical, especially in terms of an equatorial division. A separation of the earth into hemispheres by the equator finds twice as

much land in the Northern Hemisphere as in the Southern. The total area of the exposed solid surface is about 57 million square miles, equal to about nineteen times the area of the United States. Upon this surface the entire human population of the earth resides and endeavors to secure a living. Because of its physical geography, i.e., its natural variation from place to place, there are large parts of the land area which, for one reason or another, are ill suited to intensive human occupation or use.

The polar flattening and the equatorial bulging of the earth indicate it is plastic since this is the sort of deformation that would occur in any nonrigid sphere as a consequence of gravitational force and the centrifugal force resulting from its rotation. The outer zone of this plastic ball, the surface crust, apparently consists of adjacent segments that vary slightly in the average density of the rock types of which they are composed. The continental segments are thought to be made of rocks that together are slightly less

FIG. 1.1 Cumulative graph showing the relative amount of land and water surface on the earth and the average elevation and depth of the solid surface in relation to sea level. Note that most of the earth's surface is water and that most of the land lies beneath the sea.

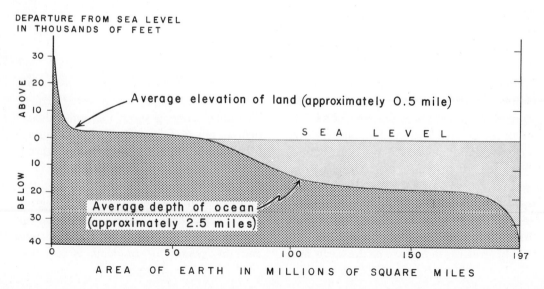

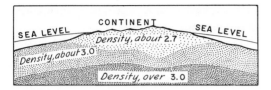

FIG. 1.2   The inferred distribution of densities of the solid materials of the earth's crustal zone.

dense (average density approximately 2.7) than those that form the crustal sections underlying the ocean basins (average density approximately 3.0). It is because of this discrepancy that the continents stand slightly higher, it is believed. The various crustal segments or blocks are thought to float, so to speak, on the subsurface in balance, a state called isostasy (Fig 1.2). Yet the relative vertical position of the materials that form the segments is transitory since the density relationships are constantly being disturbed by such events as the removal of material from the continents by streams and its deposition in the oceans. The variances that result appear to be regularly counteracted by the slow movement of the more plastic material thought to exist beneath the earth's crust. This, together with still other forces, results in the bending, breaking, and warping of the materials of the crust. These in turn cause the minor surface irregularities of lesser magnitude, such as the mountain masses and depression areas on the continents and within the ocean basins. The detailed unevenness of a surface made up of mountains, hills, and plains is of critical local and regional significance to diminutive man.

Yet it must be emphasized that the most important fact of the earth's form is its almost perfect sphericity. A large proportion of the fundamental processes that together cause natural variations in the surface from one place to another are direct or indirect consequences of this simple fact of spherical form. For example, the variation in the receipt of energy from the sun and all its consequences—such as air temperature, precipitation, and the circulation of the atmosphere and the oceans, to name but a few of the elements of physical geography—are directly attributable to the earth's being a rotating spherical body. In order, then, to understand many important things about the earth, a person must be thoroughly familiar with the geometric properties of the sphere, the circle, and the arc.

Any intersection of a plane and a sphere results in a circle that contains 360 degrees. If an intersecting plane includes the center of the sphere, the circle is termed a *great circle;* it is the largest that can occur on a sphere and divides it into hemispheres. (The equator is the great circle the plane of which is perpendicular to the earth's axis of rotation.) There can be an infinite number of great circles and they have the significant property that they all bisect one another (Fig. 1.3).

FIG. 1.3   A great circle lies in a plane that passes through the center of a sphere; consequently a great circle divides a sphere into hemispheres. A sphere can have any number of great circles arranged in an infinite number of ways, and they will all bisect one another. These concepts apply to the earth since it is a sphere.

The course along the arc of a great circle is the most direct route from one place to another on the curved surface and is thus analogous to the straight line on a plane as the shortest distance between two points. One degree of arc distance along a great circle on the earth is about 69 statute miles or 60 nautical miles. Any other circle on the earth is a *small circle,* and arc distances along small circles are shorter in miles.

These simple geometric consequences of the earth's shape and size will repeatedly be found to underlie the complex facts of physical geography that appear in the balance of the book.

EARTH MOVEMENTS

This rotating sphere, the earth, is also a planetary satellite of the sun, around which the earth revolves in an orbit some 93 million miles from it.

The earth rotates at an almost constant speed, and the time required for the surface to rotate once in relation to the sun is designated as 1 day. During each rotation most of the surface successively turns toward and away from the sun. The greater part thus experiences a period of light and energy receipt and a period of darkness and energy loss. Most places, therefore, pass twice through the boundary between light and dark, the *circle of illumination,* which is a great circle, once at dawn and again at sunset. The eastward rotation of the earth determines the direction in which the sun, moon,

FIG. 1.4   Relation of the inclination and parallelism of the earth's axis to the periods of the year. The observer of this perspective drawing is far outside the earth's orbit and slightly above the plane of the ecliptic. Compare with Fig. 1.8, which shows views of the earth in the plane of the ecliptic at the time of the solstices.

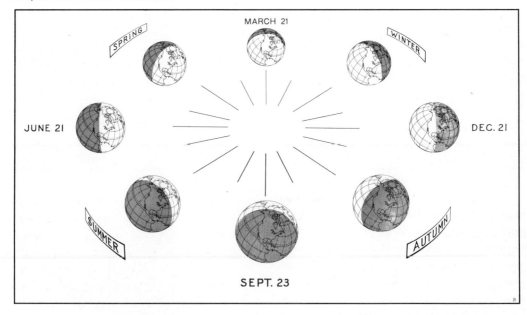

and stars appear to move across the sky and affects other earth phenomena of far-reaching consequence, such as the general circulation of the atmosphere and oceans, which will be studied later.

The earth revolves around the sun in a slightly elliptical orbit. In the course of its revolution, it moves faster when it is closer to the sun. The average time required for the earth to complete one circuit of its orbit is designated as a year. During this period the earth rotates in relation to the sun approximately 365¼ times, thus determining the number of days in the year. Primarily because of slight variations in the speed of the earth along its orbit, the time interval between successive complete rotations relative to the sun is not constant. The average rotational day is arbitrarily divided into 24 hr of constant duration.

All points in the earth's orbit lie in a plane, which includes the sun, called the *plane of the ecliptic.* The axis of the earth's rotation is inclined about 66½° from this plane (or 23½° from perpendicular to it). This angular inclination is nearly constant, and moreover the axis at any time during its orbit is parallel to the position that it occupies at any other time (Fig. 1.4). This is called the *parallelism* of the axis.

The inclination of the earth's axis and its parallelism, together with the earth's shape, its rotation, and its revolution about the sun, cause several earth phenomena that are of vital importance to physical geography. Some of these are (*a*) the distribution over the earth of the receipt of solar energy, (*b*) the changing of the seasons, (*c*) the changing lengths of day and night, and (*d*) the general manner in which the atmosphere and oceans circulate. These matters and other related ones will be discussed more fully in their connection with climate.

LOCATION ON THE EARTH

Coordinate system The earth's form and its movements are also significant as the bases upon which man has developed the system he uses to determine and describe position and relative location on the earth's surface. On an ordinary sphere there is neither beginning nor end, no natural point or line of reference from which to begin to measure the relative positions of other points. If it were not for its systematic motions and planetary relations, the earth also would have no natural point or line from which to measure distance or direction. But the fact of rotation establishes the geographic poles of the earth, and these serve as reference points for the coordinate system by means of which directions and locations are determined.

The system is similar to the familiar rectangular-coordinate system on ordinary graph paper, modified to fit the spherical earth. An infinite number of small circles is conceived parallel to the equator, as illustrated in Fig. 1.5. All, including the equator, are called *parallels,* and the earth directions *east* and *west* are determined by their orientation on the surface. Since each of the small circles is parallel to the equator, every point on a given parallel will be the same distance from the equator, the same distance from the North Pole, and the same distance from the South Pole. The distance of a point from the equator or one of the poles is called *latitude* in the earth's coordinate system and is expressed by identifying the parallel on which the point is located.

Of course a statement of latitude is not enough to locate a point since a parallel is a circle, and the point could be anywhere on it. Position east or west on a parallel, called *longitude,* may be determined by reference to a different system of circles arranged per-

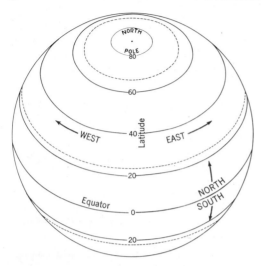

FIG. 1.5   Arrangement of the parallels in the earth's coordinate system. The parallels establish the directions east and west and provide a method for designating positions north and south. Only a few of the infinite number possible are shown here.

pendicular to the parallels. In a plane, or flat, coordinate system these lines are also parallel to one another, but on the spherical earth they must converge and intersect at the poles; they are, however, equally spaced on any parallel. These great circles are called *meridians,* and the earth directions *north* and *south* are determined by their orientation on the surface, as shown in Fig. 1.6. In practice each meridional great circle is halved at the poles to form opposite pairs of semicircular meridians extending from pole to pole.

Latitude   In numbering the earth's co-ordinate system, the great circle formed by each pair of meridians is divided into quadrants, the points of division being the poles and the two intersections with the equator. Each meridional quadrant is divided into 90° of latitude, and the numbering of the latitude proceeds from the equator (0° Lat) to each pole. Location along a meridian is established by noting the intersection of it by a particular parallel. Thus latitude is reckoned from

the equator northward to the North Pole on any meridian and, in the same way, from the equator to the South Pole. Consequently the terms *low, middle,* and *high latitudes* refer to the values of the numbering system; for example, the lower latitudes are those areas near the equator.

The lengths of the degrees of latitude are not quite identical along a meridian. On a sphere each arc unit of a great circle has the same length, of course, but the earth is not quite a true sphere. The latitude of a point is determined by observing, at the point in question, the angular difference between the horizon and some celestial body, such as Polaris (the North Star) or the sun (Fig. 1.7). A degree of latitude is, therefore, the distance north or south a person must move along a meridian in order to observe 1° change in this angle. Because of the flattening in the polar regions, a traveler must go farther along a meridian there to obtain a change of 1°.

FIG. 1.6   Adding the meridian system to the parallel system provides for an infinite number of coordinate intersections specifying the location of any and all points on the earth. The meridians themselves establish the directions north and south and provide a method for designating positions east and west.

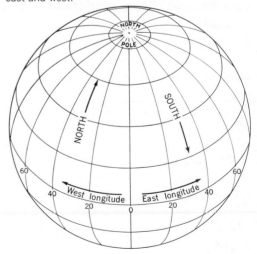

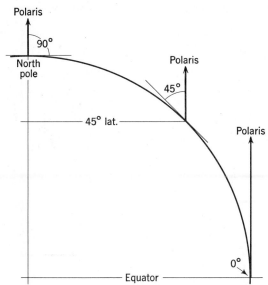

FIG. 1.7 The relation between (1) the curvature of the earth's surface (in this case north-south), (2) the angle above the horizon of Polaris, and (3) the latitude.

The first degree of latitude from the equator covers a distance of 68.7 miles, while the first degree from either pole is 69.4 miles long. Each degree of latitude is divided into 60 minutes (′), each minute into 60 seconds (″). One minute of latitude is very nearly 1 nautical mile, or about 1.15 statute miles, and one second of latitude is about 101 ft. The length of the meter, the standard of distance measurement in the metric system, is in theory one ten-millionth of the meridional quadrant, the distance from the equator to the pole.

Commonly only a few of the infinite number of meridian and parallel circles are shown on maps, such as those of the multiples of 5 or 10°. Often, however, four particular parallels in addition to the equator are indicated because they have special significance. These are the parallels of approximately 23½° N and S Lat and of 66½° N and S Lat. They are important because the sun appears at dif-

ferent angular elevations above the horizon in different regions. The parallels of 23½° N and S are called the Tropics of Cancer and Capricorn, respectively. They mark the limits of the zone near the equator within which the sun ever appears directly overhead. The parallels of 66½° N and S are called the Arctic and Antarctic Circles, respectively. They mark the limits of the polar area in each hemisphere within which the sun ever appears above the horizon continuously for 24 hr or more, or, at the same time in the opposite hemisphere, remains below the horizon for 24 hr or more (Fig. 1.8).

Longitude Longitude is reckoned east or west along the parallels, but there is no particular meridian marked by nature (as the equator is for specifying latitude), from which a system of specifying longitude may be started. All meridians are exactly alike, and any one of them could be designated as the zero meridian (0° Long). In fact, for several centuries each important country numbered a meridian that lay within its own borders as 0° Long. So much confusion resulted that, in the year 1884, the meridian passing through Greenwich Observatory at London, England, was chosen by international agreement as 0° Long. It is called the prime meridian. It intersects the equator in the Gulf of Guinea at a point which has the distinction of having 0°00′00″Long and 0°00′00″ Lat. This point is, then, the point of origin of the earth's coordinate system. The degrees of longitude in each parallel are numbered east and west to 180°, the meridian opposite the prime meridian; together the two meridians (0° and 180°) make a great circle.

The circumference of each parallel is less than that of a great circle in the ratio that is given graphically by the lengths in Fig. 1.9. Since each parallel, whatever its circumference, is divided into 360°, it follows that the

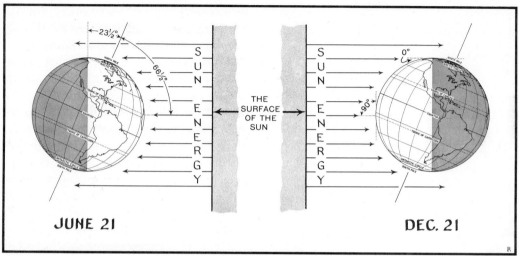

FIG. 1.8   The angular relationship between the direction of the sun's earth-striking energy and points on the earth's surface changes during the year, and thus so does the sun's apparent position in the heavens. For example, on December 21 a person on the Tropic of Capricorn would see the sun directly overhead (90° above the horizon) at noon; on the same day a person on the Arctic Circle would see the sun on the horizon; i.e., the rays would be tangent (at 0° elevation) to the earth's surface. The segments of the sun's surface shown here to scale represent only about one two-hundredth of its circumference; consequently for practical purposes they have almost no curvature.

higher the latitude, the less will be the distance represented by 1° of longitude. The length of 1° of longitude along the equator, a great circle, is 69.17 miles, which is about the same length as an average degree of latitude. At 30° N or S Lat the length of a degree of longitude is 59.96 miles, at 60° it is 34.67 miles, at 80° it is 12.05 miles, and at the poles it is, of course, nil.

Determining Latitude and Longitude   Any point on a perpendicular-coordinate system may be designated by establishing its ordinate and abscissa values; consequently, any point on the earth's surface may be located precisely by determining its latitude and longitude, i.e., that it lies at the intersection of a certain parallel and a certain meridian. Thus if a person were to say that the dome of the National Capitol at Washington was located at 38°53′23″N Lat and 77°00′33″W Long,

FIG. 1.9   Comparative lengths of the parallels in relation to the length of a great circle, as shown by the line designated as 0° Lat (the equator). Note that the sixtieth parallel is half as long as the equator.

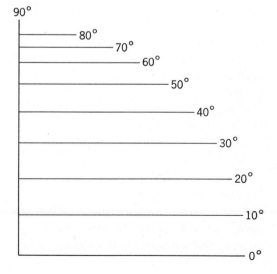

he would have stated its position on the earth to within some 10 paces.

The latitude of a place, i.e., its position in the north-south direction, is determined by instrumental observation of the vertical angle at that place between the horizon and a distant celestial body. The earth is so small relative to its distance from the stars (including the sun) that for all practical purposes the rays of light from a celestial body intercepted by the earth are parallel. Since the quadrant of latitude is divided into 90° and since the curvature along one-fourth of a meridian great circle also covers 90° of arc, a difference in arc position along a meridian will be exactly matched by the change in angular height of a celestial body. For example, at the North Pole Polaris is almost overhead; therefore its angular height above the horizon is 90°, and the latitude of the North Pole is 90°. Similarly, if Polaris could be seen from the equator, it would appear almost on the horizon, that is, at an angular elevation of 0°; and at 45°N Lat it appears halfway between the zenith and the horizon. Figure 1.7 illustrates these relationships. They may be summarized by stating that the arc distance in degrees of latitude between two parallels on the earth is the difference in the angular heights above the horizon of a given celestial body as observed in the meridional direction at the two points.

The use of stars other than Polaris to determine latitude complicates matters somewhat since corrections must be introduced to take into account the fact that other celestial bodies do not lie on the extension of the earth's axis of rotation, but tables are available to provide the necessary data.

The longitude of a place, i.e., its position in the east-west direction, is determined by observing the solar, or sun, time difference between that place and some other point of known longitude. Since the earth rotates through 360° in approximately 24 hr, it turns through about 15° in 1 hr, irrespective of latitude. Consequently, if it is 10:00 A.M. at one point and noon at another, 30° of longitude separates them. To observe one's local solar time is relatively easy; noon is the instant when the sun appears to cross the observer's meridian, i.e., when it reaches its highest point (zenith) in its daily course across the sky. This instant of time may then be compared with the solar time of some other known place by means of a chronometer (an accurate clock) that is keeping the time of the other place, or by instantaneous electronic means. The difference in time may easily be converted to degrees of longitude at the rate of 1 hr = 15° Long. Solar time will be further discussed later in this chapter.

DIRECTION ON THE EARTH

The relative location of places may be stated in directional terms as well as by identifying their latitudes and longitudes. The expression of direction on the earth is somewhat complex since it is a sphere and its coordinate system is spherical instead of rectangular.

Earlier it was seen that the path along a great circle is geometrically the most direct course between points on the earth, analogous to the straight line on a plane. Since the directions at any point on the earth are defined by the orientation of the parallels and the meridians, and since these are on a spherical surface, it follows that directional relationships change from place to place on the earth. Consequently one can describe the "beginning direction" of the great-circle course from point to point; but elsewhere along the course the angular relation between the coordinate system and the particular great circle will change, unless the great-circle course is along a meridian or the equator. Direction from one place to another is specified by stating the angle between the meridian

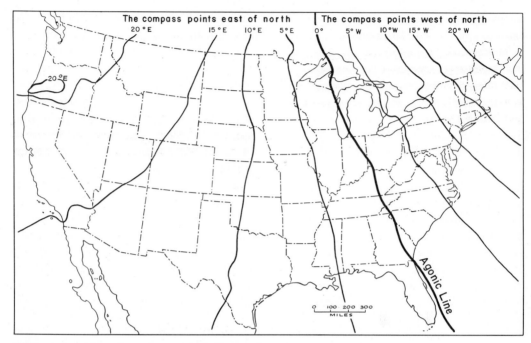

FIG. 1.10 Lines of equal magnetic declination (isogonic lines) in the United States in 1960. Only at points along the agonic line (0° declination) does the needle of the magnetic compass parallel the meridian. Elsewhere a correction must be applied to the reading.

(Generalized from a map by the U.S. Coast and Geodetic Survey.)

and the great circle at the starting point, either as a compass bearing, e.g., NE, or as an azimuth, the angle between the meridian and the great circle, usually expressed in degrees reckoned clockwise from north, e.g., NE= 45° az. The precise determination of azimuth requires astronomical observation to establish the direction of the reference meridian.

When the direction of the meridian cannot be determined astronomically, various mechanical devices or the more familiar magnetic compass may be used to find it. The needle of the compass aligns itself with the forces emanating from that great magnet the earth. Unfortunately, however, the positions of the magnetic north and south poles are not opposite one another and do not coincide with the geographical poles. The magnetic poles are even subject to slight changes of

position. In consequence, only in limited areas does the magnetic needle parallel the meridian; at most places the needle rests at an angle with the meridian. The angle varies considerably from place to place, and the magnitude of the variation at any point is called the compass declination of the point. Figure 1.10 shows the lines of equal compass declination in the United States. East of the agonic line, where declination is nil, the compass has a west declination. In some parts of the frequented oceans the compass declination is as much as 30 to 40°, and in the polar regions it shows very wide variations.

OTHER SYSTEMS OF DESIGNATING
POSITIONS OR AREAS

The spherical-coordinate system, consisting of latitude and longitude measurements with their directional derivatives, is the fundamental basis for establishing relative location on the earth. Yet for bounding small areas or locating specific positions on the land it is often inconveniently complicated, as well as subject to errors of definition and instrumentation. Consequently, in order precisely to designate parcels of land for administrative purposes, other methods are necessary.

Metes and bounds The world's most widely used method—prevalent in most of Europe and in some early-settled areas of North America, for instance—is known as metes and bounds. In this an arbitrary point is designated as a point of beginning, for example, a projecting rock, an iron stake, a tree, or some other identifiable point on the land. The land segment is then bounded by a line extending from the starting point in a given compass direction for a certain distance, then in another direction for a specified distance, and so on back to the point of beginning. This system has often led to dispute over property lines because the marked points on the ground have been lost. Moreover, the stated distances and directions have sometimes been measured inexactly, as in parts of Texas, where some of the early Spanish land grants were supposedly stated in such units of distance as the length of a lariat rope and how far a horse could walk in a given time. In most parts of the world the bounding lines do not enclose rectangular parcels of land, so that the subdivision of the land does not produce any consistent pattern of shapes oriented to the cardinal compass directions.

This lack of coordination is plainly apparent in the road patterns of many long-settled areas that were not subjected to any systematic plan of land subdivision prior to settlement. This may be seen in detailed maps of parts of North America, such as New England and Texas. In some localities of eastern North America the present small parcels of land are subdivisions of grants made by European rulers to noblemen or to the sponsors of settlement projects. In some sections, such as French Canada and French Louisiana, the present landholdings do have a pattern of rectangularity but are very long and narrow. Their narrow frontage is upon a river, and their length extends perpendicular to the river regardless of its course. Even some of the counties of the Province of Quebec have much the same shape. They were established at a time when river frontage was a most prized possession but the land of the interior had little value.

Rectangular survey In contrast, this essentially haphazard practice was not used in a large part of the United States and much of Canada, which were settled after a governmental subdivision of the land based on a rectangular-survey system. This system was applied to almost all the regions lying to the west of the earlier-settled eastern seaboard. In this system the boundaries of public and private lands are often described in detail by metes and bounds but in relation to a network of essentially north-south and east-west lines. These include selected meridians called *principal meridians* and parallels called *base lines* (Fig. 1.11). They have had the effect of dividing the land into essentially rectangular blocks. The locations of the blocks are indicated by numbered *townships* and *ranges* (Fig. 1.12).

The ranges are 6-mile-wide strips of land running north and south, each numbered to the east or to the west of a particular principal meridian. Each range is divided into a tier of townships by east-west lines 6 miles apart, each township being numbered north or south from a base line. Each survey township is thus supposed to be 6 miles square. By this system any township can be located by refer-

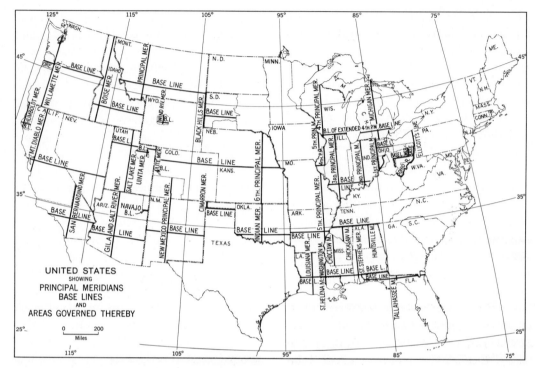

FIG. 1.11 The principal meridians and base lines which govern the land-survey system of most of the United States, except Texas and the Atlantic Coast states. The fine-dotted lines surround the areas governed by each principal meridian; some of these areas are large, some small.

FIG. 1.12 The system of designating government-survey townships by township and range numbers with respect to given principal meridians and base lines. The shaded township is T2N, R3E.

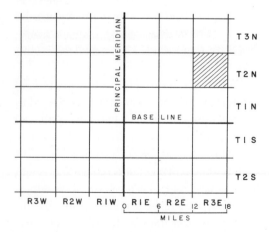

ence to its township and range numbers. e.g., township 2 north, range 3 east, usually written T2N, R3E (Fig. 1.12).

The usual survey township is further divided into 36 *sections,* each approximately 1 mile square, or 640 acres in area, whose corners are marked on the ground. The sections are numbered, beginning at the northeastern corner and ending at the southeastern, as shown in Fig. 1.13. In addition, the section is divided into quarter sections, each containing 160 acres, and these are further divided into quarters of 40 acres each, commonly called "forties." The quarter sections and the forties are indicated by the points of the compass (Fig. 1.14).

Because the meridians naturally converge

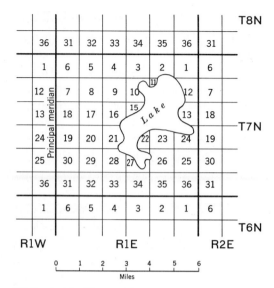

								T8N
36	31	32	33	34	35	36	31	
1	6	5	4	3	2	1	6	
12	7	8	9	10	11	12	7	
13	18	17	16	15		13	18	T7N
24	19	20	21	22	23	24	19	
25	30	29	28	27	26	25	30	
36	31	32	33	34	35	36	31	
1	6	5	4	3	2	1	6	T6N

R1W   R1E   R2E

0 1 2 3 4 5 6
Miles

FIG. 1.13 The standard system of numbering used for the sections within a township. This township is T7N, R1E.

nicipalities also are subject to change by appropriate legislation, but the government-survey townships remain.

Wherever such a basic survey framework has been employed it has left an indelible imprint on the landscape, a pattern of patchwork rectangularity easily seen from the air and on air photographs. It is even reflected in the road maps of much of the United States and Canada since the minor roads and even the field boundaries tend to be oriented with the cardinal directions.

In recent times other kinds of rectangular-coordinate grid systems have been developed to designate location on detailed military and

northward, because straight base lines cannot also be true east-west, because errors occur in surveying, and because there are sometimes lakes or streams at critical points, many corrections and other allowances have had to be made by men using the rectangular-survey system to subdivide land. Moreover, the locations of the section corners and the quarter-section corners were in the past marked by a stake, stone, mound, tree, or other device; but too often these were impermanent features, and many of them are now difficult to locate.

Civil towns or other units of political administration may or may not coincide with government townships, which exist for purposes of survey location. In thinly settled districts the civil towns often are large enough to include two or more government townships or parts of townships. In other areas one government township may be divided into two or more small civil towns. The boundaries of civil towns, villages, and mu-

FIG. 1.14 Parts of sections are described and located by quarter sections, designated by the compass position of each part in its section. The 40-acre tracts ("forties") within quarter sections are similarly described and located. For example, the shaded area (a forty) would be designated as the NE¼ of the SW¼ of, say, Sec 20, T44N, R5E, followed by either the principal meridian to which the range number referred or the administrative district, e.g., county and state, in which the area is located. A forty may be divided in quarters just as sections and quarter sections are.

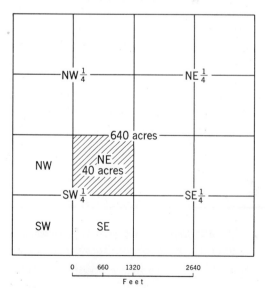

0 660 1320 2640
Feet

civil maps, in lieu of the "geographical" latitude-longitude system. Their characteristics and uses are explained in technical manuals and treatises on map use and cartography.

TIME ON THE EARTH

The movements of the earth relative to the sun cause, at each place on the earth, a variety of changes such as those of night and day and the seasons. The regularity of these movements provides the basis for the system of time and the differences of time from place to place.

There are two distinct ways of reckoning time, by clock and by calendar. From one midnight to the next is a calendar day regardless of the clock time that elapses. On the other hand, 24 clock hours are also called 1 day, and the records of the two time-telling systems must sometimes be adjusted or they will conflict.

Clock time   Clock time, as already indicated, is reckoned from the apparent motion of the sun and is called solar time or sun time, with noon on any day determined by the instant the sun reaches its zenith. Because the earth does not revolve around the sun at a constant speed, the clock interval between successive noons at any place varies a bit during the year. So for convenience an average is used, called *mean solar time*. Until about a century ago each locality kept its own time; i.e., noon was when the sun appeared directly over the local meridian. But with the development of rapid mobility this became inconvenient, and most of the world adopted a system of *standard time*.

The standard-time system, in general, allocates to 24 zones running north and south, each 15° of longitude in width, the mean solar time of the central meridian of each zone. All places within a zone then maintain the same clock time although this may depart from solar time by as much as ½ hr. Changes of clock time are then necessary only when crossing the boundary of a zone, and each change is exactly 1 hr. Because the earth rotates toward the east a timepiece is set forward, e.g., from 12:00 to 1:00, in traveling east, and backward, e.g., from 12:00 to 11:00, in traveling west. In practice, these zones are commonly bounded not by meridians but by irregular lines, the locations of which are subject to administrative changes dictated by local convenience. Figure 1.15 shows standard-time zones of the United States. In the whole system the 24 zones should each extend from pole to pole and each differ from prime meridian (Greenwich) time by an integral number of hours, but in practice the arrangement is not quite so simple. Most countries follow the general plan, but some have not yet adopted standard time at all, and a few countries employ the time of meridians that are not multiples of 15° and therefore do not differ from Greenwich time by exact hours.

Calendar time   Calendar time is reckoned by specifying that one rotation relative to the sun represents one day, and the year is the period required for the earth to complete one revolution around the sun, which is, as previously stated, the time required for approximately 365¼ rotations. This system presents no problem if someone remains at one place on the earth; but if he travels all the way around the earth he will obviously either subtract or add one rotation, depending upon which direction he goes. It will then become necessary for him either to add or subtract a day so that his calendar will match those that have remained at one place. The

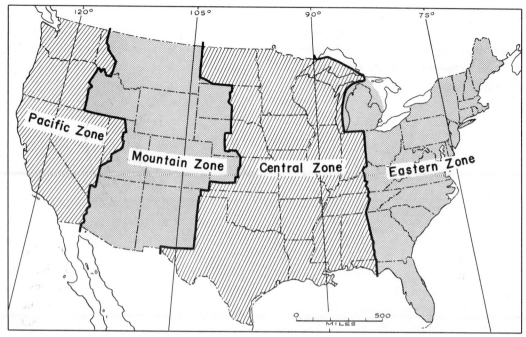

FIG. 1.15 Standard-time zones of the United States as of 1960. *(Interstate Commerce Commission.)*

total elapsed clock time is, of course, not affected, but by calendar time a day is a rotation, not 24 hr.

This may be illustrated by imagining an airplane sufficiently fast to fly in an east-west direction around the earth in exactly 24 hr. If the flier starts westward from, say, Chicago at noon on a Monday the tenth of the month, his ground speed westward will exactly cancel the eastward rotation of the earth. To him the sun will have no apparent motion; it will remain in the noon position in his sky for 24 hr. The earth will rotate under him and he will "return" to Chicago the same (to him) noon. In other words, although 24 hr has elapsed, he will not have experienced a solar day. On the other hand, for persons on the ground a night will have intervened, and it will be noon of Tuesday the eleventh. The flier will therefore have "lost" a calendar day. If he had flown from Chicago eastward instead, he would have experienced a midnight over Spain (6 hr later), noon of another day over central Asia (12 hr after leaving), a second midnight over the Pacific Ocean (18 hr after leaving), and would have returned at noon of his second calendar day, in spite of the fact that he had been traveling only 24 hr. According to his solar calendar it would be Wednesday the twelfth, while to those who stayed at the starting point it would be Tuesday the eleventh. The traveler, therefore, would have "gained" a solar day. If a person travels slowly and thus cancels or adds the 1 solar day over a longer period, the case is the same. Unless he sets his calendar ahead 1 day when making a circuit of the earth westward or sets it back when traveling eastward, his calendar will be off by 1 day on his return.

To avoid the confusion that would result from individual choice of where to reset the calendar, an international *date line* has been designated. It is located along the 180th meridian, with some small deviations agreed upon so that island groups and land areas will not be divided inconveniently. By designation of this line as the meridian where the calendar day "begins," no calendar correction is necessary except when one crosses it.

MAPS AND MAPPING

MAPS AS ESSENTIAL SCIENTIFIC TOOLS

Maps, as scientific devices, represent graphically the relative locations of many kinds of phenomena. They are used in several fields of learning, especially in earth sciences. For the student of geography the map is an essential tool, the medium for recording factual observations and their derivatives so that locational relationships and changes from place to place may be studied.

Maps are so nearly infinite in variety that they almost constitute a scientific "language" in themselves. To interpret them readily one must understand the important types of maps and their qualities. To that end the student needs to obtain considerable familiarity with three fundamental aspects of all maps. These are (a) the *scale,* that is, the size of a map representation relative to the size of that part of the earth which it represents, (b) the nature of the system of *projection* employed in transforming the spherical surface of the earth to the flat surface of the map, and (c) the meanings of the various *symbols* or devices used to show the things represented on the map.

Scale   A reduction of the earth on a globe is the form of earth representation requiring the least interpretation. The dimensions of the globe may be measured, and their relation to the dimensions of the earth may be expressed as a ratio, called the scale of the globe. For example, the earth has in fact a diam of about 500,000,000 in., so that if someone has a large globe with a diam of 50 in., then the ratio of the globe distance between any two places to the same real distance on the earth is as 50 is to 500,000,000, or more simply, as 1 is to 10,000,000, commonly written 1 : 10,000,000. This means that 1 unit on the globe represents 10,000,000 units on the earth. The scale is independent of the units of measure, but the *same units* must be used on each side of the scale. The scale may be expressed as a fraction—1/10,000,000 in this case—and called the representative fraction, or RF for short.

Maps, like globes, always have a scale relationship to the parts of the earth that they represent. Usually it is given in the form of the RF; occasionally it is expressed verbally, as for instance, "One inch represents one mile." But most often the scale is shown by means of a measured line showing the map lengths of earth units, as in Figs. 1.13 and 1.14.

Maps are sometimes described as being large-scale or small-scale. The larger the part of the earth mapped on a given size sheet, the smaller will be the RF which tells its scale; that is, the larger will be the number in the denominator. Therefore, small maps of large earth areas are called small-scale maps, and, in reverse, large maps of small earth areas are called large-scale maps. Any map showing the entire earth or any major part of it is termed a small-scale map, while a topographic map, as described later, is classed as a large-scale map.

The student should bear in mind one essential difference between the interpretation of the scale of a globe and that of a flat map. The scale of a globe, no matter how small, may properly be applied to it in all parts and in all directions, but the indicated scale never applies equally in all directions on a map. (A reason for this difference will appear below.) On very large scale maps this inequality may be ignored, but its importance increases as the scale of a map becomes smaller.

Globes and map projections　Reducing the earth with maps to help the geographer see its variations—as some other scientists enlarge their objectives with microscopes—is the job of the *cartographer,* or map maker. He may do this in two ways: he may simply make a reduced global representation of the spherical earth, or he may make his representation on a plane surface, such as a sheet of paper, by a systematic process of transformation called map projection.

A globe provides a reduced but otherwise undeformed framework for a map, since the geometry (earth measure) of the sphere has been changed only in scale, and direction and distance relationships remain in strict proportion to those of the earth. Yet a globe, in spite of this obvious advantage, has several disadvantages. Among the more serious are that (*a*) only a portion (less than half) of the globe can be seen at one time, (*b*) if it is large enough to show much detail, it is bulky and unwieldy, (*c*) its curved surface is difficult to measure on, and (*d*) it is expensive to reproduce. Most of the mechanical difficulties do not hold for a plane-surface map. It can be seen all at once, it is relatively easy to handle

or store, measuring on it is easy, and information can easily be printed on its surface. For these reasons flat maps on plane surfaces are greatly preferred to curved maps on spherical surfaces.

In geometric transformation dissimilar surfaces are said to be *applicable* if one can be bent into another without modifying the geometric relationships among the points on the surface. Thus a cylinder or a cone may be cut and laid out flat to form a plane, and neither distance nor directional relationships across the surface will be changed. A spherical surface and a plane surface are not applicable, however. The bending required to transform one to the other must involve stretching and shrinking. This unavoidably results in changing the distance and directional relationships among points on the earth represented on a flat map. Yet the other advantages of a flat map projection listed above far outweigh the disadvantages produced by the stretching and compression.

PROPERTIES OF MAP PROJECTIONS

For more than 2,000 years men concerned with maps have been devising ways of distributing the changes in distance and direction on them so that the distance-direction alterations may be allowed for by the user. In some instances it can be done in such a way that for particular uses the distribution of error becomes a definite advantage, as in certain kinds of navigational maps. There is an unlimited number of ways in which the alterations can be arranged. The majority of the widely used map projections have one or more specific useful characteristics, each of which is called a property. A property is some attribute of the spherical surface that has either been strictly retained or usefully modified in the transformation process. For example, a projection may retain on the map the same relative sizes of areas as on the earth. There are several important properties, and some projections can combine several of them; some projections have no such useful characteristics.

The only two properties which can exist all over a projection are those known as (*a*) equivalence or equal-area, and (*b*) conformality or orthomorphism. They are mutually exclusive; i.e., they cannot exist together in the same system of projection.

Equivalence   A projection is said to be equal-area when the alteration is so arranged that at any point the maximum stretching in one direction is balanced by a reciprocal compression in the perpendicular direction. The consequence is that the area of any region on the map is shown correctly in relation to the area of any other region. The equal-area quality is extremely useful in many aspects of geographical study, for if correct area relationships are not retained the student is likely to make incorrect inferences regarding spatial relationships. Because of the inescapable stretching and compression, the scale showing linear or distance relationships will vary from place to place on the projection.

Over most of an equal-area projection the scale is different in different directions at each point, and this condition causes shapes of areas, even small ones, to be deformed. Indeed, equivalent projections always deform shapes, in some instances to a very large degree. Various equivalent projections arrange the scale departures in different ways so that the inescapable deformation of angles (shapes) may be concentrated in the less used portions of the map. The map reader must be alert to make allowance for this. Figure 1.16, the equal-area map projection used for

many of the world maps in this book, shows how the deformation of shape has been concentrated in particular areas.

Conformality   The property of conformality is of particular importance in the use of such maps as topographic and navigational charts. To obtain this quality the stretching and compression is arranged in such a way that, whatever the distance or linear scale may be at any point on the projection, it is the same in all directions at that point. Since it is impossible to have the same scale at every point on any flat map, and since on conformal projections the scale must be uniform in every direction at each point, it follows that the scale must change from point to point. The larger the area represented, the greater this variation will be; on maps of the whole earth it is not unusual for the scale to be several times greater at one place than at another. Consequently, the relative sizes of areas must vary in different parts of the projection. In other words, a conformal projection must exaggerate or reduce areas relative to one another. When the scale is consistent in every direction at a point, earth directions (the compass rose) will be truly shown. This quality makes conformality useful for maps on which directions from points are important, as for example, maps used for navigation, surveying, or plotting wind directions. Although proper angles will occur at each point on a conformal projection, the great-circle directions (and their azimuths or bearings) between places far from one another will usually not be correctly shown. Similarly, shapes of small areas will be well represented on conformal projections, but shapes of large areas will be considerably deformed, as they are on all projections.

Other properties   Another property of considerable utility is that retained by those

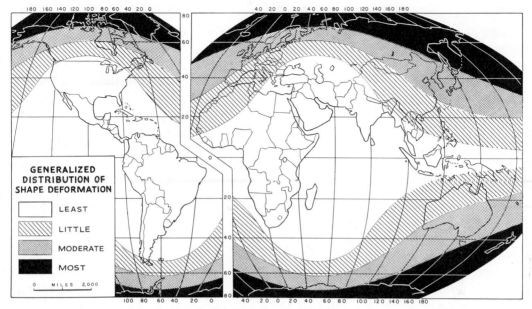

FIG. 1.16 The flat polar equal-area projection used for many of the world maps in this book, showing the areas where the shape deformation has been concentrated. The darker the shading, the more the shape deformation.

projections that are called azimuthal. This is the quality of showing correct azimuths from *one* particular point to every other point. This can be combined with another property, equidistance, which is the quality of showing correct (uniform) scale distances from *one* point to all other points. Such projections are useful in plotting radii and in figuring distances and directions of travel that follow great-circle routes, as for example, radio beams.

There are many other properties or qualities, but most of them are limited to one projection. Thus there is a projection which shows all great-circle arcs as straight lines (gnomonic); another shows rhumb lines, or lines of steady and true bearing, as straight lines (Mercator); while several show east-west directions as parallel anywhere within the representation. The properties of a pro-

jection may not be indicated in its name, and one must then turn to a treatise on cartography to find a description. One should never study a large area mapped on a small-scale map without an understanding of the distance-direction alterations introduced by the method of projection.

VARIETIES OF MAPS

Maps are employed to show the areal distribution of many kinds of things, and there are consequently many kinds of symbols. In a general way the kinds of maps and their symbols may be arranged in four groups, but the groups are neither all-inclusive nor even quite mutually exclusive. The groups are (*a*) maps employed to show areal extent, shape, or outline, (*b*) maps for showing patterns of arrangement, (*c*) maps intended to convey an impression of relative land elevation or surface relief, and (*d*) maps employed to show the areal distribution of numerical values of actual or relative quantity.

In the first group may be included all those familiar maps containing lines, shading, and color that show the extent or boundaries of areas classified upon the basis of some kind of unity. These may be countries or other political divisions, or areas of similar geologic formation, climate, landscape composition, or any other natural unity. In the second group may be found maps showing patterns of drainage, city streets and roads, other means of transportation, communication, and the relative distribution of towns and cities. In the third group are the maps that employ lines or shading arranged to produce the effect of light and shadow and thus simulate the land form.

The fourth group includes many kinds of maps with symbols, such as dots or squares denoting area, and cubes or spheres indicating volume. Each of these symbols is intended to express the existence of some numerical value in a specific locality on the earth's surface. In a sense such maps function as two-dimensional, or spatial, graphs. To a degree their usefulness is in inverse proportion to the size of the areal units for which the values are shown. Thus a few dots or squares, each representing a large unit of value and covering a large area, show generalities. On the other hand, many symbols, each representing a small unit of value and distributed properly within small units of area, show the details of a distribution.

Most such maps and their symbols are self-explanatory; if some are not, their specific quality may be determined by reference to the legend which usually accompanies a map. Care must be exercised by the map reader,

however, not to "read into" a map a greater degree of accuracy or precision than is warranted by its symbols or scale. Except on very large-scale maps, all information presented must be generalized, i.e., simplified in some way. For example, many of the maps in this book show distribution of such things as climatic regions, soil areas, and land-form differences by shading areas differently or by separating areas with lines; yet such shading and lines frequently represent only average conditions. Similarly, coast lines, civil boundaries, roads, wind-direction lines, average rainfall amounts, and other information must be greatly simplified on maps. This is necessary for two reasons: first, details cannot be represented on small-scale maps; second, the fundamental facts and patterns of distributions are not so apparent when unnecessary detail is included.

Isarithms   One frequently used cartographic device employed to show distributions of quantity on maps are the successive lines, each of which is drawn through all points that have the same numerical value. Such lines are called isarithms (Gr. *isos,* equal + *arithmos,* number). When they represent relative values expressed as ratios, such as the number of persons per square mile or the per cent of land in crops, the lines are sometimes called isopleths or simply isolines.

Isarithms are used to show distributions of many elements of geography, and these isarithms are sometimes named by combining the prefix *iso* with a term derived from the type of data. Hence one speaks of isotherms (temperature), isobars (air pressure), isobaths (water depth), and many others.

An isarithmic map is often employed, especially on large-scale maps, to show the surface irregularities of the land. Its isarithms are isohypses (Gr. *hypos,* elevation), com-

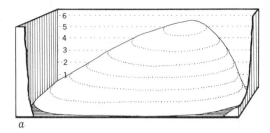

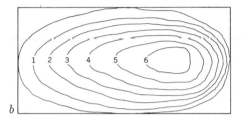

FIG. 1.17 A clay mound in a tank showing (a) the marked positions of successive water levels with a 1-in. interval between each, and (b) the positions of the water levels (contours on the mound) as viewed from directly above, i.e., as they would appear when mapped.

monly called contours. A contour is a line that passes through points that have the same elevation above sea level on the surface of the earth. The general idea of contour lines and the significance of their spacing and irregularities may be made clear by a simple illustration. The concepts thus explained may then be extended to the interpretation of the patterns of other kinds of isarithms.

If in an open tank we mold, from clay or some plastic material, an oval mound 6½ in. high that slopes steeply at one end and gently at the other, and if exactly 6 in. of water is permitted to flow into the tank, then only ½ in. of the mound will protrude above the water level. With a sharp point the position of the water upon the mound can be marked. The water level can then be lowered by 1-in. stages and the water position at each stage successively marked on the mound. The marks will appear as contour lines on the

mound, the lowest being everywhere 1 in. above the bottom of the tank, the next 2 in., and so on to the sixth, as represented in Fig. 1.17a. If the mound is viewed from directly above, as a map is, the arrangement of the lines will be that of Fig. 1.17b. From such a pattern of lines certain conclusions may be drawn which may be universally applied to the interpretation of contour and other isarithmic maps. Most important of these are that where the slope is steep the lines are close together, and that where the slope is gentle the lines are more widely spaced. On our little model the contour lines have a vertical separation of 1 in. This is called the contour, or isarithmic, interval. The numbers on the individual lines show the elevations the lines represent.

Few hills in nature are so smooth as this mound, and the example may be made more real by introducing a pair of gullies or troughs on its side (Fig. 1.18a). If the submergence is then repeated, and the lines re-

FIG. 1.18 (a) The effect that surface irregularities have on isarithms. (b) Whenever contours or isarithms cross sloping troughs (valleys) or ridges (spurs) the apexes of their bends point upslope and downslope, respectively.

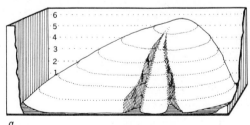

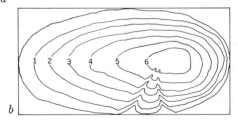

drawn, the contour lines will enter each gully, cross its bottom, and come out its other side. If the pattern of the lines, as viewed from above, is transferred to a map, the arrangement will be like that shown in Fig. 1.18*b*. From the arrangement of these lines other general conclusions become apparent. One is that when a contour, or *any* isarithm, crosses a valley or trough in any sort of distribution, it does so by a loop, the closed end of which points in the upslope direction. Between the two gullies is a ridge. On the contour map of the mound the contour lines that emerge from the gullies and pass over the ridge appear to loop so that their bends point in the downslope direction. An illustration of these principles is Fig. 1.19,

which shows "natural" contour lines marked on hill slopes as a result of wave work performed in a reservoir at different stages in the lowering of the water level.

MAPS AND PHOTOGRAPHS OF THE
EARTH'S SURFACE

For some 200 years man has been making detailed large-scale maps of the land which have helped him slowly extend his knowledge of the character of the earth's surface. These maps, called topographic maps, are a prerequisite to the scientific study of the earth's surface.

For a very much shorter time man has also been able to take precise photographs of the earth. The air photograph is somewhat like

FIG. 1.19   "Natural" contours on emerging slopes. Wave-cut lines on slopes result from the intermittent withdrawal of water from an irrigation reservoir. *(Taylor-Rochester.)*

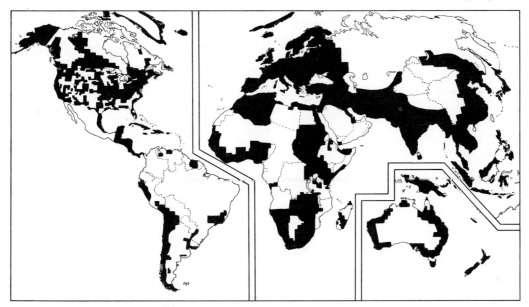

FIG. 1.20   Highly generalized map of topographically mapped areas of the world. The black areas show regions generally covered by medium- and large-scale topographic maps.

the topographic map since both are recordings of existing conditions. By the recognition of different tones of dark and light and various tonal patterns on a photograph, one is able to identify many of the physical and cultural elements of geography. With the aid of a stereoscope, overlapping air photographs may be studied in three dimensions. The ungeneralized and realistic appearance of the earth's surface in air photographs makes them a useful aid in revealing and understanding the complexities of geography. But the air photograph is not the same as a map, since it records everything a camera "sees," whereas the map is a result of a process of human selection and interpretation.

Many of the world's topographic maps are made from air photographs by analyzing both their geometric properties (photogrammetry) and the earth's image on them (photo interpretation). The air photograph thus consti-

tutes a mapping tool as well as an interpretive companion of the topographic map. The detailed knowledge of any part of the earth is gained, in part, from its maps and its air photographs; consequently a knowledge of how well the earth has been mapped and photographed indicates generally how much is known about its various parts. (Figures 1.20 and 1.21 show the extent of world coverage.) Yet it should be remembered that maps and photographs of some areas are old, of poor quality, or difficult to obtain, so that generalizations about man's knowledge of the earth based on its mapping and photographing must be made with care.

Almost all of the United States has been photographed from the air at least once, many parts of it several times. Most of the photographs are at a scale of about 3 in. to 1 mile (1:20,000); and since the photographs overlap one another, there is a tremendous

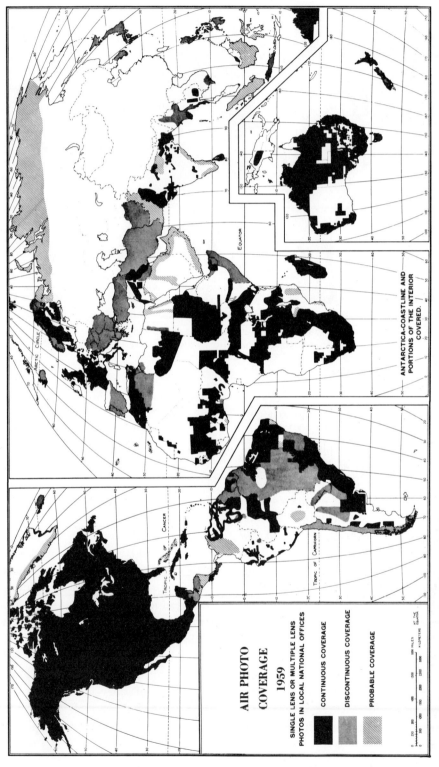

AIR PHOTO COVERAGE 1959

SINGLE LENS OR MULTIPLE LENS PHOTOS IN LOCAL NATIONAL OFFICES

CONTINUOUS COVERAGE

DISCONTINUOUS COVERAGE

PROBABLE COVERAGE

ANTARCTICA-COASTLINE AND PORTIONS OF THE INTERIOR COVERED.

FIG. 1.21 World air photo coverage. *(Kirk H. Stone.)*

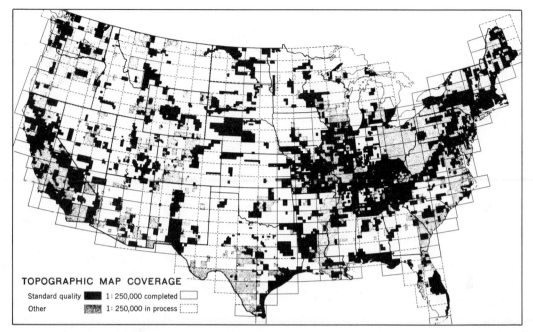

TOPOGRAPHIC MAP COVERAGE

Standard quality ▮ 1:250,000 completed ▢
Other ▨ 1:250,000 in process ⬚

FIG. 1.22 Large-scale topographic maps for about half the area of the United States were available in 1956. *(U.S. Geological Survey.)*

number of them. Topographic maps made by the U.S. Geological Survey and other governmental agencies are now available for more than half the area of the United States (Fig. 1.22). The standard United States topographic map includes a quadrangle either of $0°15'$ or $0°7\frac{1}{2}'$ of latitude and longitude. They are commonly printed at scales of $1:62,500$ (approximately 1 in. to 1 mile) and $1:24,000$ (approximately $2\frac{1}{2}$ in. to 1 mile). Some maps are printed at other scales.[1]

The topographic maps are printed in three or four colors, each showing a class of information. In black are generally shown those features that may be called cultural, i.e., pro-

duced by man, such as roads, houses, towns, place names, boundary and rectangular-survey lines, and the parallels and meridians. In blue are printed all water features, both natural and man-made, such as streams, marshes, drainage ditches, lakes, and seas; their various subclasses are distinguished by appropriate symbols also in blue. Areas covered by timber or woodland are sometimes shown in green. The contour lines, the numbers, and the other symbols related to the elevation of the land surface are printed in brown. In recent years tonal shading has been applied to many topographic maps, including some of those of the U.S. Geological Survey, in order to enhance the visual impression of the terrain. A portion of such a map is shown in Fig. 1.23.

Each map is provided with a place title, a scale, and a statement of the contour interval

[1] The Map Information Section of the U.S. Geological Survey, Washington 25, D.C., regularly publishes up-to-date indexes of the status of topographic mapping and air photography and the agencies from which the maps and photographs are available.

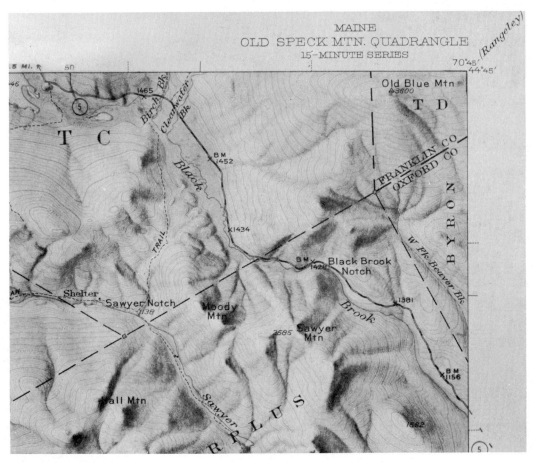

F I G . 1 . 2 3 A portion of one of the modern topographic maps of the U.S.
Geological Survey with terrain shading. These are among the best
topographic maps made anywhere.

used on that map. The contour interval employed is usually either 10, 20, 50, or 100 ft.
On the maps of extremely flat land, intervals
as small as 5 ft, or even 1 ft, are used; but
on maps of rugged mountains, intervals are
sometimes as much as 250 ft. Both the scale
and the contour interval of each map must
be ascertained before correct interpretations
of the map can be made.

Facility in interpreting maps and air photographs comes only with experience. In the
chapters to follow, the nature and arrangement of many of the land forms to be described can be made much clearer and more
realistic if use of the text is supplemented by
selected topographic maps and air photos. It
is hoped that some of these will be available
to the reader, and that he will learn to read
them so that they may contribute to his
understanding of land forms in the natural
environment. A representative list is given in
the appendix.

SELECTED REFERENCES

Chamberlin, Wellman: *The Round Earth on Flat Paper,* National Geographic Society, Washington, D.C., 1947.

Greenhood, David: *Down to Earth,* 2d ed., Holiday House, Inc., New York, 1951.

Monkhouse, F. J., and H. R. Wilkenson: *Maps and Diagrams,* Methuen & Co., Ltd., London, 1952.

Robinson, A. H.: *Elements of Cartography,* 2d ed., John Wiley & Sons, Inc., New York, 1960.

U.S. Department of Defense: *Interpretation of Aerial Photographs,* TM 5–246, 1942.

CHAPTER 2

The varieties
of surface
form

CHARACTERISTICS OF LAND SURFACES

The earth upon which man lives is characterized by a great and often pleasing variety of surfaces. High lands and low, level expanses and steep slopes, plains, tablelands, hill lands, and mountains are arranged in endless combinations. Because there are so many types of surfaces, it may seem that they are distributed over the earth without order and that an understanding of their nature and arrangement, or even a systematic descrip-

tion of them, is beyond the ability of the beginning student. Actually, however, the land surface is quite capable of objective, specific, and, if desired, quantitative description.

If many small areas are carefully compared in order to determine precisely how the land form of each is unlike that of the others, there is soon accumulated a long list of specific differences in the terrain samples.

And if this list is analyzed, it becomes apparent that the many differences may be grouped under the four major headings of (*a*) slope, (*b*) surface material, (*c*) arrangement, and (*d*) dimensions. That is, the differences between any two sections of the land surface may be expressed in terms of these four major topics.

Slope　Slope refers simply to the inclination of the land surface at a particular spot. Normally any section of the surface measuring a few miles across is made up of many small bits of sloping land, each one differing from its neighbors in steepness. Steep slopes, gentle slopes, and slopes of intermediate steepness may all be present in a single area. However, there is a great difference between one area

and another in the predominance of each of these major slope classes. For example, a section of the Texas coastal plain near Houston may be 95 per cent occupied by very gentle slopes, while in a section of hilly southwestern Wisconsin only 30 per cent of the area may be gently sloping, with intermediate and steep slopes occupying the greater part of the area (Fig. 2.1). It is doubtful that any other bit of information could tell as much about the fundamental contrast between these two regions. The figures not only suggest the contrasting appearance of the areas but also hint at important differences in the usefulness of the land.

Surface material　Most of the earth's land surface is covered with relatively fine-

FIG. 2.1　An example of contrast in slope. (a) is from the Driftless Area of southwestern Wisconsin, (b) from coastal plain near Corpus Christi, Texas. *(From U.S. Geological Survey topographic sheets: Boaz, Wis., and Petronilla, Tex.)*

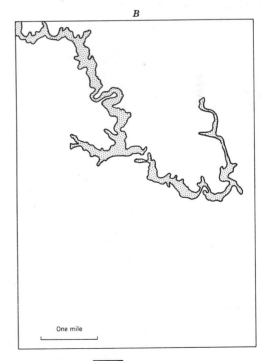

☐ Gentle slopes　▒ Moderate slopes　■ Steep slopes

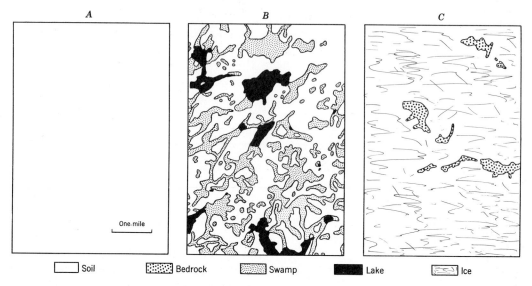

FIG. 2.2 An example of contrast in nature of surface material. (a) is from rolling prairies of northwestern Missouri, (b) from morainic plains of northern Minnesota, (c) from southern Alaska. *(From U.S. Geological Survey topographic sheets: Bethany, Mo., Ely, Minn., and Seward A-8, Alaska.)*

particled mineral matter with some partially decomposed organic debris mixed in. Wherever such soil (using the term in a very broad sense) does not make up the surface layer, it is a fact worth knowing. Surfaces of bare bedrock, of loose sand, of cobbles and boulders, of permanent ice, and of standing water are fundamentally different from soil surfaces, in appearance and feel as well as in origin and function. The character of the bedrock many feet below the surface and the chemical and detailed physical properties of even the surface layers do not as a rule belong in a list of terrain elements. But clearly the gross physical nature of the surficial materials cannot be omitted from a terrain description without running the risk of serious misrepresentation. It would, for example, be futile to attempt a characterization of Finland or of much of northern and eastern Canada without mentioning almost at the outset that standing water and exposed bedrock together probably occupy as much or more of the area

than is covered by soil. The icecap of Antarctica, the sand-dune seas of the Libyan Sahara, and the great coastal marshes of South Carolina and Georgia all owe much of their distinctive character to their unusual surface materials (Fig. 2.2).

Arrangements Arrangements are the relative positions of features within an area. Streams, ridge crests, peaks, areas of gentle slope, steep bluffs, and exposures of bare rock are all set upon the land surface in distinctive groupings that vary from place to place. Some of these arrangements, or *patterns,* may be best seen from an airplane or on a map. In some regions pattern is one of the most striking of all characteristics, especially where it departs from the usual treelike arrangement of valleys or streams and the divides between them. The remarkably parallel arrangement of ridges in the middle belt of the Appalachians between central Pennsylvania and northern Alabama, the random dotting of small isolated volcanic hills on the

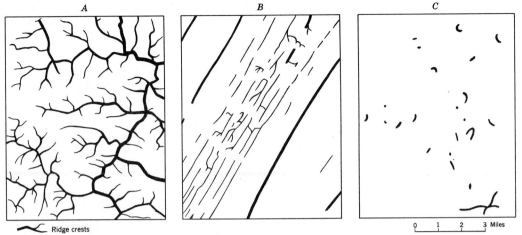

Ridge crests

FIG. 2.3 An example of contrast in pattern of ridge crests and summits. (a) is in the Driftless Area of southwestern Wisconsin, (b) in the Appalachian Ridge and Valley region of central Pennsylvania, (c) in an area of volcanic cones in south central Oregon. *(From U.S. Geological Survey topographic sheets: La Farge, Wis., Orbisonia, Pa., and Newberry Crater, Ore.)*

plains of south central Oregon, and the aimless maze of lakes, swamps, and streams in northeastern Minnesota are indispensable to any meaningful description of these regions (Fig. 2.3). The patterns distinguish the character of the terrain; they are highly significant clues to the geological history of the region; and they are clearly reflected in other geographical patterns, such as those of soils, of native vegetation, and of agricultural utilization of the land.

Vertical arrangements are also significant, especially *profiles*, a profile in this sense being the change of slope or gradient along a given line. Included here are such characteristics as the cross-section forms of valleys; the evenness, jaggedness, or presence of deep clefts in major mountain crests; and the various changes in gradient of streams from their headwaters down to their mouths. Regional contrasts in these are sometimes striking and important (Figs. 2.4, 2.5). The student of

FIG. 2.4 The continuously high crest line of the Sierra Nevada of California (a) contrasts sharply with the deeply serrated crest of the Cascade Range in Washington (b). The openings near the ends of the lower profile are railroad tunnels. *(From Army Map Service series V502: Fresno and Wenatchee sheets.)*

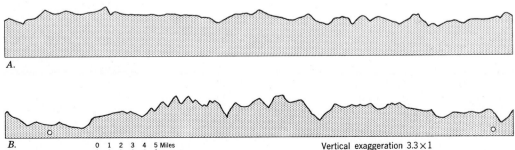

A.

B.

0 1 2 3 4 5 Miles

Vertical exaggeration 3.3 × 1

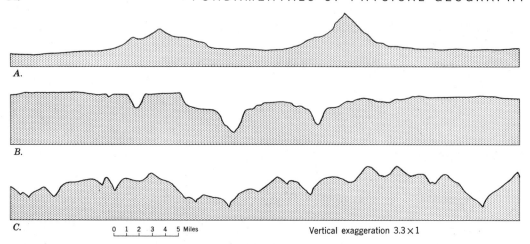

A.

B.

C.   0 1 2 3 4 5 Miles   Vertical exaggeration 3.3 × 1

FIG. 2.5 Example of contrasting transverse profiles in areas of high
relief. (a) is from Basin and Range province in Nevada, (b) from Colorado
Plateaus in northern Arizona, and (c) from Rocky Mountains of Idaho.
*(From U.S. Geological Survey topographic sheets: Sonoma Range, Nev., Diamond Creek,
Ariz., and Lolo, Idaho.)*

earth history finds cross-section profiles of
valleys and divides and the longways profiles
of streams especially valuable, for they may
sometimes be used to determine previous up-

lifts of the earth's crust in an area, earlier
variations in the volume of its streams, and
the effects of the nature of the rocks upon
the processes of erosion. These examples

FIG. 2.6 Example of contrast in texture, or spacing of valleys and
ravines. The patterns are similar, but the textures are strikingly different.
(a) is from Badlands of southwestern South Dakota, (b) from central
Missouri. *(From U.S. Geological Survey topographic sheets: Cuny Table East, S. Dak.,
and Nelson, Mo.)*

A   *B*

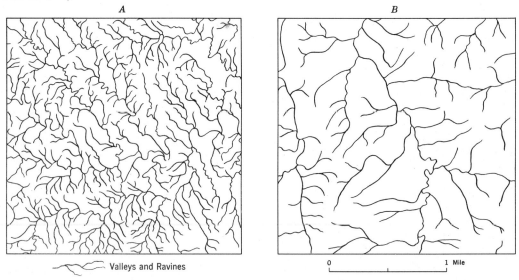

⌐⌐⌐⌐ Valleys and Ravines   0   1 Mile

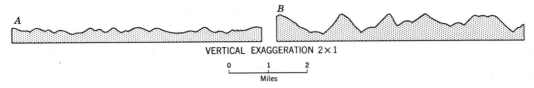

VERTICAL EXAGGERATION 2×1

0   1   2
Miles

FIG. 2.7 Contrasting local relief in two areas of rough lands. (a) is from Missouri Ozarks, (b) from Appalachians in central West Virginia. *(From U.S. Geological Survey topographic sheets: Round Spring, Mo., and Bald Knob, W. Va.)*

will suggest that profiles of the terrain may relate also to other aspects of geography, including utilization of the land by man.

Dimensions Dimensions give scale to the characterization. Without a knowledge of such numerical values as the height of ridges, the width and depth of valleys, the spacing of streams, and the size of patches of gently sloping land, it is impossible to visualize a landscape that is being described.

Important among the dimensions in the horizontal plane are the spacings of valleys, ridges and streams, and the widths of patches of gentle and steep slope, of bodies of water, and of patches of particular kinds of material. Areas similar in other characteristics are sometimes strikingly different in horizontal dimensions (Fig. 2.6). Areas in which widths and spacings of features are relatively large are spoken of as *coarse-textured;* those in which horizontal dimensions are small are *fine-textured.*

In the vertical direction, the dimensions of the terrain of a limited area are given by various expressions of *local relief,* or difference in elevation. For a general expression of local relief, the difference in elevation between the highest and lowest points in the small area is sometimes used. Or a figure may be used that indicates the average or prevalent height of crests above the adjacent valley bottoms in the area. The relief along crest lines, on local uplands, and along valley floors or streams may also be of interest. Local relief is a characteristic of considerable descriptive value, suggesting at once something of the scale of features and the degree of irregularity within the area being considered (Fig. 2.7). If the local relief in an area is only 50 ft, it is evident that the surface must be either nearly flat or marked by only small roughnesses. But a local relief of 5,000 ft immediately suggests a landscape of considerable grandeur, though without specifying what form its great features may take. When combined with data on slopes and profiles, local relief is one of the most revealing of all generalized expressions of terrain character.

TYPES OF LAND SURFACES AND THEIR OCCURRENCE

THE CONCEPT OF TERRAIN TYPES

In the preceding paragraphs it has been suggested that a land surface, even a complex one, can be effectively analyzed by considering it in terms of specific characteristics. Many can be described in quantitative terms, others with reasonable precision by words or diagrams. A complete and systematic description of the land surface of an area employs all available techniques—verbal, numerical, cartographic, and pictorial—in order to speak objectively, precisely and clearly. With such specific and systematic information, it becomes possible to compare, characteristic by characteristic, any one bit of the earth's surface with any other bit.

When large numbers of terrain samples from all over the world are so compared, certain combinations of major characteristics occur again and again in widely separated places. Given these similarities, a number of distinct types of terrain that may be recognized whenever they occur, and that together make up the entire surface of the continents, may be defined at least in the general terms of a few major characteristics. They are comparable to the climatic types defined in later chapters.

MAJOR CLASSES OF LAND SURFACES

The scheme of land-form types to be used here is based upon similarities and differences with respect to three major characteristics: relative amount of gently sloping land, local relief, and generalized profile. On the basis of the first two characteristics alone we may distinguish among (a) *plains,* having a predominance of gently sloping land, coupled with low relief, (b) *plains with some features of considerable relief,* also dominated by gently sloping land but having moderate to high local relief, (c) *hills,* with little gently sloping land and with low to moderate relief, and (d) *mountains,* which have little gently sloping land and high local relief.

The second group, plains with some features of considerable relief, may be further subdivided on the basis of whether the existing large amount of gently sloping land occurs in the lower part of the profile or in the upper part. If most of the gently sloping land lies at relatively low levels, with steep slopes rising above it, the surfaces may be designated *plains with hills or mountains.* If, on the other hand, most of the nearly level land lies relatively high, with canyon walls or long lines of bluffs (escarpments) dropping down from it, the surfaces may be called *tablelands.* If the relief is slight or if the amount of gently sloping land is not large, this profile distinction is less fundamentally significant, so it is not used here as a basis for subdividing plains, hills, and mountains. Figures 2.8 and 2.9 give examples of the principal terrain classes. Figure 2.10 shows schematically how the classes are defined.

It must be fully realized that within each of these five major classes of land surfaces, which have been defined in terms of only two or three characteristics that seem particularly important to visualization or to utility, there exists a vast variety, based upon differences in other characteristics. Some plains, for instance, are conspicuously flat and swampy, others are rolling and well-drained, and still others are simply broad expanses of smooth ice. Similarly, some mountains are low, smooth-sloped, and arranged in parallel ridges, while others are exceedingly high, with rugged, rocky slopes and great glaciers and snow fields. The subdivision that has been outlined is intended to bring out only the most striking contrasts among land surfaces and to provide a general basis for systematic discussion of land surfaces and their origin as well as the general surface character of the various continents.

WORLD PATTERN OF LAND FORM

DISTRIBUTION OF LAND SURFACES

Plate 3 shows the distribution of the major land-form classes over the earth. In

FIG. 2.8 Examples of the three smoother classes of terrain: (a) rolling plains in southwestern Iowa; (b) Canyon de Chelly National Monument in northeastern Arizona, a remarkably clear-cut example of a tableland; (c) Hopi Buttes near Winslow, Arizona, a plain with hills and mountains. [*(a) Soil Conservation Service; (b) and (c) Spence Air Photos.*]

A

B

C

A

FIG. 2.9 Examples of the two rougher classes of terrain: (a) an
extensive hill land, the Lammerlaws, in the southern part of South Island,
New Zealand, and (b) high mountain country in the Alaska Range.
[(a) White's Aviation Photograph; (b) Kirk H. Stone.]

B

addition to the five classes defined above, several significant subclasses have been shown. The conspicuously flat plains have been distinguished from the more irregular ones, the mountains of particularly high relief have been separated from the rest, and the few broad icecaps of the world have been shown by an entirely separate symbol.

The following table, which was derived directly from Plate 3, shows that the major types of land surfaces are neither equal in total extent nor evenly distributed among the continents. The more irregular types of plains are especially widespread, suggesting that conditions favoring the development of such surfaces have been common in late geologic time. On the other hand, the generation of tablelands and flat plains requires sets of circumstances that have not occurred so widely. It will be seen later that each of these kinds of surfaces demands rather specific and limited circumstances to arise at all.

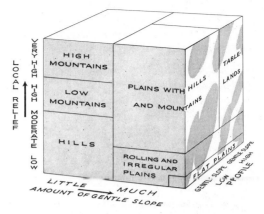

FIG. 2.10 How the principal classes of terrain are defined and how they are related to each other.

COMPLEXITY OF THE WORLD PATTERN

The world's land-form pattern is undeniably complex. However, a study of Plate 3 and other maps of surface form reveals broadly systematic arrangements and general similarities and variations among the continents that help to reduce the apparent chaos.

Percentage of Continental and World Land Areas Occupied by Major Land-surface Types

	North America	South America	Eurasia	Africa	Australia — New Zealand	Antarctica	World
Flat plains	7	18	2	1	4	0	5
Rolling and irregular plains	30	29	30	44	51	0	31
Tablelands	6	14	3	5	1	0	5
Plains with hills or mountains	9	7	10	22	19	0	11
Hills	15	8	11	11	12	0	10
Low mountains	9	13	21	13	12	0	14
High mountains	16	11	23	4	1	0	13
Icecaps	8	0	0	0	0	100	11
Percentage of world area	16	12	36	20	6	10	100

A useful starting point in considering the world pattern is the *cordilleran belts,* the great bands that contain most of the world's major mountain systems together with various basins and lands of lesser roughness. The principal cordilleran systems form a nearly continuous ring about the Pacific Ocean Basin and thrust a long arm westward through southern Eurasia to the Atlantic. Sometimes they are described as a group of three arms radiating from a "knot" in the Pamir region of the Afghanistan-U.S.S.R. frontier (Fig. 2.11). Thus both of the Americas and Eurasia have long cordilleran segments running along one side of the continent, forming for each an immense "backbone" to which the less rugged remainder of the continent is attached. Africa and Australia lack such well-marked cordilleran bands, though in each of them there is a relatively rough zone running from north to south through the eastern part of the land mass.

In the Americas and Eurasia there is, toward the Atlantic margin, secondary rough land, less rugged than the cordilleran belt opposite it. Between the two rough belts lie the most extensive plains of these three continents. In Africa and Australia the pattern is more patchy, with large areas of plains intermingled with areas of moderate roughness comparable to the secondary rough lands of the cordilleran continents. The Antarctic Continent is so largely covered by ice that little is known of the form of its bedrock surface except that it is in part ruggedly mountainous. It is believed possible that the "continent" beneath the ice may actually involve more than one land mass.

INDIVIDUAL CONTINENTS

North America   North America is a roughly average continent in the proportional occurrence of the various types of land form. Along its western side is a broad and com-

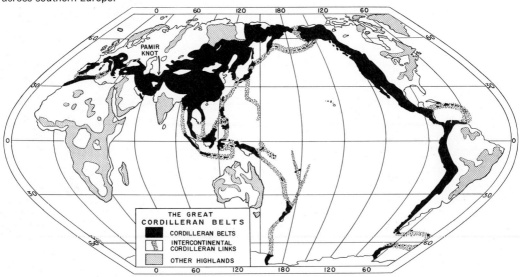

FIG. 2.11   The great cordilleran belts of the world are all interconnected. They may be considered as three great arms radiating from the Pamir knot, two of them embracing the Pacific Ocean Basin, the third reaching westward across southern Europe.

plex cordilleran belt that occupies most of Alaska, more than a quarter of Canada and the United States, and all but an interrupted east-coastal strip in Mexico and Central America. In the United States and northern Mexico, where it achieves a width of about 1,000 miles, the cordillera is made up of loosely linked mountain strands separated by extensive basins and tablelands, considerable parts of which do not drain to the sea. North and south of this section it becomes narrower and more continuously rough.

The extensive secondary rough land of North America includes the Ozark-Ouachita and Appalachian-New England areas, irregular margins of the great Canadian Shield, and the major portion of the Arctic Islands. Most of this area is made up of hills and low mountains, but in the eastern Arctic the ruggedness becomes extreme and icecaps become prominent. Greenland accounts for nearly one-tenth of the world's area of icecap.

The North American plains lie between these two bands of rougher land, with a further extension along the Atlantic Coast in the southeastern United States. The interior plains, with significant exceptions, are irregular and rise gradually toward the west, reaching elevations of 3,000 to 6,000 ft at the base of the Rocky Mountains. The northern sections are notable for their abundant lakes and swamps. The southeastern plains are low and frequently marshy near the coast, rising and becoming better-drained and more irregular inland.

South America South America is similar to North America in having a western cordillera, secondary rough lands to the east, and extensive plains between. However, the nature of the three parts is strikingly different.

The South American cordillera, the Andes, is higher, more continuous, and much nar-

rower than that of the northern continent, its greatest width being no more than 500 miles. Except in the extreme north and south there are no real breaks in the mountain wall, and in the central section the elevation of the divide continuously exceeds 10,000 ft for a distance of 2,000 miles. In the widest central section are broad basins at great elevation, strongly resembling those of the high uplands of Tibet.

The secondary rough land is in two sections, separated by the lower Amazon plains. The northern and smaller section, known as the Guiana Highlands, is largely a loose array of groups and ranges of low mountains rising from the plains. The much larger Brazilian Highlands are a great platform that rises gradually from the Amazon lowlands toward the southeastern margin, where it drops abruptly to the sea. Most of the rough part of this section is along the high southeastern edge; the interior parts are upland plains and tablelands.

The plains of South America occupy nearly half the continent and form the major part of the drainage basins of its three greatest river systems, the Orinoco, the Amazon, and the Paraguay-Paraná. They lie at low elevations and contain (especially the southern basin) larger areas of flat land than are found in North America. The plains reach broadly to the Atlantic near the river mouths, and on the west abut directly, at low elevation, against the foot of the Andes. Only in the extreme south is there a more elevated section, the Plateau of Patagonia, a counterpart for the High Plains of North America.

Eurasia Eurasia is by far the largest, the roughest, and the most complex of the continents. Less than one-third of its area is plain, and that is split into numerous pieces. Like the Americas, it may be regarded as having a cordillera, a secondary rough land, and inter-vening plains, but these are vastly different in form, position, and proportion from those in the New World continents.

The Eurasian cordillera covers nearly half of its land mass. In the west, from Spain to western Iran, it is of moderate width, and is composed of loosely linked mountain systems separated by broad, low basins, some drowned by the sea, and broken by numerous low, transverse gaps such as the valley of the Rhone River and the straits of the Bosporus and Dardanelles. Two strands of mountains, completely separated from the rest by the narrow straits of the Mediterranean, form the Atlas Mountains of northwest Africa. In the Middle East the basin levels become higher and the low breaks disappear. In and just beyond the Pamir knot the mountains surge to extreme heights and begin the fanwise spreading that carries the cordillera into all parts of eastern Asia. This section of the con-tinent, with its tangled ranges and huge inter-montane basins, is the most complex and extensive cordilleran area in the world. The belt even continues into the sea along the rugged island chains of Indonesia and Japan and hurdles the Bering Sea to join with the backbone of the Americas. Along the northern margin of the cordillera are a number of areas of hills, low mountains, and tablelands, the largest being the extensive upland of central Siberia.

The principal plain of Eurasia occupies much of the northwestern quarter of the con-tinent. Like the plains of South America this great wedge of smooth land lies at low ele-vations, even to the very foot of the cordil-leran ranges. As in North America the north-ern part of the plain contains many lakes and swamps. The flat lowland of northwestern Siberia is the most extensive swampland in the world. The dry southeastern part of the plain does not drain to the open ocean but to the immense salt lakes called the Caspian and Aral Seas. In addition to this most ex-tensive plain, Eurasia possesses several others of considerable size, most notably those of Iraq, of north India and Pakistan, and of north China and Manchuria.

The secondary rough land of Eurasia is small and divided, occupying the Scandina-vian Peninsula and much of the British Isles. It is largely open hill-and-low-mountain country, though in Norway it achieves con-siderable elevation. The Ural Mountains form a curious and unique isolated north-south band of rough country in interior Russia.

The Arabian and Indian Peninsulas are an element in Eurasian geography that has no counterpart, for location, in the Americas. These peninsulas, lying beyond the cordil-lera, are both tilted platforms, highest on the west, that bear some resemblance to the Brazilian Highlands and are even more closely related to sections of Africa. The Arabian Peninsula may in all respects be considered a detached fragment of Saharan Africa, just as the African Atlas is a detached strip of Europe. There is little to distinguish its sur-face from that of northeastern Africa, which faces it across the Red Sea. Peninsular India is higher and more irregular, much like southeastern Brazil and parts of west central Africa.

Africa   Africa differs from the three con-tinents already discussed in that it has no true cordilleran backbone. High mountains are scarce. Surfaces smoother than hill lands make up nearly three-quarters of the total area. From the southern Sahara southward, Africa may be regarded as a series of broad, shallow basins separated by somewhat higher swells or thresholds. Generally speaking, the basin surfaces are largely plains, while the swells are commonly hill-studded plains or are carved into hills or low mountains. The long line of swells that traverses eastern Africa from north to south is especially high and in many places rugged and broken. The detached block of Madagascar is somewhat similar to the rougher sections of this swell. This central and southern part of Africa is moderately elevated (principally to the south and east), and the outer swells drop with varying degrees of abruptness to the sea or to relatively narrow coastal plains.

Saharan Africa is generally lower than the southern part of the continent. It is largely plain and low tableland, with several areas of hilly or mountainous terrain. The trough of the Red Sea and the rugged swell adjacent to it separate the Sahara from the similar Arabian peninsula.

Australia Australia somewhat resembles northern Africa, being largely low-lying and smooth-surfaced. Along the eastern margin of the continent runs a swell of moderate elevation and roughness, the closest approach to an Australian cordillera. As in northern Africa, most of the interior is dry, and considerable areas of it do not have through drainage to the sea.

By way of contrast, New Zealand is distinctly cordilleran, with predominantly rough terrain that also characterizes the Indonesian and other islands north and northeast of Australia along the same general structural line.

CHAPTER 3

How surface form develops

TIME AND PROCESS

The shortness of man's span of life led ancient peoples into a false idea of the permanence of the natural features of the earth's surface. Since little change could be seen, even over a space of several generations of mankind, it was natural to think of the landscape as essentially "given" and unchanging. Only along certain river courses and seacoasts and near unusually active volcanoes could significant changes be noticed, and these could be regarded as exceptions, perhaps as willful acts of the gods.

But even now, when something is known of both the vast reaches of geologic time and the extreme changeability of land surfaces, man's short life is a poor yardstick with which to measure and understand the rates of earth-shaping events. It is like trying to express the distance from the earth to the moon in inches: the resulting numbers are so large they are meaningless. It is difficult to realize how much can be accomplished over millions of years of geologic time by the almost imperceptibly slow processes that can be seen at work today. Yet a simple computation shows that a canyon 1,000 ft deep could be cut in no more than a million years by a stream eroding its bed at the modest rate of just over 1 in. per century. In the history of the earth's surface development, there has been abundant time for slow processes to alter the surface greatly and repeatedly. The lands in their present form are in no way permanent but represent only a momentary stage in a long and complex history of change.

The natural processes that have produced and are producing alterations of the terrain are in a general way known and understood, though there is much yet to be learned about the details of their workings. It is convenient to group them into two major sets: (*a*) those that move, or locally change the composition of, the rocky crust of the earth (*tectonic* processes), and (*b*) those that move material about from place to place over the surface, picking up here and depositing there (*gradational* processes). These two sets of happenings go on at the same time and, as will be seen, commonly work in opposing directions. The land surface at any moment in earth history therefore indicates the existing state of affairs in a never-ending war between tectonics and gradation.

CHANGES IN THE CRUST

Nature of the crust The rocky outer shell of the earth was originally termed the "crust" of the earth because it was thought to enclose a completely molten interior. Although it is now believed that most of the interior is not liquid but very dense solid material, the term has been retained to refer to the thin outermost layer composed of the familiar types of rocks that occur at the surface (Fig. 3.1). These crustal materials are much less dense than those of the layers beneath. The crust probably averages less than 20 miles in thickness, and is much thinner beneath the ocean floors than under the continents.

Especially important to the development of surface form is the fact that the crust, although it seems very rigid, is actually not so in relation to the tremendous forces that attack it. Furthermore, the layers immediately beneath it, which are evidently extremely hot and dense solid-rock materials, are capable of very slow flowage or other deformation, much like an exceedingly stiff or viscous

FIG. 3.1 Internal structure of the earth. The heavy outer line represents the crust, too thin to be shown otherwise.

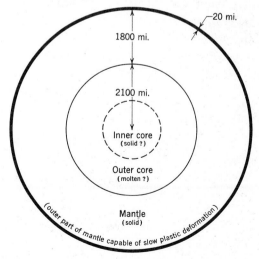

FIG. 3.2   A portion of a folded rock structure that has been exposed in a stream valley. *(U.S. Geological Survey.)*

liquid. This combination of relatively weak crust and somewhat unstable underpinning makes possible the deformation of the crust, provided there are forces strong enough to produce it. Since there is abundant evidence that the crust has in fact been warped, buckled, and shattered, it is clear that such forces do exist though little is yet known of their nature or causes.

Movements of the crust   Examination of the existing structure and arrangement of rock layers at or near the surface of the earth indicates clearly that over the long reaches of geologic history the crust has been subjected to almost every conceivable sort of bending, breaking, uplift, and depression. Rock strata originally laid down as horizontal sheets of sediment on the shallow sea floor are now found gently inclined, warped into broad domes and basins, or thrown into gigantic wrinkles such as would be obtained

by jamming an immense carpet against an unyielding wall (Fig. 3.2). In places the crust has broken under the stress, and the sections on the two sides of the break have slipped vertically or horizontally relative to one another. When bending or breaking, sections of the crust have been raised or lowered, so that, for example, rocks containing fossil sea life may be found thousands of feet above the present sea level. Almost everywhere rocks are more or less shattered as a result of having been subjected to severe stresses at some time in the near or distant past.

Examples of crustal movement   A few examples may give a clearer picture of the variety of crustal movements that can occur.

The American Middle West is an excellent case of relatively simple and gentle warping of the crust. Here between the Appalachian and Rocky Mountains, the rock strata, mostly ancient marine sediments, have been cast into a series of shallow domes and basins. Rarely are the beds inclined at angles of more than a few degrees. However, because of the long distances involved, a single stratum may appear at the surface in one locality, only to descend to a depth of several thousand feet below the surface a few hundred miles away. Much of the warping appears to have occurred long ago in geologic time. Even considering its gentle deformation, this area must be regarded as one of the more stable parts of the earth's crust.

The central strip of the Appalachians displays much more intense disturbance of the crust. Rock strata similar in age and nature to those in the Middle West have been folded into a remarkable series of long, nearly parallel wrinkles measuring thousands of feet in height and several miles from crest to crest.

In many mountainous areas, such as the Alps, the Himalayas, and parts of the Rockies, folding of the rocks has been still more vigorous and so complicated by fracturing of the crust as to produce a jammed and broken structure of bewildering complexity (Fig. 3.3). In some of these areas it is estimated that the crust has been shortened by several tens of miles by horizontal compression and buckling.

In some places folding appears to have been less significant than breaking and displacement (faulting) of the crust. Prominent fractures (faults) develop, and over a long period of time vertical or horizontal slippages may occur repeatedly along them. By this means large blocks of the crust may be raised, lowered, or moved horizontally tens, hundreds, or thousands of feet relative to adjacent sections (Fig. 3.4). The towering east face of the Sierra Nevada Range of California owes its great height to large-scale upward movement of the mountain block along a series of faults that follow the eastern base of the range (Fig. 3.5). Many of the smaller ranges of Nevada and western Utah are raised or tilted fault blocks, as is the high Wasatch Range that rises immediately behind Salt Lake City. In eastern Africa an extensive series of trenchlike valleys has been formed by movements along parallel faults in such fashion that long strips of the crust have been left depressed between higher blocks to either side. The Red Sea and the Dead Sea occupy northerly parts of this valley system (Fig. 3.6).

It should not be thought that large-scale folding or faulting occurs in single swift

FIG. 3.3 Simple and complex deformation of the crust. (a) shows simple open folding in the Appalachian Ridge and Valley region in West Virginia and Pennsylvania. (b) shows combined folding and compressional faulting in the Rocky Mountains of southeastern Idaho. [*(a) After U.S. Geological Survey Geological Folio 179; (b) after U.S. Geological Survey Professional Paper 238.*]

A. Simple folding

B. Complex folding and faulting

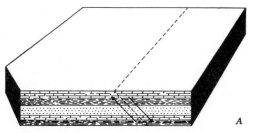

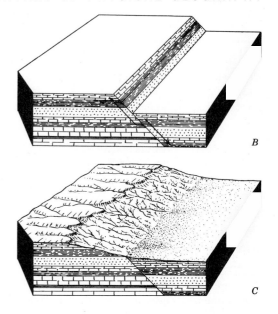

FIG. 3.4   Development of a normal fault in stratified rock: (a) the strata before faulting; (b) fault, showing direction of displacement and the fault scarp (cliff); (c) modification of the fault scarp by erosion. *(V. C. Finch.)*

cataclysms. Instead the movements proceed very slowly, sometimes intermittently or even jerkily. During historical times it has been possible to record some crustal movements, but none has been extreme in size. The coast of the Baltic Sea, for example, has been rising at a rate of about 3 ft per century, while the outer part of the Mississippi River Delta in Louisiana is apparently sinking at a similar rate. On the other hand, displacement along fault lines is often sudden, the result of an abrupt giving way to stresses that have

FIG. 3.5   The rugged eastern face of the Sierra Nevada in California is a dissected fault scarp. Mount Whitney, at right, rises nearly 8,000 ft above the gentle slopes in the foreground. *(Spence Air Photos.)*

built up over a considerable time. These sudden movements often produce strong vibrations, or earthquakes, that may travel long distances through the crust. Yet observed fault displacements in single earthquake-producing movements rarely exceed a few inches, and never more than a few tens of feet. In the violent San Francisco earthquake of 1906, the maximum observed displacement was 21 ft, indicated by the horizontal offset of a road. It must be remembered, of course, that however small or slow folding and faulting are, the time available for their operation is great. It is clear that processes of the order indicated by these examples can produce immense changes in the crust if they are enabled to proceed over a period of a few million years.

Molten material in the crust Normally both the crust and the layers of material beneath it are in the solid state in spite of the high temperatures that prevail below the surface. Yet repeatedly during geologic history, large masses of material in the deeper crust or immediately beneath the crust have become molten and forced their way toward the surface. The complex reasons why these molten masses develop are not well understood, though the masses are known to come into being most frequently in areas of active crustal deformation.

The upward movement of the molten materials and the various phenomena that accompany that movement are collectively known as *vulcanism*. Gases are given off, water in the ground is boiled into steam, and the molten rock forces its way upward, partly by melting the rocks above it and partly by passing through fractures. The various rising materials sometimes reach the surface, causing the often spectacular events known as volcanic activity (extrusive vulcanism). Most of the molten material cools and hardens again into solid rock before reaching the surface (intrusive vulcanism).

In extrusive vulcanism much rock material, as well as quantities of gases and steam, is forced out onto the surface of the earth. Some is emitted rather quietly as molten rock or lava; some is vigorously blown out in solid form, in particles varying from fine dust to large boulders. Some volcanoes characteristically erupt in a series of explosions, often of tremendous force. This happens when the vent of the volcano has been sealed over by quick-hardening lavas, allowing extreme pressures to build up underneath. Vesuvius is a familiar example of an explosive volcano.

FIG. 3.6 An immense system of fault valleys (grabens, or rift valleys) extends through much of east Africa and neighboring areas. *(From Machatschek and others.)*

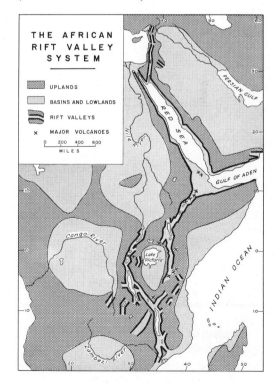

FIG. 3.7 The volcano Parícutin, Mexico, in violent eruption. Typical steep-sided cinder cone. *(American Museum of Natural History.)*

Krakatau, in Indonesia, and Katmai, in Alaska, have created two of the greatest explosions of human record: each mountain nearly destroyed itself by blasts of unbelievable violence. As would be expected, the percentage of solid material, or ash, in the products ejected by explosive volcanoes is high (Fig. 3.7). On the other hand, many volcanoes emit slow-cooling lavas that have less tendency to plug the vents. Such eruptions are quieter and often produce a much lower percentage of ash. The volcanoes of Hawaii are of this type.

Effects of crustal disturbances Both crustal movement and vulcanism produce two quite different sets of results that are important to the development of surface form. First, each immediately and directly produces irregularities in the surface. But further, each invariably leaves behind an arrangement of diverse rock materials in the crust, a *rock structure,* upon which the surface-sculpturing forces will thereafter have to work. In the long run the second effect is the more far-reaching. The surface irregularities are soon destroyed or altered beyond recognition by the sculpturing processes, while the rock structures, reaching deep into the crust, may persist for eons, always modifying, through their variations in resistance, the activities of the sculpturing processes that are at work upon them.

Geologic structure, indeed, is important to the development of land form largely because of differences in the rate at which the various structured rock materials yield to sculpturing. Some rocks are much more resistant than others, and hence will continue to stand firm when neighboring materials have been eroded away. Areas where resistant rocks are at the surface will tend to remain as heights and ridges, while weak-rock areas will be eroded to valleys and lowlands.

The pattern of strong and weak rocks at the surface is largely set by the structure, and therefore by the history of crustal disturbance. Areas where the crust has been stable normally show simpler structures and simpler patterns of surface geology than areas where the crust has been strongly deformed or invaded by molten materials. Layered rocks that have been tilted or folded will occur at the surface in bands of varying thickness and pattern, with different bands displaying differing degrees of resistance. Intrusive rocks, those that have cooled and hardened from a molten state without reaching the surface, will occur in masses, sheets, and fingers of varying sizes, that commonly differ from the surrounding rocks in resistance. They can affect the course of surface sculpture only when the rocks overlying them have been stripped away (Fig. 3.8). This may be long ages after the vulcanism which placed them occurred.

Although movements of the crust are largely responsible for the major differences that exist in the elevation of the surface, the forms that occur on the elevated or depressed sections are often not direct results of crustal disturbance. For as soon as crustal disturbance begins to produce any irregularity of the surface, the sculpturing forces go to work on it, cutting into the raised sections and depositing in the low. Therefore by the time the crustal movement is completed, the surface may have been powerfully modified by surface sculpture, and may bear little resemblance to the surface form that would exist had there been no erosion or deposition. A glance at Fig. 3.3, for example, reveals a striking lack of correspondence between the form of the present mountain surface and the shape of the underlying folds.

Only where crustal disturbance has been so recent and so rapid that the sculpturing forces have been utterly unable to keep pace do land forms occur that can be said to be distinctly tectonic in their origin. Some of the more striking examples of this are (*a*) volcanic cones, produced by the accumulation of ash and lava about an active vent, (*b*) extensive lava plains, formed by the emission of quantities of highly fluid, slow-cooling lavas, (*c*) fault scarps, which are cliffs resulting from large vertical fault displacements, and (*d*) smooth domes, swells, and similar features, usually small, that indicate relatively rapid and recent folding. Usually even these forms show a certain amount of gullying and other modification by streams, glaciers, or gravity. Strongly sculptured counterparts of them are much more common.

But tectonically produced surface forms,

FIG. 3.8 A vertical sheet of intrusive rock (a dike) that stands in relief because it is more resistant to erosion than the rocks on either side of it. Near Spanish Peaks in southern Colorado. *(U.S. Geological Survey.)*

like all others, are, by geologic time scales, short-lived. It is probable that even a great mountain range can be destroyed by the surface forces in no more than 20 to 40 million years, and the major portion of the destruction would occur in the first few million. Rock structures, on the other hand, as long as they are not stripped away by surface erosion, will last indefinitely. The folded structure of the Appalachians is perhaps 250 million years old, that of the Scottish Highlands perhaps twice as old. Numerous generations of surface forms have developed and vanished on these structures, but always their development has been strongly affected by the nature and arrangement of the underlying rocks, that is, by the structure that was formed so long ago.

World pattern of crustal disturbance
There are vast differences from place to place over the earth in how much the crust has been disturbed in past times and in how active it is now. Some areas appear to have suffered strong and repeated disturbance over a long span of geologic time and are still

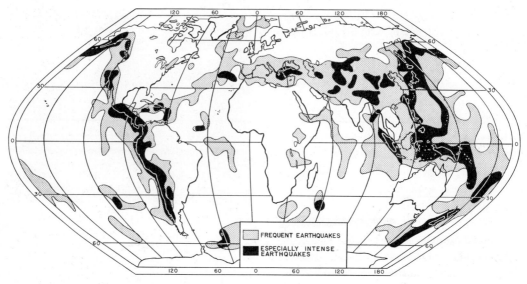

FIG. 3.9   The principal earthquake regions of the world. *(After Leet.)*

active. Others have not undergone anything more severe than mild warping for hundreds of millions of years. Still others indicate, by their disordered structures involving ancient rocks, that they were active zones in times past, but show no evidence of recent deformation.

The location of areas of past deformation may be determined from geological maps that show disordered structures of various ages. Areas of present disturbance can be located by the occurrence of earthquakes (Fig. 3.9) or volcanic activity (Fig. 3.10), by significant changes in level along coasts, and also simply

FIG. 3.10   The principal volcanic regions of the world. *(After Karl Sapper, Vulkankunde.)*

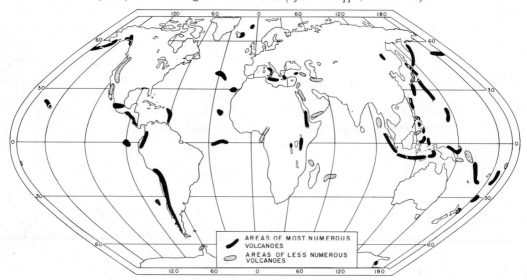

by the occurrence of mountains or other features of high relief (Plate 3). These maps all show the areas of greatest disturbance in late geologic time to be especially concentrated in the cordilleran bands that encircle the Pacific Ocean Basin and extend across southern Eurasia. In earlier geologic time several other areas were active, notably parts of the Atlantic borderlands. Especially stable sections of the crust include central North America, interior South America, parts of northern Europe, and much of Africa and Australia. The reasons for this pattern of crustal disturbance are not well understood as yet and will not be discussed here.

CHANGES AT THE SURFACE

THE IDEA OF SURFACE SCULPTURE

Any process that can pick up soil or rock material at some point on the earth's surface and move it somewhere else can thereby change—sculpture—the surface form. Where the picking up (erosion) occurs, the surface is lowered; where the material is subsequently laid down, the surface is raised. In a complex combination, such erosion and deposition work upon surfaces and structures modified by crustal disturbances, and the diverse forms of the land surface are produced.

The specific natural *agents* that are able to move surface materials are several: running water (both in streams and in thin unchanneled sheets), glacier ice, the wind, waves and currents in lakes or the sea, and gravity. Gravity, an erosional and depositional agent in its own right, is also significant in the working of the other agents. The result is that when material is picked up and moved by any agent, it most commonly comes to rest at a lower elevation than where it began. The long-run effect is for higher parts of the surface to be lowered by erosion and low sections to be raised by deposition, thus reducing the over-all surface irregularity. The surface may be locally roughened for a while by the cutting of erosional valleys in uplands; but eventually, through the widening of the valleys and the lowering of the high ground between them, the surface becomes relatively smooth. It is for this reason that the agents working at the surface are often called the gradational agents.

BREAKDOWN OF ROCK MATERIALS

Processes of rock breakdown None of the gradational agents is able to accomplish much in working against solid, massive bedrock. All are far more effective if the material to be moved is in the form of relatively fine grains or particles. But even coarse chunks are more easily moved than unbroken rock. Therefore the processes by which rock is rotted and broken, collectively referred to by the somewhat misleading term *weathering*, are very important preliminaries to the work of surface erosion.

There are two interrelated groups of processes that contribute to rock breakdown. One is simply mechanical breaking of the rock, or disintegration. The other is chemical alteration of the rock substances, or decomposi-

FIG. 3.11 Jointing in granite. Joint planes commonly occur in sets, all the members of which have the same directional trend. The sets may be vertical, inclined, or horizontal.
(U.S. Geological Survey.)

tion. The two go on at the same time and actually aid one another; for on the one hand, cracking of rock makes for easier pene-

FIG. 3.12 Angular rock debris covering surface of ground at 11,000-ft elevation in the Beartooth Range, Montana. At these high altitudes, low temperatures favor mechanical weathering by freezing water but inhibit chemical weathering.

tration of chemical agents (chiefly water), and on the other hand, decomposition rots and weakens rock masses so that they can be more easily broken.

Mechanical breaking   Rocks are broken mechanically in several ways. Much breaking occurs far beneath the surface as a result of stresses produced by crustal deformation, heating, cooling, and compaction. Thus most rocks are found to be shot through with small cracks (joints), and some are quite shattered, by the time they are exposed to the surface by erosional stripping (Fig. 3.11). Then near the surface the rocks are attacked by other agents. Tiny plant roots invade crevices and pore spaces and crack the rocks by the tremendous pressures they exert as they grow. Water freezes in similar openings and exerts breaking pressures as it expands upon changing to ice. Bits are loosened from the surface by the impact of moving fragments on stream beds, by the blasting of wind-blown sand, by slides and avalanches, and by extreme heating under forest fires or where lightning strikes. Some maintain that extreme day-to-night temperature changes, especially in desert areas, may cause enough irregular expansion and contraction to strain rocks to the breaking point, but this is debatable. Mechanical breakup therefore may be found occurring everywhere, though most intensively where strong crustal deformation has taken place, where tree roots are abundant, and where alternate freezing and thawing is frequent (Fig. 3.12).

Chemical decomposition   Rocks are chemically decomposed principally by water containing in solution various substances, notably carbon dioxide, that increase its chemical aggressiveness. These substances are in part given off by plant roots, in part released during the decay of organic remains on and in the soil, and in small part carried down by rain water from the atmosphere. One would naturally, and correctly, expect chemical decomposition to be most rapid where water is abundant, and least active where water is scarce or is frozen much of the time. High temperatures keep water unfrozen and also favor rapidity of chemical reaction. Hence the humid tropics should be most favored realms for chemical decomposition, while in the deserts, the polar areas, and the high-mountain zones decomposition should be slow. The truth of this is demonstrated by the prevalence, in humid regions, of a cover of fine-particled soil and partially decomposed rock at the surface (Fig. 3.13). But in dry and very cold areas such a cover is usually patchy and thin, and the angular fragments produced by mechanical breaking are more in evidence, not because they are more abundant there than elsewhere, but simply because they are not covered by finer debris.

Rock resistance There are many kinds of rocks, and they react variously to the attacks of the disintegrating and decomposing agents. These differences stem from the chemical composition of the rock materials and the size and arrangement of the grains or particles of the rock.

Rocks are made up of particles of various substances called minerals, each of which has its own well-defined chemical composition and physical properties. Some minerals are soluble or otherwise unstable chemically under conditions that are common near the earth's surface. These, of course, are especially liable to decomposition. Other minerals are highly stable chemically under normal surface conditions and thus resist decomposition. Some minerals are physically hard and difficult to break. Others are easily crushed or split.

FIG. 3.13 Bedrock grading upward into weathered rock and soil.

Since rocks differ in the minerals of which they are composed, they differ in their resistance to attack. Those that are made up largely of unstable minerals are easily decomposed, while those that contain chiefly stable or hard minerals resist breakdown. Also important are the arrangement and size of the mineral grains. In some rocks the grains are intricately interlocked and closely spaced, so that breakage is resisted and water penetration is slow. In others the particles are loosely cemented or are in the form of poorly joined plates or sheets, so that they readily break or split. Water penetrates easily into porous rocks, thus speeding the rotting process.

Though space does not permit a lengthy discussion of specific rock types and their resistance, a few examples will illustrate the subject. The common rock limestone is made up largely of the mineral calcite, which under surface conditions is quite soluble. Thus limestone decomposes rapidly in humid areas. In dry regions, however, chemical attack is less active, and the dense, tight texture of many limestones tends to protect them against disintegration, so that in the desert limestone is often a relatively resistant rock. Granite is made up of coarse grains of the minerals quartz and feldspar. Quartz is hard and chemically very stable. Feldspar, on the other hand, is hard but decomposes fairly readily. Thus in humid climates the feldspar grains decompose to become clay, and the quartz grains fall apart but retain their identity as grains of sand. Even in dry regions granite, being somewhat porous, is easily penetrated by what little water there is. This causes slight rotting on the surfaces of the feldspar grains, which weakens the bonds that hold the rock together and furthers disintegration.

Sandstones are usually composed of grains of quartz cemented by some other substance. If this substance is a weak material, such as clay or iron oxide, the sandstone may disintegrate readily. Or if the cement is a soluble substance, such as calcite, the sandstone is easily rotted. Some sandstones have been cemented by silica, chemically the same as quartz, and these (called quartzites if the cementing is especially firm) are perhaps the most resistant of all common rocks, chemically and mechanically and in all environments.

The importance of differences in rock resistance as they affect surface sculpture has already been suggested. Where nonresistant rocks outcrop at the surface, rock breakup is relatively rapid, and erosion and valley development can proceed swiftly. In areas of resistant-rock outcrop, materials small enough to be moved are produced only slowly and sparingly. Erosion is hindered, the cutting of valleys and general lowering of the surface lags, and the area comes in time to stand above its surroundings because of the staunchness of its foundation. This is *differential* or *selective erosion,* an important control of surface sculpture.

THE ACTUAL MOVING OF SURFACE MATERIALS

PICKING UP, CARRYING, AND DROPPING

It is convenient, for purposes of study, to divide the work of any sculpturing agent into three parts. The first, *erosion,* includes the detaching and picking up of material from its original position. The second, *transportation,* is the carrying of the material from the place of erosion to the place where it is to be deposited. The third, *deposition,* is the laying down of the material at the end of the transportation line. To a degree this division of processes is somewhat artificial, for it is often difficult to say precisely where one ends and the next begins. It is also difficult to draw a fine line separating rock weathering and erosion. However, each of the processes is governed by its own set of laws, and for this reason it is valuable to consider them as distinct from one another.

Each of the sculpturing agents works in its own way, with its own peculiarities and therefore with its own results. Thus, for example, running water has a strong tendency to become narrowly channeled, while glacier ice, especially if very thick, is less subject to channeling, and wind and gravity are still less so. Hence running water is the prime producer of well-defined valleys; the other agents work more broadly. The sizes of particles that will be picked up, transported, and deposited by running water or by wind depend closely upon the velocity at which either of these agents is moving. This makes for marked place-to-place differences in erosive power, selectiveness in sites of deposition, and a high degree of sorting by size among the deposited materials. Ice and gravity, on the other hand, have no particular mechanism for sorting materials by size. Their deposits are notably jumbled mixtures of all sizes of particles and chunks. Because of such differences, it is important to consider the work of the agents separately.

THE WORK OF RUNNING WATER

Occurrence and importance A considerable part of the water that falls on the land surface as precipitation runs downslope across the surface in response to the pull of gravity. While it may start moving as a thin sheet of water on the slopes, it is always seeking the lowest place and the easiest line of flow. Therefore it soon becomes concentrated in well-defined channels, which progressively join with other channels to form larger and larger streams. Because there are few parts of the earth's surface where there is no running water, there are few landscapes that do not show the effects of its sculpturing activity. It must be rated, along with gravity, as one of the most important of the sculpturing agents.

Water erosion Apart from the work of waves, which will be considered later, water erodes by four principal means: (*a*) the impact of raindrops striking against a bare soil surface, (*b*) the striking against the stream bed of solid particles that are already being carried, (*c*) the force of eddying currents in the moving mass of water, and (*d*) the dissolving of material with which the water comes in contact. High velocities of flow, such as will develop where there are steep gradients and deep waters, increase the force of particle impact and also the amount of eddying, and hence increase erosional power. A cover of vegetation on the surface protects the soil against raindrop and particle impact and decreases the speed of flow, thereby

tending strongly to protect the surface against erosion. Rains of the heavy-downpour type are productive of great amounts of surface runoff in a short time, and thus are especially favorable to erosion.

Other factors affecting the erosive power of running water are the size, cohesiveness, and solubility of materials available for it to move. As the size decreases from boulders through gravel to very fine sand and coarse silt, the ease of erosion becomes steadily greater. Fine silts and especially very fine clays, however, are surprisingly difficult to erode, because of the strong tendency of the tiny, flat particles to cling tightly together.

Hence conditions especially favorable to rapid erosion are heavy downpours of rain, surfaces bare of vegetation, steep gradients, and materials that are soluble or that are largely of fine-sand–coarse-silt size. Least favorable are infrequent and gentle rains, a thick cover of vegetation, flat surfaces, and either unusually coarse or exceedingly fine materials.

Transportation by running water Particles that have been dislodged from the stream bed are transported in several ways (Fig. 3.14). Materials too heavy to be raised from the bottom may simply be rolled or shoved along by the force of the current and the impact of other particles. Somewhat smaller grains are thrown up into the current and carried downstream until they settle, strike the bottom, bounce up again, and so proceed by a series of leaps. The finest particles are so light that they can be kept off the bottom entirely by the force of the churning eddy currents. Material in solution is, of course, indistinguishable from the water itself. In terms of the mode of transport it is possible to distinguish a bed load that is rolled

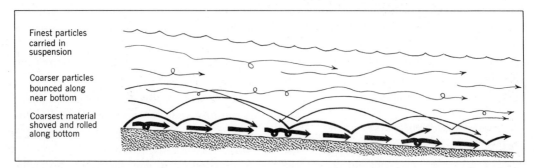

Finest particles
carried in
suspension

Coarser particles
bounced along
near bottom

Coarsest material
shoved and rolled
along bottom

FIG. 3.14   Ways in which solid materials are transported by running water.

or bounced along the bottom, a suspended load carried in the body of the stream, and a load carried in solution.

The ability of a stream to transport eroded material depends upon the volume of water and upon the speed of flow. Naturally a large stream has a greater carrying capacity than a smaller one. But with a given amount of water, a difference in the speed of flow has a profound effect upon the amount and size of material that can be moved in the various ways. As the velocity increases, the amount of solid material that can be transported increases manyfold, and larger and larger particles are shifted from the bed load up to the suspended load. A sluggish stream may move clay as suspended load, and small amounts of silt and fine sand as bed load. A swift stream, on the other hand, may move even coarse sand in suspension and may be able to roll sizable boulders along the bottom. It should be noted that although clay is rather difficult to erode, it is the easiest of all solid materials to transport. Also, the carrying of material in solution is not affected by velocity, but only by the chemical condition of the water.

Deposition by water   Deposition is simply the end of transportation. Wherever the carrying power of a stream is reduced below the degree necessary to handle the existing load, some of that material will drop out. Since carrying power depends upon speed and volume, deposition results from a reduction of either speed or volume. Slowing of a stream occurs at places where the gradient becomes less or where the stream flows into a lake or the ocean, both common occurrences. Decrease in stream volume in a downstream direction is less common, but often occurs in dry areas. There a stream may receive little nourishment from the surrounding desert, while losing much water through evaporation to the atmosphere or soaking into the ground.

As carrying power is reduced, the first materials to be discarded are the coarsest parts of the bed load, followed by the remainder of the original bed load and the coarser particles from suspension. The finer suspended load, especially clay, will remain in suspension even at very low speeds. Deposition of clay requires that the water be virtually at rest.

Development of valleys   Because running water is so readily channeled, much of its erosional activity is concentrated along narrow lines of flow. The result is that the principal work of water erosion is the cutting of valleys. To be sure, thin sheets of water moving down slopes also do some stripping of surface soil, but under natural conditions this work is small compared with that accomplished by the channeled flow.

In stream beds the erosional force is directed chiefly downward, so that valley deepening is the principal erosional effect. However, such downcutting cannot go on indefinitely. The mouth of a stream cannot be lowered as long as the sea or lake level does not change, and the rest of the stream bed cannot be cut below the level of the mouth, or *baselevel*. The result is that as erosion continues, the gradient of the stream becomes gentler, first near the mouth and then successively farther and farther upstream (Fig. 3.15). But as the gradient decreases, the speed of flow, and hence the cutting power, also decreases, so that erosion becomes progressively less active and eventually almost ceases, except perhaps for solution. The lower reaches of the stream normally reach this condition first, the headwaters last.

In an actively eroding stream there may be significant irregularities in gradient, with falls and rapids intervening between gentler stretches, as a result of different rates of erosion on rocks of differing resistance (Fig. 3.16). In time, however, these features are evened out and the gradient becomes smooth.

As a valley is being deepened, runoff water

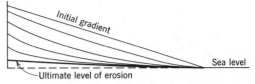

FIG. 3.15   Idealized development of a stream profile. Lower reaches of stream achieve gentle gradients first, resulting in concave profile.

flowing down its sides becomes channeled and cuts secondary or tributary ravines that flow into the main valley. As time goes on these become more numerous and extend themselves headward into the upland areas between the principal valleys (Fig. 3.17). If runoff water is abundant, this may happen rapidly, but if runoff is slight because of dryness, flatness, or porous and absorbent surface materials, tributary development may be very slow.

Stream deposits   Deposits left by streams take the form of thin sheets of material, usually rather well sorted by size and distinctly layered. Any stream-deposited material is called *alluvium*. If the stream is flowing in a well-defined valley, the alluvium is deposited in the valley bottom as a long, flat strip that becomes thicker and broader as deposition continues. In time of flood the stream will often spread out over the entire strip, for

FIG. 3.16   Effects of rock resistance upon stream profile. Weaker rocks erode more rapidly and allow stream to achieve gentle gradients, while resistant outcrops, because they yield more slowly and are undercut from below, develop steep gradients, rapids, and falls.

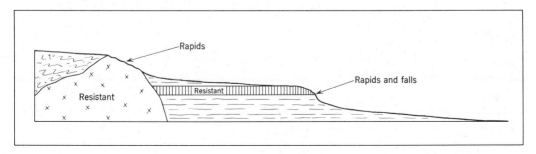

FIG. 3.17 As a gully grows in length by headward erosion, tributary gullies branch from its sides and grow in like manner. *(F. W. Lehmann, C.B.&Q. Railroad Company.)*

which reason such a deposit is called a floodplain. If deposition occurs where the stream is not in a valley, the deposit will take the form of a broad, flat, fan-shaped sheet, across which the stream channel may shift rather freely. Such a deposit, if made on dry land, is called an alluvial fan (Fig. 3.18). If laid down in water at the mouth of a stream, where it is normally flatter and more marshy, it is known as a delta.

Alluvial materials, except for clays and very coarse debris, are easily reworked and re-eroded, especially at floodtimes, when the streams are particularly powerful. For this reason stream channels on alluvial surfaces are continually being altered and shifted. If the stream is a steep one that is depositing sand and gravel, it tends to develop a wide, shallow channel, choked with many sand bars and low islands (braided channel). If the stream is sluggish and is flowing on silty materials, it tends to develop a very winding (meandering) course, with looping bends that are continually changing form and are occasionally cut off from the main stream (Fig. 3.19). Between these two extremes are many intermediate types. Channels on alluvial fans and on deltas commonly branch in a downstream direction, spreading out from the head of the deposit. Alluvial-surface streams will be more fully discussed in the next chapter.

THE WORK OF GRAVITY

Gravity as an earth-moving agent Streams and glaciers flow in direct response to the pull of gravity, and the ways in which they move earth materials are conditioned by the fact that gravitational force is always present everywhere. Indeed, the force of gravity is well known as a contributing factor in the operations of all other gradational agents. But the work of gravity as an essentially independent gradational agent in its own right is much less familiar, and its importance was in the past grossly underestimated.

Just as gravity's pull urges water or ice to flow, so also does it exert a continuous downward pull on the layer of weathered and broken materials that blankets the surface. That layer, of course, is rarely a fluid mass; it is rather an agglomeration of rigid particles and chunks of various sizes, each particle being supported by those beneath it. But if in any way the support is undermined or weakened or if the material of the layer becomes lubricated, as it may through satura-

tion with water, then gravity can act. The surface mantle moves downslope, either particle by particle or in large masses. Such movements are collectively referred to as *mass movement* or *mass wasting.*

How and where mass movements occur Removal of support for the surface materials is commonly caused by active erosion at the foot of the slope (or of a section of the slope). This may be accomplished by a swift downcutting stream, a valley glacial tongue, a stream on an alluvial plain widening its channel during floodtime, or by waves cutting at the base of a coastal bluff. By all of these processes slopes become oversteepened, support for the upper part of the slope becomes insufficient, and that upper part slips down.

FIG. 3.18 A small and steep alluvial fan in Nevada. The apex of the fan lies at the mouth of the gully from which the fan material was eroded. *(John C. Weaver.)*

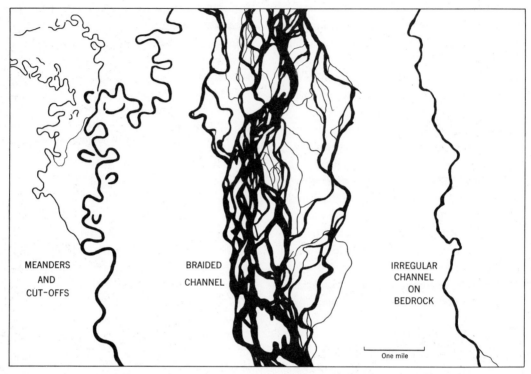

MEANDERS
AND
CUT-OFFS

BRAIDED
CHANNEL

IRREGULAR
CHANNEL
ON
BEDROCK

One mile

FIG. 3.19   A sluggish stream on a floodplain commonly exhibits a pattern of shifting meanders. A stream moving and depositing quantities of sand and gravel often develops a complex system of intertwined, shallow, sand-choked channels. Streams cutting on bedrock characteristically show relatively narrow channels of irregular pattern. *(From U.S. Geological Survey topographic sheets: Fairbanks D-1, Alaska, Fairbanks C-1, Alaska, and Fairbanks A-4, Alaska.)*

One circumstance favorable for this is present when the lower part of the slope is based upon rock materials that are weaker and more easily weathered and eroded than those above. This results in oversteepening, sometimes to the point where the resistant rocks above come to stand in cliffs, or may even overhang the receding slope beneath. Another favoring factor is the presence of slanting joints or other fracture planes in the rocks, slippery clay layers in the subsoil, or other such features: all may serve as surfaces along which the "hanging" hillside material may break away or slip down. Often nowadays man plays a part by making excavations in places where they undermine slopes.

Saturation of the ground is especially likely to occur and cause mass movement as a result of long-continued rains or the melting of quantities of snow. It is not surprising, then, to find that actual flowing of the surface mantle occurs rather frequently in areas that have a pronounced rainy season and in areas that experience a rapid seasonal thaw, but infrequently elsewhere.

Kinds of mass movements   Mass movements differ from one another in the amount of material moved, the sizes of particles involved, and the form and speed of the movement.

On steep slopes the motion is likely to be rapid, sometimes extremely so, and may involve materials of every conceivable size, including immense boulders. These rapid movements may involve a single rock or a huge mass of material. They are often produced by the gradual erosional undermining of a steep slope, on the side of which is poised a mantle of soil and weathered or jointed rock. Often the dislodgment of the particle or mass is triggered by some particular occurrence such as a heavy rain, the entry of water into a joint or a separation between layers as a lubricant, a slight earthquake, or some excavation by man. The particle or mass breaks loose, falls, rolls or slides down the slope, and comes to rest near the base. Some

such landslides and rock falls achieve tremendous size and may be highly destructive (Fig. 3.20). Most, however, are small and inconspicuous.

Saturation of soil by heavy rain or melting may result in actual flowage of the soil like a thick liquid. Commonly the saturation becomes significant only in a limited area on a given slope, and usually in a clayey subsoil layer. Eventually the material of the layer becomes highly plastic, and a patch or tongue of it begins to flow, usually at a slow but visible rate, carrying the surface layers along with it. Occasionally such earthflows are very large, but usually they are small and move only a few yards before losing much of their water content and coming to rest (Fig. 3.21).

In high-latitude and high-altitude areas,

FIG. 3.20   The Gros Ventre landslide of 1925, near Jackson Hole, Wyoming, produced an immense scar on the mountainside and temporarily dammed the creek flowing in the valley below. *(U.S. Forest Service.)*

FIG. 3.21 Earthflow resulting from rain saturation of the ground on a shaly hill slope in eastern Ohio. The lower slope shows turf bulges resulting from flowage beneath the sod; the upper slope shows tension cracks. *(U.S. Soil Conservation Service.)*

the deeper ground may remain frozen for some time after the surface layers have thawed. The water from melting cannot escape downward by infiltration, so the surface layers become so wet as to be jellylike. The soil may then ooze slowly downhill over an entire extensive area of sloping land. This process is known as solifluction.

The most widespread, continuous, and hence most important of all forms of mass movement is, oddly enough, the slowest and least evident of all. This form, called creep, is not a single process, but rather the sum total of all processes by which individual soil particles can be moved a fraction of an inch downhill. There are many such causes. The filling of cracks, burrows, or root cavities comes mostly from the uphill side. The growth of frost crystals lifts particles and then upon melting permits them to settle downhill. Soil expands or swells when it is wetted, heated, or frozen, and contracts again when it dries, cools, or thaws. Such expansion and contraction is greatest in the downhill direction because of gravity. Soil is forced downhill by the prying action of wind-blown trees and shrubs or by the weight of walking animals. In these and other ways the soil on *all* slopes is slowly and steadily moved downward, grain by grain. Though the movement itself is imperceptible because of its slowness, its results are visible in various forms (Fig. 3.22).

Importance of mass movement   Aided only by unchanneled rainwash, mass movement must accomplish all of the gradational activity there is on the slopes and uplands that lie between stream beds. And since these have a total area many times as large as that of the stream beds themselves, the accomplishment is great.

The swifter and more localized forms of

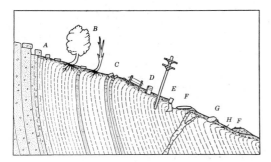

FIG. 3.22 Common evidences of creep:
(a) moved joint blocks; (b) trees with curved
trunks; (c) downslope bending and drag of
fractured and weathered rock; (d) displaced posts,
poles, etc.; (e) broken or displaced retaining walls;
(f) roads and railroads moved out of alignment;
(g) turf rolls downslope from creeping boulders;
(h) stone line near base of creeping soil.
*(C. F. S. Sharpe, Landslides and Related Phenomena,
Columbia University Press, New York, 1934. Reproduced by
permission of author and publishers.)*

mass movement, such as landslides and earth flows, usually leave behind obvious marks on the surface. Normally there is a sunken scar on the upper slope where the material has broken loose, and at the lower end of the scar a jumbled, humpy accumulation of the debris that has come down (Figs. 3.20, 3.21). Where prominent cliffs occur, chunks and blocks often break loose singly, and fall and roll to the base of the slope. Often they accumulate there in large quantities, forming what is known as a talus slope (Fig. 3.23).

These rapid and concentrated forms of mass movement are important chiefly in mountainous and hilly areas where steep slopes prevail. In many of those areas they undoubtedly account for a large part of the transfer of debris from the slopes to the valley bottoms, where it may be carried away by streams or ice tongues. It is because of their concentrated occurrence that they are less important, in total result, than the more unobtrusive creep, which occurs everywhere a

weathered mantle lies on even a gentle slope.

Creep, however, does not produce well-defined landforms. It urges the entire mantle downslope. Instead of forming scars and localized accumulations, it serves to drive back the entire expanse of a slope. The material that has crept down may be carried away by streams or other transporting agents, or it may accumulate in a thickening sheet, gentling the lower part of the slope and masking it against further weathering and erosion. Creep probably has most relative importance in humid areas that have a thick mantle of weathered material and a well-established cover of vegetation. Under such conditions creep can proceed at a significant rate, but surface erosion outside of the stream beds is negligible. Here, then, creep may be the chief means of modifying the slopes between streams. On the other hand, where the

FIG. 3.23 An extensive talus slope at the foot of a cliff. Beartooth Range, Montana.

vegetation cover is sparse or open, surface erosion by rainwash is much more important, though creep will still occur.

THE WORK OF MOVING ICE

Definition of glaciers   Glaciers are not simply inert masses of ice and snow but rather accumulations of ice so thick that they actually move in response to gravity. The movement is much in the manner of the flow of very viscous liquids, like the traditional "molasses in January." Rates of movement of glaciers rarely exceed a fraction of an inch per day, though exceptional rates of several feet per day have been recorded.

Since ice must become 150 to 200 ft thick before it will begin to flow, glaciers form only where there is the possibilty of an un-

FIG. 3.24   Nysne Glacier, Peary Land, northern Greenland. Note the collecting basins from which the glacier tongue flows and the surface markings that indicate the flowing movement. Ridges of ice-deposited debris (moraines) border the ice tongue, and a braided stream of meltwater flows across the sand it has washed out from the ice margin.

(Geodetic Institute, Copenhagen, copyright.)

usual accumulation of ice carrying over from year to year. If more snow falls during a cold season than can be melted during the following summer, then the unmelted residue is added to the accumulation of the next year. The old, buried snow changes gradually into solid ice under the effects of compression and partial melting and refreezing. In a relatively short time a great thickness can be built up. Such circumstances are most often encountered in areas having unusually heavy winter snowfall but short and cool summers.

Antarctica and Greenland have most of the existing ice-covered area of the earth. Elsewhere glaciers are confined to the moister and colder mountain regions. Dryness and summer heat are enemies of glacier development, and many high mountain ranges and even some large areas within the polar circles have no glaciers because of snowfall insufficient to last out the summer.

The ice in a glacier will always move, in the main, downslope and away from the center of thickest accumulation, following the paths of least resistance (Fig. 3.24). As it spreads beyond the region of accumulation into neighboring areas of lower elevation, warmer and longer summers, or less snowfall, its outer margins are attacked by melting. The ice will continue to spread until its edge reaches the point of balance between the rate of movement and the rate of melting. Thereafter, as long as conditions do not change, the edge of the glacier remains in the same place, though the ice is in continuous movement from the source to the edge. If climatic conditions change so that the supply of ice is lessened or melting is increased, the glacier begins to shrink under the attacks of melting. If melting is decreased or the ice supply is increased, the edge of the glacier advances until it reaches a new point of equilibrium.

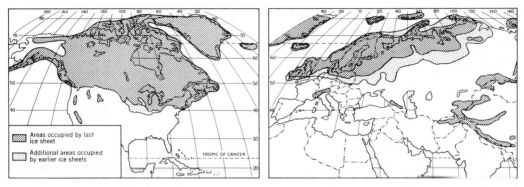

FIG. 3.25 Extent of former continental glaciers in North America and Eurasia. *(After Flint.)*

Former continental glaciers If glaciers had not once been more extensive than they are now, they would be of little interest as sculptors of the land, for the surfaces beneath the glaciers are effectively hidden. However it is well known that at times during the last million years glaciers of tremendous size have spread over large parts of the Northern Hemisphere continents. In North America they originated to the east and west of Hudson Bay and covered, at one time or another, all of Canada and the northeastern and north central United States. In Eurasia they developed in the Scandinavian highlands and spread over most of northern Europe and northwestern Siberia. Most of eastern Siberia and much of Alaska were not glaciated in spite of their coldness, probably because of insufficient snowfall (Fig. 3.25).

Outside of the areas of these continental ice sheets there was, at the same time, a general expansion of glaciers in high mountain valleys all over the world. The Rocky Mountains in the western United States, for example, which now are almost bare of glaciers, were heavily glaciated, much as the Alps and high Himalayas are now. There were no continental glaciers in the Southern Hemisphere except on Antarctica because there are no

large land masses in the upper middle latitudes where they could have grown.

Why such immense glaciers developed during this great ice age, or Pleistocene period, is not at all clear. Unquestionably climatic changes in the direction of cooler summers and greater snowfall were involved, but the reason for these changes lies in the realm of theory.

Even the course of glacial history is most imperfectly known. It is generally believed that ice sheets formed, spread, fluctuated, and finally melted away several times (possibly four) during the Pleistocene period. The last major expansion reached its maximum not far from 20,000 years ago, did not finally disappear from the northern edge of the United States until perhaps 8,000 years ago, and reached approximately its present state only about 5,000 years ago. This last glaciation fell well within the period when man had become widely established over the earth, and must have had profound effects upon his existence. By the time the last ice sheet had vanished, history had reached the early stages of the sedentary civilizations of Babylon and Egypt.

The effects of glaciation were widespread and complex. The surfaces actually covered by the ice were modified by erosion and deposition, and were also evidently considerably depressed by the weight of the ice, rising again when the ice melted. Valleys and plains adjacent to the ice received deposits of debris carried from the glacial edge by meltwater. Throughout the world sea levels were greatly lowered as more and more water became tied up in the ice sheets, only to rise again as the glaciers wasted away. Accompanying the whole affair was a complex series of climatic changes, affecting not only the glaciated areas but much of the rest of the world as well. The study of all of these events and their history and interrelation is still in its infancy, and undoubtedly there are yet many fascinating discoveries to be made.

Erosion by glaciers   The investigation of how glaciers erode and deposit is greatly complicated by the fact that it is almost impossible to see just what is happening underneath glaciers now in existence. Much of our notion of how glaciers rework the surface is inferred from the forms left behind on surfaces from which the ice has lately melted away. Hence our knowledge has grown slowly, and there are strong differences of opinion, especially with regard to how glaciers erode.

Apparently glaciers can erode in three ways.

First, and probably the most important by far, is the process known as plucking or quarrying. In this the plastic ice molds itself about particles of the weathered mantle or blocks of bedrock and then drags them out of place as the ice mass moves on forward (Fig. 3.26). Quarrying is most effective where the surface materials are loose or jointed. A second erosional technique is that of grinding or abrasion. Quarried rocks that are partly imbedded in the lower surface of the ice are dragged across bedrock outcrops like grains on a giant sheet of sandpaper, scraping and gouging as they go. Grooved and polished rock surfaces testify to the work of this process, though it is no doubt much less effective than quarrying. Third, and least important, is a bulldozerlike shoving effect at the front of the ice. Probably this process is significant only locally, as, especially, where the ice edge readvances over loose heaped-up debris dropped earlier.

Undoubtedly the greatest effect of glacial erosion is the stripping of the weathered mantle from the surface over much of the area covered. There is also active quarrying of strongly jointed or conspicuously weak bedrock. Projecting crags are removed or reduced in size. Bottleneck valleys oriented

FIG. 3.26   How a glacier erodes by plucking and abrasion.

Abrasion by debris dragged over surface

Joint blocks removed by plucking

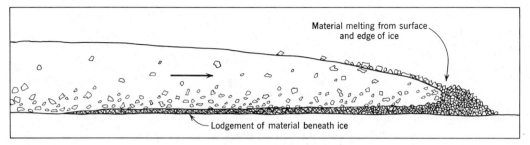

Material melting from surface and edge of ice

Lodgement of material beneath ice

FIG. 3.27   Near its edge, an ice sheet suffers melting on both upper and lower surfaces. Thus some of the debris it contains is lodged beneath the ice, and the rest is deposited at the edge.

in the direction of ice movement seem especially liable to strong erosion. But generally speaking the extensive and thick continental ice sheets were not strongly channeled, so that their erosional work was inclined to be patchy, producing irregular depressions rather than integrated valleys. Erosion by glacial tongues in mountain valleys is, of course, confined to the bottom and lower sides of the valleys.

Transportation by glaciers   Glaciers are highly competent transporting agents, able to carry material of all sizes, including immense boulders. The debris eroded by the glacier itself is concentrated near the base of the ice. But valley glaciers may also carry quantities of material that has been dumped onto their surfaces by mass movement or washed down the valley sides. This material is concentrated near the surface, though some may reach considerable depth in the ice because of later covering by snow.

Deposition by glaciers   A glacier deposits its load by melting away from it. Melting occurs toward the edges or outer margin, of the ice, and works both upward from the ground and downward from the upper surface (Fig. 3.27).

As a result of melting on the lower surface, the debris carried in the lower part of the ice is lodged beneath the glacier. Melting down-

ward from above exposes more and more debris on the surface of the ice, so that some mountain-valley glaciers are almost completely obscured near their lower ends by a thick cover of rock and sand. This debris is deposited along the edges of the glacier as the ice melts.

There is no mechanism for selectivity in either the transporting or depositing process. Therefore glacial deposits are commonly jumbled mixtures of material varying in size from clay to huge boulders (Fig. 3.28). By this they can usually be easily distinguished from water-laid deposits, which almost always show some degree of sorting and layering (Fig. 3.29).

Glacial deposits are called *moraines*. Those believed to have been laid down by lodgment beneath the ice are ground moraines; those deposited along the ice edge are marginal moraines. The material itself is called *till*.

Moraines will be found throughout the glaciated area, for at some time or other every part of the area covered by the ice will have been in the vicinity of the glacial margin. However, within this area, the till will have been unevenly distributed in patches, heaps, ridges, and blankets of unequal thickness. The deposits will normally be thickest in valleys, "downstream" from sources of easily eroded material that furnish quantities of till,

FIG. 3.28   An exposure of glacial till showing the unassorted clay, pebbles, and boulders of which it is composed. *(Wisconsin Geological Survey.)*

and in the outer parts of the glaciated area. Deposits will be thin or absent on hilltops, in areas of especially resistant rock, and in the source regions of the ice.

Meltwater flowing from the ice margin may carry out quantities of finer debris, to deposit it as alluvium across plains or in valley bottoms. Such deposits, called *outwash,* are not strictly glacial, but outwash and till deposits are both commonly included under the general term of *glacial drift.*

Till deposition modifies in varying degree the landscapes over which it is laid down. The resulting forms depend upon the thickness and stoniness of the till and upon the form of the underlying surface. Characteristic moraine features will be discussed farther on, but one point may be mentioned here. The tendency of moraine deposition to be irregularly heaped and to be concentrated in valleys has the effect of obscuring old drainage lines and of leaving behind an irregular surface of rises and depressions without any well-organized valley system. Thus glacial deposition tends to destroy existing stream channels and to produce irregular, "pockmarked" surfaces. It was noted above that glacial erosion has somewhat similar effects.

Because there is a significant difference in age between glacial deposits from the early Pleistocene and those from the late Pleistocene, there is also a considerable difference in the freshness and degree of preservation of the surface features that the ice produced. Those formed by the later ice sheets are generally clearly defined and little-altered. Those formed during the middle and early Pleistocene are commonly so changed by stream erosion and mass movement as to be unrecognizable. Only the distinctive character of till deposits reveals the glacial history of these "old drift" areas.

THE WORK OF WIND

Where and how wind works The wind is a much less important producer of surface forms than are water, gravity, and ice. This is true principally because the wind can erode only under certain limited conditions. In particular, the wind is almost powerless to erode unless the surface is nearly bare of vegetation, and then can erode only if the surface material is fine and dry. For this reason the work of the wind is confined to the deserts or semideserts and to those few areas in humid regions, such as beaches, river beds at low water, and, nowadays, plowed fields, where there is little plant cover.

Where it is able to work, the wind erodes, transports, and deposits in much the same manner as running water, except that there is little channeling. Erosion is accomplished by the force of eddy currents near the surface and by the impact of particles already being carried (sand-blasting effect). The wind moves material by rolling or bouncing it along the ground or by carrying it in suspension. Deposition occurs where surface irregularities, including vegetation, check the speed of the wind near the ground, or where the wind velocity decreases simply because of the atmospheric-pressure pattern. Rain falling through the dust-laden air will often carry most of the suspended material down with it.

The wind can rarely move material larger than coarse sand. Sand is carried as "bed load" of the air stream, that is by rolling or bouncing, and seldom rises more than a few feet above the ground. Silt and clay can be carried in suspension, and thus may reach great heights and may travel long distances. Fine red soil traceable to the plains of western Oklahoma has, for example, been observed to fall on the decks of steamers in the Atlan-

tic. Because it remains close to the ground, sand usually does not move far from its source region. Finer material, on the other hand, may be spread as a thin blanket over a huge expanse downwind from its place of origin.

Wind erosion Erosion by the wind, like that by ice, tends to be widespread or patchy rather than channeled. Thus it may lower the surface rather uniformly over a broad area without producing any pronounced surface forms. On occasion it scours out shallow depressions in favored places where the vegetation has been destroyed, where the material is especially loose and fine, or where the velocity is increased by a natural bottleneck. A common occurrence is for the wind to winnow out the finer particles from mixed surface material, leaving behind a coarse-textured gravelly or stony cover (Fig. 3.30).

Wind deposition The deposition of fine suspended material is so broad and un-

FIG. 3.29 A cut through an outwash plain, showing sand and gravel washed free of clay and rudely stratified according to size. *(Wisconsin Geological Survey.)*

FIG. 3.30 The pebbles and sand-blasted rock fragments of an unusually coarse wind-sorted surface cover on the floor of Death Valley, California. *(Eliot Blackwelder.)*

concentrated that it modifies the surface strongly only if it continues for a long time and leaves a very thick layer. Most of the extensive deposits of silty, unlayered, buff-colored, limy material called *loess,* common in the middle western United States, eastern Europe, and north China, are believed to have originated as wind-blown silt.

By contrast, sand is usually deposited in heaps rather than smooth sheets, and thus sand deposition does produce distinct land forms. These features, called dunes, are common in some desert regions and along many coasts.

FIG. 3.31 A wave breaking. *(F. P. Shepard.)*

THE WORK OF WAVES AND CURRENTS

Occurrence   Like that of winds, the work of waves and currents is narrowly confined. Along the thousands of miles of the world's coasts and lake shores, however, this work is a prime factor in shaping the surface forms. Though waves and currents also occur in the open seas, they can erode only along the shore and in shallow water where their activity can reach to the bottom. It should be emphasized that the currents being discussed here are not the slow, large-scale, world-wide drifts set up by prevailing winds and water-density differences. These are instead local, relatively swift movements that occur along the shores and in narrow inlets as a result of winds and tides. Such currents may reach velocities of several miles per hour, and are quite able to pick up and move loose sand or fine debris.

Wave erosion   The largest part of the actual erosion, however, is accomplished by waves. When a wind-driven wave enters shallow water, it drags on the bottom, steepens to a sharp crest, and finally breaks or pitches forward in a plunge of water and foam (Fig. 3.31). In large storm waves tons of water (and sometimes sand and rock as well) are flung forward and downward, striking against the shore or the shallow bottom with tremendous violence. Under favorable conditions the erosive force generated is probably as great as any found in nature. The water flung toward the shore is then drawn again seaward by gravity, flowing beneath oncoming waves as an undertow current. These currents are sometimes strong enough to move out quantities of material loosened by the breaking wave.

Where the water maintains a depth of 10 to 20 ft close to the shore, waves will not break until they are almost to the land. Their erosional force is then spent against the land itself, driving it back and cutting sea cliffs. If, on the other hand, the water becomes shallow far out, the principal wave breaking occurs a long distance from shore and the force of erosion is expended against the bottom, deepening the water at that point and casting some of the loosened debris up ahead of the breakers in the form of a bar.

Transportation and deposition Material dislodged by waves or fed into the water by streams is carried by wave-generated or tide-generated currents either outward into deeper and quieter water, or along the shore until it reaches a sheltered spot. That carried outward is deposited to form a shelf of sediment that tends to build slowly seaward. Fine material may be carried far out and spread thinly over vast areas of deeper water. Material is carried along the shore chiefly by zigzag in-and-out movements produced by

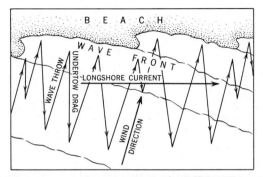

FIG. 3.32 The zigzag path of a pebble under the combined forces of oblique waves, undertow, and longshore current.

waves that strike the coast at an oblique angle (Fig. 3.32). In storms these currents may be remarkably strong, and quantities of sand may be moved along until they reach the sheltered waters of a bay or the protected lee of an island or projection of the coast. There the sand is dropped in the form of a bar or beach.

SELECTED REFERENCES

Finch, V. C., G. T. Trewartha, A. H. Robinson, and E. H. Hammond: *Physical Elements of Geography,* 4th ed., McGraw-Hill Book Company, Inc., New York, 1957.

Flint, R. F.: *Glacial and Pleistocene Geology,* John Wiley & Sons, Inc., New York, 1957.

Gilluly, J., A. C. Waters, and A. O. Woodford: *Principles of Geology,* 2d ed., W. H. Freeman & Company, San Francisco, 1959.

Leet, L. D., and S. Judson: *Physical Geology,* 2d ed., Prentice-Hall, Inc., Englewood Cliffs, N.J., 1958.

Lobeck, A. K.: *Geomorphology: An Introduction to the Study of Landscapes,* McGraw-Hill Book Company, Inc., New York, 1939.

————: *Geological Map of the United States* (with text), C. S. Hammond & Co. Inc., New York, 1941.

Longwell, C. R., and R. F. Flint: *Introduction to Physical Geology,* John Wiley & Sons, Inc., New York, 1955.

Sharpe, C. F. S.: *Landslides and Related Phenomena,* Columbia University Press, New York, 1934.

Thornbury, W. D.: *Principles of Geomorphology,* John Wiley & Sons, Inc., New York, 1954.

Wooldridge, S. W., and R. S. Morgan: *An Outline of Geomorphology: The Physical Basis of Geography,* 2d ed., Longmans, Green & Co., Ltd., London, 1959.

CHAPTER 4

Plains

ORIGIN OF SMOOTH SURFACES

Plains were defined in Chap. 2 as surfaces consisting predominantly of gentle slopes, with low relief. The detailed features of plains result from recent operations of the various surface-sculpturing agents, but for plains to exist at all a specific set of conditions able to produce low relief and much gentle slope must have existed sometime in the past.

High relief is the result of either crustal disturbance that has raised parts of the surface above their surroundings or the cutting of deep valleys in an upland surface. But for valleys to be cut deeply, the upland surface must be far above the baselevel of erosion, and the usual way it has gotten there is by

uplift of the earth's crust. So it is generally true that high relief requires preceding crustal disturbance and that without it relief will be low. As has already been suggested, many of the world's most extensive plains lie in areas where the crust has been stable in late geologic time.

However, low relief can occur in areas of disturbed crust if a broad surface has been uplifted so recently that valley cutting has not yet gone very far. Much of the upland of central and southern Africa fits this condition. Also, some depressed sections of the crust have low relief because they have served as receptacles for extensive and smoothing deposition. Examples are the Central Valley of California, the Ganges Plain of north India, and the Mesopotamian plains of Iraq in the Middle East.

For two reasons gentle slopes usually accompany low relief. One is that on low-relief surfaces streams usually have gentle gradients and therefore cut down slowly. This gives ample time for surface erosion and mass movement to keep most valley sides from becoming very steep. Second, with so little valley deepening, valley floors often begin to widen out while there is much upland still uncut by tributaries. Where this has happened most of the surface is occupied either by valley floors or by smooth uplands and is therefore predominantly gentle in slope, even if the valley sides happen to be steeper than average.

PLAINS SHAPED BY RUNNING WATER

STREAM-ERODED PLAINS

Characteristics and varieties The majority of plains owe their surface detail chiefly to the erosional work of streams, aided by slope wash and mass movement. The distinguishing characteristic of these plains is widespread integrated systems of stream valleys. The differences among individual stream-sculptured plains are definable in terms of the size, spacing, cross-section form, and pattern of these valleys and of the divides between them.

Differences in tributary development also provide an excellent basis for making distinctions among stream-sculptured plains. Some plains are crossed only by a few major valleys, with broad, almost uncut uplands between them. Tributaries of any considerable length are few, though there may be fringes of short ravines along the sides of the principal valleys. A plain having these characteristics is sometimes said to be "youthful," not because of its age in years, but because reduction of the upland has hardly more than begun (Fig. 4.1a).

On other stream-cut plains the landscape is occupied by a close network of valleys and

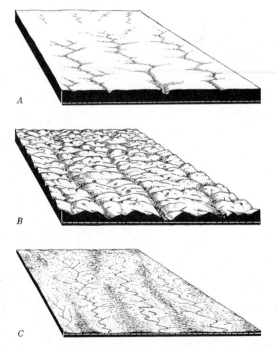

FIG. 4.1 The ideal stages in the development of a land surface by stream erosion, from youth (a) through maturity (b) to old age (c). The dashed white line indicates the baselevel toward which the streams are working. *(V. C. Finch.)*

tributaries. The original upland surface is gone, or nearly so, and the surface is made up largely of sloping valley sides (Fig. 4.1b).

A rolling, dissected plain of this kind is termed "mature," for the valley system is fully established, though much gradational work still remains to be done.

These differences in degree of tributary development are partly a matter of the amount and effectiveness of surface runoff. Some surfaces pass quickly into maturity, while others remain youthful almost indefinitely. Characteristics favoring slight runoff and therefore slow tributary development and the maintenance of youth are marked flatness of the upland, porous and absorbent surface material, a protective blanket of vegetation, and light or gentle rains. On the other hand, a sloping upland, fine and impervious surface material, sparse vegetation, and torrential rains favor much runoff, rapid tributary growth, and quick achievement of maturity.

A good case of a persistently youthful surface is the High Plains of western Kansas, Oklahoma, and Texas. Here the original surface was extremely smooth, the material is rather porous, there has been a dense cover of sod, and the climate is semiarid. The area has been exposed long enough for one to expect that erosion would have made considerable headway, but instead valleys are few, and most of the surface remains as if untouched (Fig. 4.2). Somewhat similar conditions exist in the plains of southern Russia.

On the other hand, rolling, typically mature plains occupy large sections of the American Middle West, especially in southern and western Iowa, northern Missouri, and eastern Kansas and Nebraska (Fig. 4.3). The more advanced erosion here is probably due not to greater age, but to a more rolling initial surface, easily eroded surface material (much of it loess), and, possibly, to more frequent heavy rains.

Valley form and size   Stream-sculptured plains also exhibit great differences in the cross-section forms of their valleys, especially

FIG. 4.2   The remarkably smooth surface of the High Plains in southwestern Kansas, an old depositional plain upon which stream erosion has made little headway. *(U.S. Soil Conservation Service.)*

FIG. 4.3   The rolling surface of a mature plain in northwestern Missouri.

in the width that the valleys have achieved. Thus, for example, in the southern half of Illinois valleys are narrow and relatively steep-walled, while in much of southwestern Missouri, central Oklahoma, and north central Texas valleys are extremely wide, their smooth floors occupying the major portion of the land area.

Like tributary development, the width of valleys in plains is largely controlled by time and the rate of erosion (Fig. 4.4). As erosion proceeds, valley walls are worn back by wash and creep, and the valleys widen at the expense of the higher ground between them. Valley widening, like tributary development, is strongly affected by the amount of surface runoff and the ease of erosion of the surface material. If there is little runoff, valley widening will have to depend almost wholly on creep, and thus will be slow.

Even in youthful and in mature plains there may be some large valleys that have become quite wide, though by definition valley floors occupy a small percentage of the total area of such surfaces. But once the tributary net is complete and the original upland de-

stroyed, then valley widening and reduction of the height of divides become the chief erosional processes. Valley floors expand until they make up the larger part of the area. Divides become smaller, lower and less conspicuous, and finally the entire surface is reduced to a low level and erosion practically ceases. Such a surface is said to be in the stage of "old age," and is given the rather misleading name peneplain, which means almost a plain (Fig. 4.1c). Small hills or mountains that are the last remnants of disappearing divides are common features on plains in advanced stages of erosion. From

FIG. 4.4   A stream that cuts down rapidly relative to the rate of valley widening develops a narrow, steep-sided valley. Slow downcutting permits valley widening to open up a broad, flaring profile.

Valley widening slow relative to valley deepening

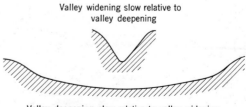

Valley deepening slow relative to valley widening

FIG. 4.5   Spencer Mountain, a monadnock on the partially redissected
old-age erosion surface of the Appalachian Piedmont, near Gastonia,
North Carolina. *(V. C. Finch.)*

the example of isolated Mount Monadnock
in New Hampshire, the name monadnock is
given to these last vestiges of former height
(Fig. 4.5).

Patterns of streams and divides   As a
general rule, tributary streams develop at
open acute angles to the main stream. This
gives to the stream system a branching pattern

FIG. 4.6   Random dendritic stream patterns develop where there are no
strong local contrasts in rock resistance (a). If the original surface has a
pronounced slope, the branching pattern is drawn out in a downslope
direction (b). *(From Army Map Service series 1:250,000: Charleston and Moab sheets.)*

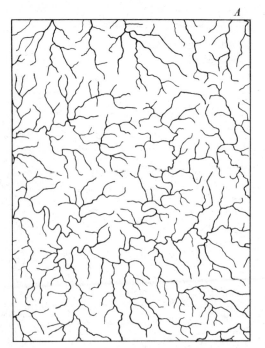

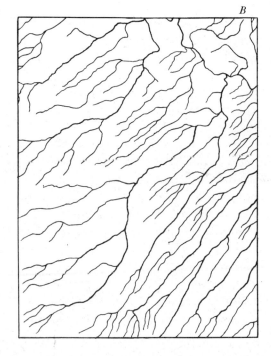

A   *B*

like that formed by the limbs of a tree. If the surface on which the streams develop is gently inclined, the branches may be spread broadly as on an oak, while if the inclination is steeper, they may be drawn out lengthwise as on a poplar. But they are still treelike, or to use a technical word that means the same, dendritic (Fig. 4.6).

If the stream pattern is not dendritic, it usually means one of two things. Either (*a*) there was some striking peculiarity of the slope on which the streams formed, as when streams radiate from a center like a new volcanic cone or a dome, or (*b*) there are strong local variations of rock resistance.

Effects of rock resistance The effect of local variations in rock resistance is simply to favor the development of valleys in places where the rock materials are most easily

weathered and eroded. The resulting valley pattern will not be dendritic but will instead conform to the pattern of rock weakness. This is most strikingly developed in hilly and mountainous lands, where relief is high, and features are on a large scale (Fig. 4.7). Yet even on plains some streams have achieved an unusual angular pattern by developing along prominent systems of joints where weathering is rapid. Roughly parallel stream patterns also form sometimes on plains that cut across the edges of upturned rock layers of contrasting resistance.

More important for plains, though, are the effects of rock structure upon the broader pattern of major divides and valley systems. Broad patches or bands of relatively resistant rock tend to stand out as areas of higher ground in which valleys are narrower and

F I G . 4 . 7   Stream patterns affected by structure: (a) parallelism resulting from erosion on parallel bands of rock of contrasting resistance; (b) angularity imposed on dendritic pattern by erosion on strongly jointed rocks. *(From Army Map Service series 1:250,000: Charlottesville and Lake Champlain sheets.)*

A

B

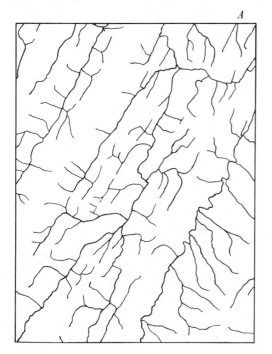
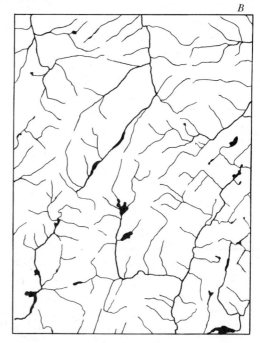

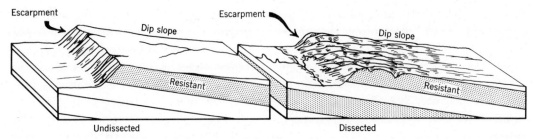

Escarpment   Dip slope   Escarpment   Dip slope

Resistant   Resistant

Undissected   Dissected

FIG. 4.8   Form and structure of cuestas. Example at left is sharp and regular. Dissected form at right is more typical, especially in humid regions.

less advanced in their development than elsewhere. Patches and strips of weak rocks advance more rapidly toward old age, and become lowlands or elongated valley systems. The development of alternating strips of higher, rougher land and lower, smoother land is very common, occurring almost anywhere that there are gently inclined sedimentary strata of varying resistance. Central and southeastern North America, northern France, and southern Great Britain are among the regions in which this type of development occurs. The higher and rougher belts, developed where the resistant strata outcrop, are termed cuestas. Usually they have quite abrupt escarpments along their higher margins (Figs. 4.8, 4.9).

Erosional plains in dry lands   Erosional plains in dry lands differ from those in humid areas chiefly in the extent to which certain kinds of features occur. These differences from the humid areas stem from slow weathering, streams that flow only when it rains, and a surface unprotected by vegetation in dry lands.

Most of the sculpturing there takes place during the rare heavy rains. Absence of vegetation and the prevalent thinness of the weathered mantle favor runoff, and the bare surface is readily attacked by erosion. Quantities of debris are stripped from the slopes and carried down the many ravines and gullies into the valleys and basins below. But the material is usually dropped without being carried far, for once the rain ceases and the stream leaves the area, the stream dwindles, losing its carrying power.

Thus it is that desert plains are likely to have unusually rocky and roughly gullied slopes and uplands, and on the other hand, lowlands that are more or less thickly covered with alluvium and therefore smooth. These features give desert plains their distinctive character.

FIG. 4.9   Northern France is a structural basin in which the rock strata dip generally toward Paris from all sides. Erosion on this structure has produced rings of cuestas with escarpments facing outward. *(V. C. Finch.)*

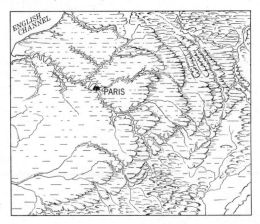

ENGLISH CHANNEL

PARIS

KINDS OF
WATER-LAID PLAINS

General characteristics   Most of the world's smoothest plains are the surfaces of extensive deposits laid down by water. Some of these deposits have been dropped by streams along their courses or at their mouths. Others have accumulated upon the floors of lakes or on shallow sea bottoms, and have become exposed through a change in water level or an uplift of the land. In all kinds, the materials are normally well-sorted, layered, and loose.

Such plains are flat, but they are not truly featureless. Stream channels are nearly always present. Usually there are also various slight swells and depressions, and the latter often contain shallow lakes or marshes. Streams shift their channels readily in the loose sedimentary materials, so that scars of abandoned channels are almost as characteristic as active streams.

Floodplains   Alluvial deposition is responsible for the flat bottomlands that are so characteristic of the floors of gentle-gradient valleys. Sluggish flow and, in some instances, decreasing volume render the streams in such valleys incapable of carrying all the sediment load fed to them by their tributaries, and excess sediment is deposited along the valley bottom as a floodplain. Under normal low-water conditions a stream on a floodplain is confined to a definite and somewhat wandering channel. But during periods of heavy runoff this channel may prove inadequate to carry the vastly increased discharge from the tributaries, and the stream then overflows its banks and spreads in a thin sheet over much or all of the floodplain surface.

Sandy materials and braided channels
Stream channels on alluvium are extremely changeable because of the ease with which the loose material may be eroded (Fig. 3.19). A relatively swiftly flowing stream, able to move sand and gravel, has a tendency to develop a very wide, shallow channel which the stream entirely covers at high water. In the channel are many shifting sand bars, around which are branching and rejoining threads of deeper water and swifter current. At low water only the deeper threads of the channel carry water; the rest of the bed is exposed (Fig. 4.10). This is the classic braided channel, widely seen in sediment-charged streams emerging from mountain valleys, flowing from the margins of glaciers, or passing through areas of loose, coarse, sedimentary materials. Excellent examples of braided channels are provided by most of the larger streams of the High Plains east of the Rocky Mountains, such as the Platte, the Arkansas, and the Canadian Rivers.

Silty floodplains and meandering channels
At the other end of the scale are the silty floodplains of slow-flowing streams. Here the stream channel is narrower and more sharply defined, and usually exceedingly sinuous, or meandering (Fig. 4.11). Its loops and bends change form rather rapidly; individual loops are often cut off entirely by the stream's breaking through the narrow neck of land at the base of the curve.

During floods silt-depositing streams of this type characteristically drop the major part of their load immediately as the waters leave the deep channel and begin to spread across the plain. This results in the formation of slightly raised strips of ground along the sides of the channel. These low swells, called natural levees, provide the highest, best-drained, and most useful land on the floodplains (Fig. 4.12). The lower lands behind them are poorly drained and sometimes permanently

FIG. 4.10   The braided channel of the Rio Grande in northern New Mexico. During flood the entire belt of channels and sandy islands will be covered with water. *(Spence Air Photos.)*

swampy. The scars of abandoned channels and cutoff meander bends, each with its own natural levees, are common features over most of the floodplain surface. The great plain of the lower Mississippi is the most extensively

FIG. 4.11   The floodplain of a meandering stream, showing cutoffs and scars formed by shifting of the channel. Laramie River, Wyoming. *(J. R. Balsley, U.S. Geological Survey.)*

studied floodplain of the silty type, but smaller examples are numerous.

Between the wide braided channels on the one hand and the narrower channels that freely meander on the other are many intermediate types, usually showing rather wide, shallow beds with numerous sand bars, swinging but not looping courses, and an absence of natural levees.

Use of floodplains   Because they are flat, are developed on loose and relatively fine

FIG. 4.12   A cross-section diagram illustrating typical floodplain features. The highest ground is along the natural levees.

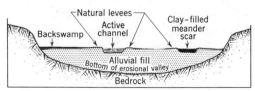

material, and have easy access to water, flood-plains are often eagerly sought as agricultural lands. Sometimes, though by no means always, their soils are more fertile than the older soils on the neighboring uplands. How-ever, floodplain agriculture is always beset by the problem of floods, with their destructive-ness to crops, buildings, and livestock. Even excepting actual floods, much of the land is likely to be permanently swampy or subject to waterlogging by heavy rains. While these problems can be attacked by various flood-control and drainage programs, such measures are expensive and not always worth the cost and effort they involve.

Alluvial terraces   After a floodplain has been formed, the stream's gradient, its volume of flow, or the amount of sediment load being fed into it may change in such a way that the stream starts eroding once again. It will then cut down into its earlier deposit, leaving only shelflike remnants along the valley sides. Such alluvial terraces are very common. In some valleys several terrace levels may be seen, in-dicating that the stream has repeatedly changed its activity from deposition to ero-sion (Fig. 4.13).

Alluvial terraces have many of the advan-tages of floodplains, without the dangers of flood and poor drainage. Therefore they often serve as agricultural lands or as the sites of towns or of transportation routes. However, they tend to be less well-watered and, because their soils are older, less fertile than the bot-tomlands themselves.

Deltas   Deltas, as previously stated, are the plains formed by alluvial deposition at the mouths of streams. Here the stream's velocity is checked as it enters the body of standing water. The sediment load is dropped on either side of the principal line of flow and often also in a bar opposite the open end of the channel.

FIG. 4.13   Development of alluvial terraces by renewed downcutting in an older deposit of alluvium. Natural levees border the present stream course. *(V. C. Finch.)*

By continued deposition the delta grows both outward and laterally. Often the channel divides around the bar at its mouth, and each branch extends itself seaward as the delta grows. In this way the stream acquires nu-merous branching outlets, known as dis-tributaries, and the delta becomes complex and fan-shaped (Fig. 4.14).

Most large deltas are composed chiefly of silt and fine sand, and show some of the characteristics of silty floodplains. Natural levees are often well-developed, and meander-ing channels are common. Swift streams en-tering a lake or the sea may build sandy deltas. These commonly have relatively steep gradients and display braided and shifting channels. They are essentially alluvial fans built in the sea instead of on the land.

Some deltas reach great size. Those of the Mississippi, the Nile, the Volga, and the Gan-ges, for example, all exceed 100 miles in width (Fig. 4.15). That of the Yellow River (the Hwang Ho) is a plain more than 300 miles wide. Many deltas, though large, are not conspicuous on the map because they are built in the ends of large arms of the sea. The Colorado, Sacramento-San Joaquin, and Tigris-Euphrates deltas are examples (Fig. 4.16).

Not all streams form deltas. Many lack the necessary sediment load. Others enter the sea where the water is too deep or wave action so strong that the sediment is spread broadly

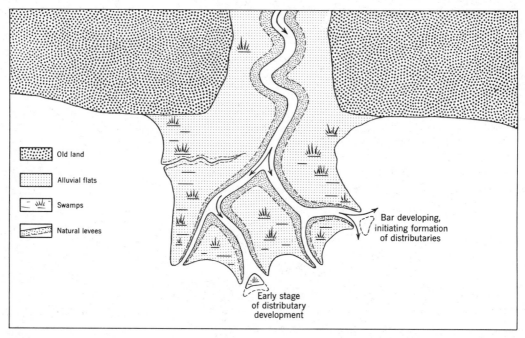

FIG. 4.14　Characteristic features of a delta plain.

over the sea bottom without building up to the surface. The St. Lawrence and the Congo both deposit most of their load in interior basins and reach the sea with too little sediment to produce deltas in the deep waters that they enter.

Deltas, like floodplains, are sometimes use-ful agricultural lands because of their flatness, their water supply, and often their fertility. But, they are also subject to floods and often contain much swampy land (Fig. 4.17). The natural levees may offer the only delta land that can be used without diking, draining, or pumping. Yet useless delta land

FIG. 4.15　Delta outlines and channels.

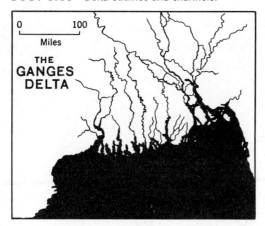

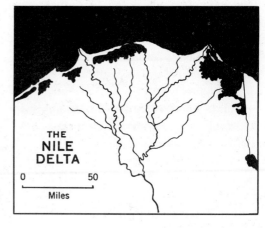

can be reclaimed, as the Netherlands has shown. Most of that country lies on the great combined delta of the Rhine and the Maas Rivers and several smaller streams. Much of it was originally either swamp or shallow sea floor. Now, by means of centuries of dike building, pumping, and flushing out of salt, huge areas of highly productive land have been virtually created there by man (Fig. 4.18). Indeed, the Netherlands serves as a remarkable example of what can be done in reclamation of deltas when the demand for land is sufficiently intense and the initiative and the necessary technical knowledge are available.

Alluvial fans   The alluvial fan is similar to the delta as a spreading form developed by a stream dropping its load because of an abrupt checking of the velocity. But with the alluvial fan the break in speed is the result of a sudden decrease in the stream's gradient: most fans are formed by streams emerging from steep mountain canyons onto plains or flat valley floors. The material dropped is largely the coarser bed load of gravel, sand, and sometimes coarse silt. The large fragments are dropped first, near the mouth of the canyon.

Like most other sand-moving streams, those that form alluvial fans commonly have wide, shallow, braided channels. They continually choke themselves with debris and shift from one side to the other, so that the deposit takes on the shape of a spread fan (or half of a low, flat cone) with the apex at the mouth of the canyon. The surface of the fan bears the marks of many diverging sandy channels, most of them dry (Fig. 4.19).

Piedmont alluvial plain   Some alluvial fans are only a few yards across; the broadest ones extend out several tens of miles from the mountain front. At the foot of an elongated

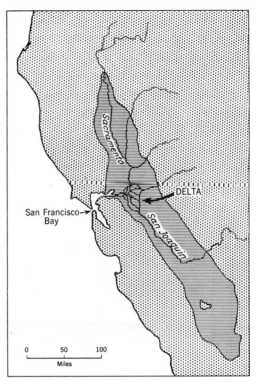

FIG. 4.16   An arm of the sea once reached through San Francisco Bay into the heart of the Central Valley of California. The combined delta of the Sacramento, San Joaquin, and other rivers that drain the valley has been built in the head of this embayment, far from the open sea.

mountain range many fans may develop side by side, eventually growing together to form an extensive gently sloping alluvial apron or piedmont (foot-of-the-mountain) alluvial plain (Fig. 4.20). Most of the southeastern part of the Central Valley of California is a plain of this type. Much of Los Angeles stands on a similar plain that has been built out into the sea from the mountains north of the city. Alluvial fans and aprons surround most of the small ranges of Nevada and western Utah.

The High Plains that stretch eastward from the Rocky Mountains of Colorado and New Mexico into Kansas, Oklahoma, and

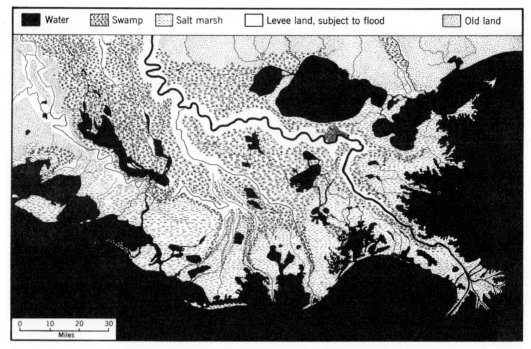

| ■ Water | ▨ Swamp | ▦ Salt marsh | ☐ Levee land, subject to flood | ▨ Old land |

FIG. 4.17   The Mississippi River Delta has fringing areas of salt-marsh grass and reeds, belts of wooded swamp, and strips of tilled levee lands. Note that the levee lands grow narrow downstream and disappear. *(V. C. Finch.)*

FIG. 4.18   The extent of reclaimed land in the Netherlands in relation to the area of the Rhine River delta.

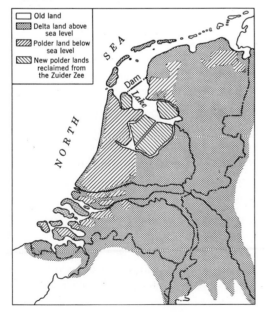

☐ Old land
▨ Delta land above sea level
▨ Polder land below sea level
▨ New polder lands reclaimed from the Zuider Zee

Texas owe their remarkably smooth upland surface to alluvial deposition. During successive uplifts of the mountains great quantities of alluvium were eroded and spread eastward as a piedmont alluvial plain of enormous size. More recently the streams crossing the plains have begun to erode and have cut valleys in the surface, but only at wide intervals, so that there are still broad expanses of smooth upland remaining (Fig. 4.2). A similar plain, but almost uncut, lies to the east of the Andes in eastern Bolivia, western Paraguay, and western Argentina.

Lake plains and coastal plains   The areas of plain which are former lake bottoms or portions of shallow sea bottom from which water has disappeared are many. Lakes are short-lived, by the scale of geologic time, for they are inevitably subject to filling by washed-in sediment or to draining by down-

FIG. 4.19   These large alluvial fans at the eastern foot of the Sierra
Nevada of California are beginning to merge, forming a piedmont alluvial
plain. *(Spence Air Photos.)*

cutting of the outlet. Other lakes disappear as a result of increasing dryness of the climate. So it is not surprising that there are many lake beds not now occupied by lakes. Similarly, small uplifts of the land or lowerings of the sea level, both of which have occurred frequently, expose strips of surface that were formerly parts of the sea bottom just offshore.

On lake bottoms and coastal sea bottoms sediment is likely to be spread broadly and evenly, sometimes to a considerable thickness. Thus their surfaces tend to become quite smooth, with only a very gentle slope away from the shore. Certain plains of this origin are among the most featureless surfaces in existence (Fig. 4.21). Because they are usually low-lying, stream erosion is slow and shallow. Swamps or shallow lakes may occur in the slightly lower sags in the surface. Around the margins of the plain there are often beaches, terraces, or other features that indicate the position of the former shorelines.

The outer part of the southeastern plains of the United States, along the south Atlantic and Gulf Coasts, is one of the more extensive examples of a surface lately emerged from the sea. It is low, flat, sandy, and swampy, with only feeble stream erosion (Figs. 4.22, 4.23). The area farther inland

FIG. 4.20   A piedmont alluvial plain is formed by the growing together of many extensive alluvial fans at the foot of a mountain range.

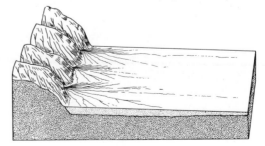

FIG. 4.21   The extremely level surface of a glacial-lake plain near Saginaw, Michigan. *(V. C. Finch.)*

was also once covered by the sea, but has been exposed long enough and is now far enough above baselevel that erosion has made strong headway. Many other coasts of

the world have strips of emergent sea bottom along them, but most of these are relatively narrow. The margins of Hudson Bay, especially the southwestern, show remarkably broad belts of low, flat, poorly drained land marked by innumerable parallel lines of raised beaches. These are apparently the result of a rather rapid but irregular rise of the land following the melting of the last continental glacier.

The exposed floors of former lakes are also common, and some are very extensive. Some of the largest known are in North America. Large parts of northwestern Minnesota and the eastern Dakotas, and most of southern Manitoba are occupied by a flat plain that represents the bottom of a huge lake, larger than any of the present Great Lakes, that existed near the end of the Pleistocene period.

FIG. 4.22   The flat, marshy surface of the Florida Everglades, part of a relatively new plain not yet dissected by streams. *(V. C. Finch.)*

FIG. 4.23 A flat but well-drained section of the West Gulf Coastal Plain in Texas. *(V. C. Finch.)*

This body of water, which is known as Lake Agassiz, came into being when the northward-flowing drainage of the area was dammed by the edge of the melting ice sheet. At present the surface is nearly featureless, with the Red River cutting slightly into the lowest part and several sets of low beach ridges visible around the margins. There are several smaller plains of similar origin in the north central part of the continent (Fig. 4.24).

Another set of lake plains exists in the Basin and Range province of Nevada and surrounding states. These represent the beds of lakes that existed in the extensive structural basins of that area during times when the climate was moister than it is now. This probably occurred more than once during the late Pleistocene and possibly at least once since the Pleistocene. Two of these lakes, named Bonneville and Lahontan, occupied extensive areas in western Utah and western Nevada, respectively. Great Salt Lake is a shrunken remnant of Lake Bonneville, and the Bonneville Salt Flats, famous for auto-

mobile speed trials, are part of the former lake floor.

Among the larger lake plains elsewhere in the world are part of the smooth elevated basin of the Congo River, and several basins along the southern margin of the Sahara Desert, including that containing the remnant Lake Chad.

FIG. 4.24 Map of the plain of glacial Lake Agassiz, with the plains of other ice-margin lakes that existed at various times during the wastage of the Wisconsin ice sheets. Also shown are some of the spillways through which these lakes drained when their normal drainage was blocked by the ice.

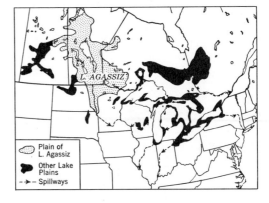

L. AGASSIZ

Plain of
L. Agassiz

Other Lake
Plains

Spillways

PLAIN SURFACES AFFECTED BY ICE, GROUND WATER, AND WIND

KINDS AND FEATURES OF GLACIALLY MODIFIED PLAINS

Glacial modification of the surface
Nearly a third of the continental area of the world was occupied by ice at one time or another during the Pleistocene period. However, not all of that area is now characterized by distinctly glacial land forms. Only in those sections covered by ice in late Pleistocene time (called Wisconsin in this continent) are the glacially produced features well enough preserved to give distinctive character to the surface. The older glaciated surfaces have been so modified by running water and mass movement that their glacial history can be inferred only from the presence of material recognizable as till.

Surfaces glaciated in Wisconsin time are shown in Fig. 3.25. The land forms of these areas are quite varied, and not all of the

FIG. 4.25   Areas of late glacial deposition commonly display numerous lakes, swamps, and wandering streams.

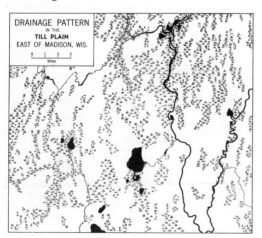

areas are plains. However, there do exist throughout recurrent types or associations of features that reflect the patchy, irregular, unchanneled erosional and depositional activity of the great ice sheets. A significant part of that activity involved virtual obliteration of the old stream courses and the production of a surface in which there were many shallow enclosed depressions and few continuous valleys. For this reason lakes, swamps, and aimlessly wandering streams are found almost everywhere in the lately glaciated country, though they are rare in stream-eroded landscapes. It is these features that are the most obvious and impressive novelties to a person coming into glaciated country for the first time (Fig. 4.25).

Most of the area of glaciated plains is dominated by depositional features. Only in scattered sections is the drift so patchy or so lacking that bedrock surfaces scoured by erosion are broadly exposed. These appear to be chiefly in areas where the bedrock is especially resistant and where the original surface was relatively rough.

Till surfaces   Since the major portion of the glaciated surface is depositional, it will be well to consider some of the characteristic features of drift-covered surfaces. These assume many forms because of differences in (*a*) the roughness and shape of the surface on which the drift was laid down, (*b*) the thickness of the drift, (*c*) the amount of rock, sand, and clay in the drift, and (*d*) the specific local conditions of deposition.

Effects of till deposition   Except where the original surface was unusually smooth, the deposition of till usually had the effect of making the surface smoother than it was. Till was deposited thickly in the valleys and only thinly on the hilltops. If the original terrain had slight relief, the till might completely obscure the older forms, producing an entirely new surface. If, on the other hand, the original terrain was hilly or the drift rather thin, the old hilltops may be still visible as elements in the landscape, even though they are thinly covered with till (Fig. 4.26). This kind of partial control of the surface form by preglacial bedrock features is common in the northern United States, Canada, and Scandinavia. Where it occurs, lakes and swamps are especially likely to be found along the larger old-stream valleys that are now only partly filled by drift. An excellent example is the chain of lakes at Madison, Wisconsin.

Where the deposition of till has been the controlling factor in shaping the landforms, the surface is ordinarily smoothly undulating to moderately rolling. Steep and angular slopes are rare; features are usually rounded, and bedrock outcrops are few (Fig. 4.27). Some of the clayey or silty till surfaces, such as those in northeastern Illinois, north cen-

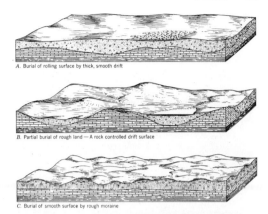

A. Burial of rolling surface by thick, smooth drift

B. Partial burial of rough land — A rock controlled drift surface

C. Burial of smooth surface by rough moraine

FIG. 4.26 The effects of glacial deposition vary with the roughness of the buried surface and the thickness of the drift. *(V. C. Finch.)*

tral Iowa, and the eastern Dakotas, are among the smoother sections of the continent. Stony and gravelly till sustains steeper slopes and hence normally displays more irregular surfaces than fine till.

Distinctive surface features of till deposits Among the more distinctive features of till surfaces are the marginal moraines, the strips of thicker drift that accumulated along the edge of the ice sheet when the margin remained long in one place. Here debris was dropped as at the end of a

FIG. 4.27 The undulating surface of a till plain. *(Wisconsin Geological Survey.)*

FIG. 4.28   Small kettle ponds surrounded by boulder-strewn knobs in a marginal moraine near Whitewater, Wisconsin. *(V. C. Finch.)*

great conveyor belt, partly by the ice melting from around it, partly by being washed over the edge of the glacier by meltwater.

Marginal moraines usually appear in the landscape as bands of somewhat rougher, higher, and often stonier land than that to

FIG. 4.29   The unusually rough, knobby surface of the Kettle Moraine, in eastern Wisconsin. *(John R. Randall.)*

either side (Fig. 4.28). Some are narrow, low, and inconspicuous; others are broad strips of knobby, pitted, lake-strewn country that can hardly fail to be noticed by the traveler. In the United States one of the most conspicuous is the high, rugged Kettle Moraine of eastern Wisconsin, formed between two tongues, or lobes, of the late Pleistocene glacier (Fig. 4.29). Another is the broad series of moraines in western Minnesota that forms a belt of unusually rough knob-and-kettle surface 25 to 50 miles in width. An important group of European moraines can be traced as a belt of irregular lake-dotted country that extends from Denmark through north Germany and Poland to the vicinity of Moscow. Narrower but very prominent moraines also cross southern Finland from west to east.

Many till plains exhibit elongated ridges and grooves that extend in the direction of ice movement. In some areas these take the form of low, streamlined hills of drift that are called drumlins (Fig. 4.30). The origin of such features is not well understood, though it probably involved the riding of the ice over old moraine deposits or over material lodged beneath the ice by melting. Recent investigations, especially in Canada, have disclosed that linear features of this kind are much more widespread than was formerly thought.

The lakes and swamps that are common to most till surfaces are simply collections of water in the low sags and depressions in the drift surface. They are most abundant where the surface is especially rough because of marginal-moraine deposition or the presence of an irregular preglacial surface underneath. Most of the lakes are shallow. Nearly all are destined for early disappearance because of filling by sediment and swamp debris as well as rapid lowering of the outlets by erosion of the unconsolidated drift.

Outwash surfaces Outwash surfaces can occur both within and beyond the limits of the area covered by the ice. Meltwater streams may carry debris tens or hundreds of miles from the ice margin to deposit it in

the form of floodplains along established valley bottoms or as fans and sheets across smooth plains.

With one significant exception the features of outwash surfaces are those common to other alluvial plains of comparable type. The surfaces are usually conspicuously flat and exhibit various patterns of stream channels (Fig. 4.31). Since the finer silts and clays are normally carried in suspension clear out of the area of origin, the outwash deposits in the vicinity of the ice margin are usually sands and gravels, reasonably well stratified. A peculiarity of some outwash surfaces is the existence of sizable depressions, often rather steep-sided, and usually containing lakes or swamps. These are not normal alluvial features, but are found principally in outwash plains laid down within the glaciated area. During wasting away of the glacier, individual masses of stagnant ice are left in front of the retreating glacial margin, to be largely or completely buried in outwash. Eventually the mass melts away from beneath the deposit, and the surface sags down into the space it occupied.

Outwash deposits are widespread about

FIG. 4.30 A drumlin on the till plain of central New York. Its shape indicates that the ice movement was from right to left. *(U.S. Geological Survey.)*

FIG. 4.31 The nearly flat surface of an outwash plain. *(Wisconsin Geological Survey.)*

the former glacial margins and throughout the glaciated areas. A few areas have received unusually thick and extensive deposits because of conditions that favored the pouring of large amounts of meltwater into a restricted space. Southern Michigan, for example, received outwash from glacial tongues to the west, north, and east, and is notable for such deposition (Fig. 4.32). The Baltic Coast of Denmark, Germany, and Poland received quantities of outwash that was trapped between the ice front to the north and higher ground to the south.

Glaciated surfaces with little drift Some glaciated surfaces have little drift. They occur principally in the rougher parts of the crystalline rock regions of Canada, Scandinavia, and Finland. In these areas the thin preglacial soil cover was extensively removed, especially from the higher spots, and the resistant bedrock yielded little new drift. Locally, shallow basins were excavated in the bedrock, and lakes now occupy them. Patchy drift was deposited in the low spots, but especially on the uplands the naked bedrock has been left exposed (Fig. 4.33). These bare rock surfaces were in many

places crudely smoothed by the action of the ice, and often show grooves or scratches that indicate the direction in which rocks were dragged across them by the glacier. Joints, fault lines, and other bands of weaker material show especially clearly because they have been etched out by selective erosion.

Ice-scoured surfaces of this kind are generally of low human utility because of their thin, stony, and patchy soils, their irregular surfaces, and the large amounts of standing water. Rapids and falls provide some useful water-power sites, and valuable mineral deposits have been discovered in some of these areas of ancient rocks, but for the most part they offer little to man.

PLAINS AFFECTED BY UNDERGROUND SOLUTION

How solution affects the surface Relatively limited areas of the world's plains owe their surface form primarily to the work of agents other than running water or moving ice. The most significant are those showing the effects of subsurface solution and those modified by wind action.

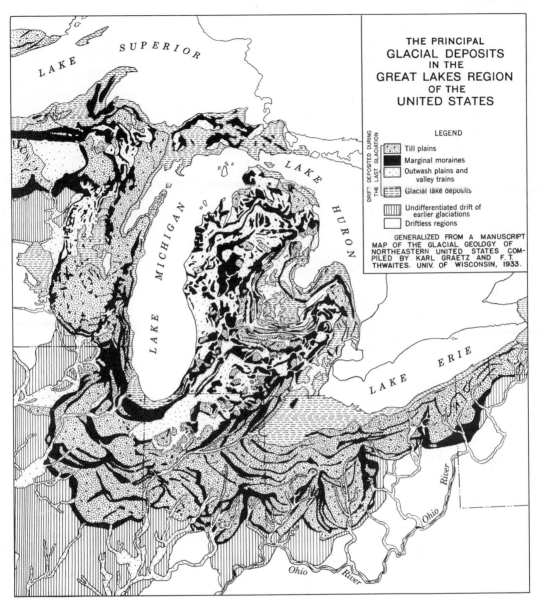

FIG. 4.32 The pattern of arrangement of the drift deposits in the Great Lakes region. *(Reproduced by permission of F. T. Thwaites.)*

Subsurface solution is highly significant only in regions underlain by relatively pure limestones. Water in the ground makes its way along joints and between layers of the limestone and enlarges these openings by dissolving the rock. In time the mass becomes honeycombed with cavities, some of them of cavernous size. This weakens the structure of the rock, and parts of it collapse. If breakdown occurs near ground level, the

FIG. 4.33   The rounded uplands and rock basins of an ice-scoured surface in northern Canada, where vegetation is scant. Note the different elevations of the lakes. *(Royal Canadian Air Force.)*

surface sinks down, forming a depression, or sinkhole (Fig. 4.34).

Solution features   Sinkholes are of all sizes, but those in plains areas are usually no more than a few feet or at most a few tens of feet in depth, and from a few yards to a large fraction of a mile in diameter (Fig. 4.35). They may have openings at the bottom through which surface water can escape to underground passages. But sometimes the opening becomes stopped with clay and other debris, so that a small lake is formed.

These depressions are the most distinctive

feature of topography in which solution has played a part. Where they are closely spaced and small, the surface strongly resembles morainic topography. In addition, however, solution areas commonly have strikingly few surface streams. A small stream will run on the surface for a short distance and will then disappear into a sink opening or small hole, pursuing the rest of its course underground. In many depressions and valleys streams emerge from caves or springs, sometimes diving again into the ground some distance downstream.

Sizable areas of solution-marked plains

FIG. 4.34   Sinkholes and their relation to solution cavities beneath the surface. *(V. C. Finch.)*

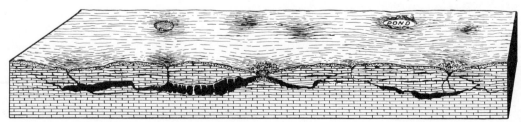

occur in northern and northwestern Florida; smaller areas are numerous and widespread. Several highly spectacular solution landscapes of high relief exist in various parts of the world, most notably in western Yugoslavia, but these cannot be classified as plains.

PLAIN SURFACES SHAPED BY THE WIND

Occurrence and characteristic erosional features Wind-shaped plain surfaces are largely confined to the dry parts of the world. Even there the effects of wind action are usually less important than the work of water. Except for the few great seas of sand dunes, wind-produced features are mostly minor details on surfaces sculptured principally by water.

Wind erosion produces three kinds of noticeable features. Some broad, shallow, enclosed depressions that cannot be other-

wise explained are attributed to wind erosion resulting from destruction of the vegetation by some local cause. These features, called blowouts, are common in arid and semiarid regions. Also attributable to the wind are the various polished, etched, and curiously formed bedrock features produced by sandblasting during strong winds. The most extensive products of wind erosion are the gravel plains left behind by the selective removal of fine particles from the surface layers of mixed alluvium. This "desert pavement" occupies broad areas in most of the world's dry lands (Fig. 3.30).

Depositional features The only pronounced surface forms directly attributable to deposition by the wind are sand dunes. They have developed chiefly from thick alluvial deposits of lowland basins and in some instances from the residual weathering products of sandstones (Fig. 4.36).

Where sand is thick and abundant, dunes commonly form as series of great waves sim-

FIG. 4.35 Limestone plain with numerous small sinkholes, some containing ponds. Near Park City, Kentucky, south of Mammoth Cave. *(H. Ray Scott, National Park Concessions, Inc., courtesy Kentucky Geological Survey.)*

FIG. 4.36 The billowing, wind-rippled forms of one of the small patches of sand dunes in the American desert. Death Valley National Monument. *(George A. Grant, National Park Service.)*

ilar in form to waves in the sea. However, where strong winds may come from various directions, these waves are distorted into pyramids and other more complex forms. Where the sand is less plentiful, dunes are usually separated from one another, sometimes forming almost perfect crescents (*barchans*) with the horns pointing downwind.

FIG. 4.37 Common types of sand dunes. In all the examples shown, the prevailing direction of strong winds is from left to right.

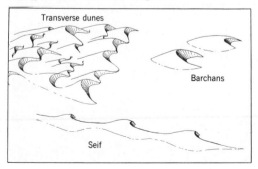

Long, peaked ridgelike forms (*seifs*) are also common (Fig. 4.37). Many dunes, especially the smaller ones, are moved along progressively by the wind, not as a mass but grain by grain. Roads, irrigated fields, and even towns, in the Sahara and elsewhere, have been engulfed by moving dunes.

Perhaps because of the striking forms and movements of dunes, it is a common belief that most deserts are largely covered by them, but this is not true. Dunes are rather rare in the Americas, and even in the Old World they occupy a minority of the desert lands (Fig. 4.38).

Dunes also occur as features of sandy surfaces in humid lands, especially adjacent to beaches. Usually, however, they do not move far from their place of origin, but tend to be confined by the growth of vegetation.

The deposition of wind-blown loess (page 70) may serve to cover the land with an

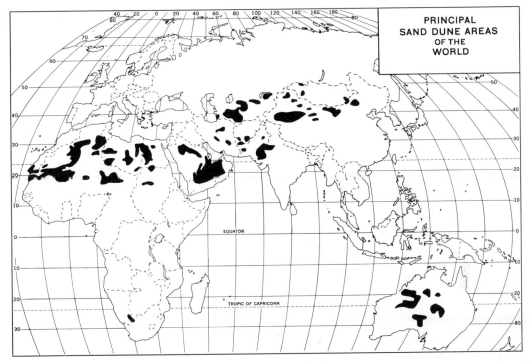

FIG. 4.38 Extensive areas of sand dunes are largely confined to the deserts of the Eastern Hemisphere continents.

extensive blanket of silt several inches or even many feet thick (Fig. 4.39). But the smooth-surfaced loess accumulations, unless they are unusually thick, do not greatly change the form of the preexisting terrain, unlike sand deposits. Because of the relative ease with which loess is eroded, and because of its propensity for maintaining steep slopes, areas of thick loess are nonetheless commonly rather strongly dissected by streams, and in places have become quite picturesque (Fig. 4.40).

FIG. 4.40 An eroded and slumped hillside in deep loess in central Nebraska.

FIG. 4.39 Loess deposits are widespread in the United States. *(From C. F. Marbut, U.S. Department of Agriculture.)*

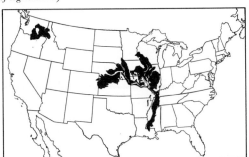

CHAPTER 5

Surfaces rougher than plains

HILLS AND MOUNTAINS

ORIGIN AND DEVELOPMENT

Basic nature; tectonic background Hill and mountain lands are distinguished from other types of surfaces by the fact that the majority of their slopes are too steep to be described as gentle. In addition, most hill lands have local relief of several hundred feet, and the relief of mountains is still higher.

As previously mentioned, high relief can develop only if parts of the area are built or carried far above their surroundings by crustal deformation or vulcanism, or if the entire area is brought so far above the baselevel of erosion that streams can cut deeply into the surface. In either instance tectonic activity of considerable strength is necessary. So it is no surprise to find that the world's mountains occur in strongly disturbed parts of the crust.

Furthermore, a considerable amount of the disturbance must have occurred late in geologic time; otherwise the surface irregularities would already have been smoothed out by gradation. In most mountain areas major crustal disturbance appears to have taken place several times, with long intervals between. In these instances the present mountains are simply the latest of several generations that have existed in one place. Thus, for example, the first (and strongest) crustal deformation in the Appalachian Mountain region took place some 250 million years ago, but the mountains produced at that time were soon destroyed. An unknown number of generations of mountains have come into existence and been destroyed in the area since then, and the present ones are not more than a few million years old. The latest disturbance was a broad, rather modest upwarping of the old complex structures, with carving out of the existing forms by differential erosion.

Steep slopes naturally accompany high relief. Streams that have far to go in order to reach baselevel commonly achieve steep gradients and cut down rapidly, producing steep-sided, often canyonlike valleys. As suggested earlier, a predominance of steep slopes is rather rare in areas of low relief, where slow downcutting is more the rule. Hills of low relief usually require unusual conditions for their development, conditions that favor concentrated runoff and especially swift erosion. Thus such hills are especially likely to develop in dry areas, limestone areas, and loess areas.

It is worth emphasizing that extensive areas of hills are rarely if ever simply worn-down mountain lands. Where mountains have been worn down to moderate relief, their valleys have ordinarily been so widened by erosion and mass wasting that only widely

separated clumps or lines of high-standing remnants are left. Broad expanses of hills such as the Ozarks and the hills of eastern Kentucky and West Virginia have been formed by the cutting of a close network of narrow valleys in extensive masses of the crust that have been only moderately uplifted. The relief has not, in late geologic time, been appreciably larger than it is now.

Sculpturing   The sculpturing of rough lands is accomplished by the same agents that shape the surface features of plains. It is therefore not necessary to recapitulate the principles of surface development but only to consider their application to these surfaces of higher relief and predominantly steeper slopes.

Mountain and hill lands are all carved out of masses of the crust that have been lifted up or built up significantly by crustal deformation or vulcanism. The forms taken by the various ranges, groups, ridges, valleys, and peaks depend first upon the nature of the gradational agents and the form and geologic structure of the mass on which they have to work. Most mountain forms are erosional; that is, they are produced by such processes as stream cutting, mass movement, and glacial quarrying. Only the occasional uneroded fault scarps, volcanic cones, lava flows, and alluvial features are exceptions.

CHARACTERISTICS

STREAM ERODED FEATURES

Valley forms and patterns   The majority of streams in rough lands are still cutting down rapidly. Their gradients are steep and irregular, with many rapids and falls. Because valley deepening is going on actively, there is no chance for valley floors to open out; so the cross sections are commonly V-shaped. Where the rocks are especially resistant to

FIG. 5.1   The Black Canyon of Gunnison River, Colorado, a narrow gorge cut by an active stream in resistant rock. *(W. T. Lee, U.S. Geological Survey.)*

weathering, valley widening is so slow in comparison to deepening that a slitlike gorge develops (Fig. 5.1). Where rocks are weaker and stream gradients gentler, valley sides are much less steep, provided there is enough surface runoff or mass movement to wear them back.

In those rough lands where erosion has proceeded for a long time, the principal streams have attained gentle gradients and their valleys have begun to widen and to develop open floors. Many of the tributary valleys, however, are still steep and V-shaped. Eventually the continued widening of the principal valleys tends to parcel the rough land into separated masses and spidery ridges. Such areas are likely to offer much more usable land and somewhat easier paths of access than those in which erosion is less far advanced.

As in plains, the pattern of valleys and ridges will be dendritic unless there are pronounced local variations in rock resistance or peculiarities in the arrangement of original slopes (Fig. 5.2). However, because complex rock structures and irregular arrangements of slopes on the original uplands are almost the rule in mountainous areas, departures from the dendritic pattern are common. And because the relief is great, these peculiarities are more obvious and more significant than they are in plains (Fig. 4.7).

Slopes, peaks, and ridges   The steep slopes of hills and mountains favor rapid wash and active mass movement on the valley sides. Landslides, avalanches, and sudden floods are not uncommon. On especially steep, rocky mountainsides sizable blocks of rock, dislodged by weathering and ice wedging, roll or fall down the slopes, accumulating in steeply inclined piles or fans called talus or scree (Fig. 3.23). Hillside soils are characteristically thin and stony because of the continual stripping of the surface by erosion.

Most peaks and ridges are simply what has been left after the cutting of adjacent valleys. Their pattern is determined by the pattern of the streams. Sometimes this arrangement is strongly conditioned by variations in the resistance of the rocks, with ridges and peaks upheld by outcrops of unusually resistant rock. In a few mountain areas many or all of the individual high peaks are volcanic cones.

In erosional mountains, as in stream-eroded plains, upland divides are continuous and high during the earlier stages of development. In time, however, the divides become narrowed to relatively sharp crests and from then on are subjected to irregular lowering. Notches appear at the heads of major valleys and then at tributary heads (Fig. 5.3). As the number and depth of the notches increases, the divides change from continuous high ridges to lines of well-defined peaks separated by lower gaps or passes. The existence of such gaps may be highly important to the location and relative ease of transport routes through a mountainous area.

Some areas of hills or mountains are remarkable for the close spacing and extreme sharpness of their gullies, ravines, and ridges. Such intricacy of sculpture is fairly common in dry lands, where the surface is not protected by vegetation and gullying is the rule. In a few regions of the world there are hill lands of almost incredible ruggedness and complexity. The famed Badlands of the western Dakotas are an excellent example (Fig. 5.4). These have been carved out of weakly cemented, easily eroded sandy silts in a semiarid climate. Small-scale features of the same sort can often be seen on dirt fills and old mine dumps that have been allowed to remain for years without a plant cover.

Effects of structure   The form and the rock structure of the upraised mass of the crust can have strong effects upon the mountains or hills that are carved from it. These effects are seen sometimes in the form and pattern of major features and sometimes in relatively minor details of slope and crest.

Where crustal disturbance or volcanic outpouring has occurred very rapidly and recently, the shape and pattern of the uplifted section of the crust is clearly visible in the form and outline of the mountain mass itself. One of the most striking examples is to be seen in the Sierra Nevada of California. This great range is sculptured from an immense tilted fault block nearly **400** miles long. The precipitous fault scarp, in places more than 8,000 ft high, faces eastward, and the tilted surface of the block slopes more gently toward the west (Fig. 3.5). Both slopes have been deeply cut by streams and

FIG. 5.2   Aerial view in the Allegheny hill region of West Virginia shows it to be a stream-dissected upland with a dendritic valley pattern. *(John L. Rich. Courtesy of the "Geographical Review," American Geographical Society of New York.)*

valley glaciers, but the general form and the size of the range are those of the block. Such fault-block ranges are not uncommon, though few are as large as this one. Other ranges and groups of mountains and hills show forms and outlines produced directly by rapid and recent folding or doming.

More commonly, however, uplift occurs so slowly that by the time it is completed the upraised mass has already been strongly eroded, so much so that the resulting moun-

FIG. 5.3 Brown Pass, a saddle-shaped notch in Glacier National Park,
Montana. The white arrow point touches the crest of the pass, which crosses
the Continental Divide. Note talus slopes at foot of cliffs at right.
(National Park Service.)

tains or hills bear little direct relationship to
the form of the uplift except in general extent
and outline. In these cases the complete structure of the mass can be deduced only by
inference from what is left of it. Often the
amount eroded away is larger than the bulk
of the mountains or hills that remain.

It was mentioned earlier in this chapter
that in most rough lands there is evidence
that uplift has occurred repeatedly and that
the present mountains and hills are not the
first ones to exist. In these situations it is
almost a rule that the earlier disturbances
were the most violent and complex, and that
the later ones tended to be simply broad

general uparchings of relatively modest
height. But these upwarped masses are still
rooted on the older and much more complex structures, which not infrequently
include rocks of high resistance. As a result,
differential erosion becomes very important
in determining patterns of ranges and valleys
within the broadly upwarped area.

Some of the most remarkable examples of
the effects of structure are found in the
Appalachian Highlands of the eastern United
States. The present mountains are the result
of erosion on a broadly upwarped section of
the crust in which are some very old and
complex structures. The western part of the

highlands is underlain by nearly horizontal rock strata. Since, within a limited area, there are not great differences in rock resistance, the valley patterns are dendritic, and the entire area is carved into a jumble of hills and low mountains (Figs. 2.9*a*, 5.2). The easternmost section of the highlands is developed on a highly complex structure, but one in which the ancient rocks involved do not vary much in resistance. Here again the mountains display a typical dendritic pattern (Fig. 5.5). Between these two areas, however, is a long belt of layered rocks that were in ancient times thrown into a remarkable series of long, parallel wrinkles. The layers now outcrop in parallel bands and vary greatly in resistance. Erosion on this structure has etched out valleys along the bands of weaker rock, leaving the edges of the resistant strata standing in relief as long ridges (Figs. 5.6, 5.7). Somewhat similar features are found in the Ouachita Mountains of Arkansas and in the Jura of eastern France.

Less striking, though not less significant, effects of structure are common. Thus, for example, most of the ranges of the Rocky Mountains of Wyoming and Colorado owe their present height above their surroundings to the superior resistance of their rocks, which are the roots of earlier, folded mountain structures.

Rock structure has many effects upon the smaller features of rough lands, just as it does in plains. Resistant outcrops stand out as ridges and peaks or form ledges and cliffs on the hillsides (Fig. 5.8). Joints, fault lines and nonresistant outcrops become sites of rapid erosion and therefore serve to localize

FIG. 5.4 The intricately dissected terrain of the Badlands of western South Dakota.

FIG. 5.5   The irregular, peaked ridges and eroded basins of the
southern Blue Ridge, Great Smoky Mountains National Park, North Carolina.
(National Park Service.)

valley cutting. Scarcely a slope, a crest, or a
stream course fails to show at least some
effect of the underlying rock structure.

FIG. 5.6   Series of diagrams in chronological
sequence to illustrate the erosional development of
linear ridges. *(V. C. Finch.)*

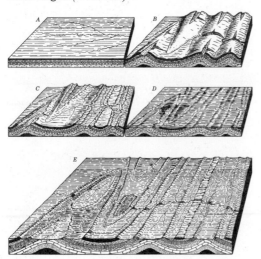

GLACIAL FEATURES

Mountain glaciers   Large areas of hill-
and-low-mountain lands in northern North
America and northwestern Europe were
completely overrun by the continental ice
sheets of the Pleistocene period. The higher
mountains in those areas, as well as elsewhere in the world, supported large glacial
tongues in their valleys; indeed, many still
do. Both continental and valley glaciers had
significant effects upon the land forms, and
the still-existing glaciers are significant forms
in themselves.

From their broad, snow-covered areas of
accumulation on the upper slopes and
especially in the valley heads, mountain
glaciers extend far down the valleys into the
zone of melting. The tiny, almost extinct
glaciers of the western United States rarely
exceed a mile in length, but in the Rocky
Mountains of Canada and in the Alps glacial

tongues 5 to 10 miles long are common. Some of the largest valley glaciers are in southern Alaska and the Himalayas, where lengths of 20 to more than 50 miles are recorded (Fig. 5.9).

The upper parts of mountain glaciers are often concave in form, with snow-covered, sometimes smooth surfaces. Toward the lower ends, however, the snow cover melts away in the summer, exposing a rather rough surface deeply slashed in places by open cracks or crevasses, especially at sharp turns in the valleys and where the gradient abruptly increases. Wastage of the ice by melting and evaporation uncovers masses of rock debris contained within the glacier, so that the lower ends of many glaciers are almost obscured by a cover of rubble.

Effects of continental glaciation Mountain and hill areas that have been over-ridden by continental ice sheets appear to have suffered much the same kinds of modification experienced by glaciated plains. The ice tended, in general, to smooth the surface by eroding away crags, projecting peaks, and small spurs, and by depositing drift in the valleys and ravines (Fig. 5.10). In a few places, where valleys were oriented in the direction of glacial flow, the ice was able to erode conspicuously in moving through the bottleneck. As in plains, the drift-clogged valleys are often the sites of numerous lakes and swamps. The northern Appalachians and the Adirondacks in New York State, the uplands and mountains of New England, and most of the Laurentian highlands of eastern Canada are rough lands that have been modified by overriding continental glaciation.

Effects of valley glaciation While broad ice sheets have the general effect of smoothing the topography, valley glaciers have quite the opposite effect, for their work

FIG. 5.7 Winter aerial view along one of the parallel ridges of the Appalachian Ridge and Valley region in Pennsylvania. The resistant stratum that forms the ridge dips sharply to the left. The Susquehanna River cuts through the ridge, forming a water gap. *(Fairchild Aerial Surveys, Inc.)*

is restricted to the valleys themselves. Within each valley they work vigorously, clearing weathered rock and talus from the valley bottom and sides, plucking in jointed bedrock, scouring on rock projections, and dumping their transported load farther down the valley and along the sides of the ice tongue. Thus the walls of glaciated mountain valleys are commonly steeper and freer of debris than are those of typical stream-cut valleys. Valley floors often descend in a series of

FIG. 5.8   View northward along the eastern front of the Rocky Mountains
near Denver, Colorado. Massive crystalline rocks at extreme left. In center are outcrops
and long hogback ridges on steeply inclined sedimentary strata. Mesa in
right background is capped by an old lava flow. *(T. S. Lovering, U.S. Geological Survey.)*

FIG. 5.9   Head of Susitna Glacier in central Alaska. Several tributary glaciers, descending
from high snowfields, join to form a large glacial tongue in the foreground. Note the many
cirques at the glacier heads, the crevasses at sharp turns and in steeper sections of the
glaciers, and the prominent medial and lateral moraines in the foreground. *(Bradford Washburn.)*

FIG. 5.10   Keuka Lake, one of the Finger Lakes, rests among the smooth-sloped glaciated hills of western New York. Contrast with Fig. 5.2 *(NYSPIX—Commerce, Albany, N.Y.)*

FIG. 5.11   Head of a glaciated mountain valley. A large cirque in background, with precipitous rock walls and a small remnant glacier. Characteristic stepped-down valley profile with lakes and waterfalls. *(Hileman, from Glacier National Park.)*

steps, and are marked by lakes strung like beads along a cord, some of them occupying shallow depressions in the bedrock, some dammed by moraines. Rapid weathering and wearing back of the bare, steep valley walls may reduce intervening divides to jagged, knife-edged ridges. Many valley heads look as though they had been excavated from the mountain masses by tremendous scoop shovels. Such steep-walled valley heads are termed cirques (Fig. 5.11).

This combination of abrupt slopes, sharp peaks and ridges, much exposed rock, numerous lakes, and prominent moraine ridges gives to valley-glaciated mountains a particularly spectacular quality, which is enhanced if there are still large glaciers and snow fields present (Fig. 5.12). It is true that many of these characteristics are sometimes found in mountains that have been subjected to especially vigorous stream erosion but never glaciated. But the recurring combina-

FIG. 5.12 Valley-glaciated mountains of the alpine type. Note the large abandoned lateral moraine in the foreground, indicating that the glacier was once larger than it is now. Mount Athabasca, Alberta, Canada. *(Canadian Pacific Railway Co.)*

tion of such features, and most significantly the presence of lakes and moraines, is the special mark of mountain glaciation. Nearly all of the truly great and high ranges of the earth display glacial features, some of modern development, some dating from the Pleistocene. Those ranges in which the glacial features are especially rugged and in which living glaciers still exist are often termed alpine mountains.

VOLCANIC MOUNTAINS

Occurrence While many of the world's rough lands are carved out of rocks that have originated through vulcanism, relatively few mountains have actually been constructed primarily by volcanic activity. The map of volcanic regions shows that volcanoes are largely confined to Central America, parts of the Andes, certain of the Atlantic islands, Italy and Sicily, eastern Africa, and the island chains of the western and northern Pacific. The majority of the great mountain systems, including the Rockies, the Alps, and the Himalayas, are nonvolcanic, although there is evidence of local activity in past times. Yet nearly all of the volcanic areas do lie in the mountain belts. The same strong crustal disturbances that have led to the development of the great mountain systems have undoubtedly favored the formation of molten pockets near the base of the crust and have provided the zones of weakness through which these materials have escaped to the surface.

Volcanic cones Strictly speaking, the truly volcanic mountains are the cones that have been built up by the accumulation of lava and ash about eruptive vents. Such cones form as essentially isolated features, ranging in size from insignificant hillocks to magnificent peaks thousands of feet high and

several miles in diameter. As a general rule the cones formed by explosive eruption involving ash are steep-sided, while those formed by the effusion of slowly hardening lavas are very broad and gentle. Parícutin (Fig. 3.7) and Vesuvius are examples of the former, the Hawaiian volcanoes of the latter (Fig. 5.13). However, the majority of cones are actually made up of layers of both lava and ash, and so are intermediate between the two extreme varieties. Fujiyama, the beautiful dormant volcano of central Japan, is a composite cone of this type (Fig. 5.14).

Fresh volcanic cones are usually smooth and symmetrical in form and display one or more well-defined craters, but erosion soon destroys this perfection. Once the volcano has ceased to be active, its crater is breached by ravines and its flanks become scarred and irregular. Mount Hood, Mount Rainier, and the other great peaks of the Cascade Range in the northwestern United States have all been dissected and roughened in varying degree by the work of both streams and glaciers (Fig. 5.15). Eventually, extinct cones become so reduced that they can scarcely be recognized for what they are. Occasionally destruction of a cone is hastened by explosion or collapse that destroys the top of the cone, leaving an immense depression (caldera) larger than any normal crater. Crater Lake in Oregon occupies a caldera of this kind (Fig. 5.16).

In some areas volcanic cones are so closely grouped in clusters or lines that they form mountain ranges or groups by themselves. The high-peaked and almost continuous range that extends the entire length of the island of Java, for example, is made up almost entirely of volcanic cones. Much more commonly, however, the cones are incidental features in areas of complex mountains formed

FIG. 5.13   The great "shield" volcanoes on the island of Hawaii. The summit of Mauna Loa (13,018 ft), with several craters, in the foreground; the broad cone of Mauna Kea (13,784 ft) in the background. The largest crater shown is 2 miles long and nearly 2 miles wide. *(Official U.S. Navy photograph.)*

FIG. 5.14   The symmetrical cone of Fujiyama rises more than 12,000 ft above Suruga Bay and its bordering alluvial plains. *(H. Suito.)*

chiefly by crustal deformation. Thus, for example, the cones of the Cascade Range and of the Andes have been constructed on top of or among mountains formed by the erosion of complex upraised masses of lava, ash, and various older rocks.

Erosional mountains developed on volcanic materials   Where thick and extensive accumulations of lava and ash have been upraised and deeply dissected, the resulting mountains, though composed of volcanic materials, are actually erosional features and do not owe their form directly to the volcanic activity. Much of the San Juan

FIG. 5.15 Mount Hood, Oregon, is an extinct composite volcanic cone, deeply eroded by water and ice. *(U.S. Forest Service.)*

FIG. 5.16 Crater Lake, Oregon, occupies a deep caldera formed by the collapse and destruction of the upper part of a great volcanic cone. Wizard Island (foreground) is a younger cone formed later. *(National Park Service.)*

FIG. 5.17 The Abajo Mountains in eastern Utah. This mountain group is a dissected intrusive mass (laccolith) about 6 miles in diameter and rising nearly 4,000 ft above the uplands of the Colorado Plateaus. *(W. Cross, U.S. Geological Survey.)*

FIG. 5.18 Agathla Peak, a great volcanic neck in northeastern Arizona. *(American Museum of Natural History.)*

Mountains of southwestern Colorado, the most extensive mass in the Southern Rockies, is carved in this way out of old volcanic debris.

Small intrusions sometimes form domelike bulges on the surface. These too are attacked by erosion and are sculptured into isolated peaks or small groups of mountains. Navajo Mountain, northeast of the Grand Canyon, is such a feature as yet but slightly dissected. The Henry Mountains, La Sal Mountains, and Abajo Mountains of eastern Utah have been more deeply carved into rugged mountain groups (Fig. 5.17). Because of the superior resistance of their rocks, the fillings of volcanic vents and the last remnants of small intrusive domes sometimes remain standing as striking towers after the surrounding materials have been eroded away (Fig. 5.18).

SURFACES COMBINING SMOOTHNESS AND HIGH RELIEF

GENERAL NATURE

Large areas of the continents are occupied by surfaces in which much gentle slope and relatively high relief are combined. These surfaces would, indeed, be plains, were there not certain widely spaced features on them having steep slopes and considerable height or depth. The distinction has already been drawn between those surfaces in which relief is provided chiefly by canyons or cliffs falling away below a smooth upland (tablelands) and those in which spaced hills or mountains rise above an extensive plain (plains with hills or mountains).

Since smooth surfaces usually imply a dominance of gradational processes and since high relief cannot occur without significant uplift of a part of the crust, it is clear that these rough-and-smooth surfaces are combinations in origin as well as in configuration. Commonly the smooth plain and the interrupting irregularities must be accounted for by quite separate series of events.

TABLELANDS

Origin   Tablelands, with their relatively smooth uplands and deep, steep-sided valleys, are like youthfully dissected plains in which the valleys are unusually deeply cut. Such deep cutting requires that the original surface shall have been lifted far above base-level. Thus most tablelands have originated as plains of various kinds that have in relatively late time been uplifted or built up far enough to permit deep dissection by streams.

However, preservation of the upland surface against dissection during such deep cutting requires that tributary development be unusually slow. Hence the conditions that retard tributary growth—(*a*) flatness, (*b*) porous and absorbent surface materials, (*c*) a solid vegetation cover, (*d*) light rains, and (*e*) resistant surface strata—are even more important to the existence of tablelands than to the maintenance of youthful plains. It is not mere coincidence that most tablelands are found in rather dry areas. Nor is it surprising that many tablelands are capped by nearly horizontal strata of unusually resistant rock or by sheets of porous gravel.

Characteristics   The detailed features of tablelands are chiefly products of recent gradational activity and are not fundamentally different from features already discussed in connection with plains and rough lands. The uplands may be typical stream-eroded plains the details of which depend upon rock structure and history. Many, having developed under dry climates on nearly horizontal rock strata of varying resistance, show features typically produced by those conditions. Narrow, steep-walled ravines, low cliffs and ledges, small, flat-topped mesas, and rocky terraces combine to give such uplands the

appearance of being miniatures of the larger tablelands of which they are a part. Other uplands show features of alluvial or glacial deposition. Still others are capped by lava flows or ash deposits.

Canyons and cliffs are so characteristic of tablelands as to demand special attention. The existence of canyons is favored by the very factors responsible for tablelands in general. Late, strong uplift of the surface favors rapid downcutting. The conditions that favor preservation of the upland also inhibit valley widening. So the valleys become deep but not wide, and canyons and gorges are the result. Their excessively slitlike appearance is, of course, something of an illusion; rarely are they as deep as they are wide. (Fig. 5.19).

The lines of cliffs (escarpments) that form the margins of many tablelands usually originate either as canyon sides or as fault scarps, though some are formed by differential erosion. They are worn back by erosion and mass movement but retain their steepness. In time they may retreat many miles from their original position. As they do so, the tableland surface becomes smaller and smaller and eventually disappears entirely. Usually the escarpment is highly irregular, with many ravines and projections (Fig. 5.20). Often fragments of the tableland are detached from the main mass by erosion and form spectacular flat-topped hills (mesas or buttes) and columns in front of the escarpment. Such features are called outliers (Fig. 5.21).

The upland surfaces of tablelands are in many places smooth enough to be easily traversable, even to serve as agricultural land. However, they are often rather dry, and may be too far above the streams to irrigate. The canyons and escarpments may provide major obstacles to transportation and may even make access to the uplands unduly difficult.

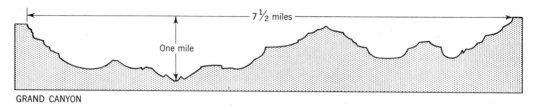

GRAND CANYON

7½ miles

One mile

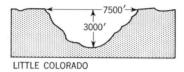

7500'

3000'

LITTLE COLORADO

FIG. 5.19   Cross-section profiles of the Grand Canyon of the Colorado River at Powell Memorial and of the canyon of the Little Colorado River about 2 miles above its mouth. Vertical and horizontal scales are the same.
(From U.S. Geological Survey topographic sheet: Grand Canyon National Park, east half.)

Occurrence   The principal tablelands of North America, all in the western part of the continent, differ in rock structure and in the manner in which they have developed. The several tablelands about the Colorado River in Utah, Arizona, New Mexico, and Colorado are strongly uplifted erosional plains on gently warped rock strata. The climate is dry, but a number of large streams emerging from the more humid mountains round about have cut profound canyons as they cross the up-

land (Fig. 5.22). In parts of eastern Washington and Oregon are tablelands carved out of thick and extensive accumulations of highly porous lava. Again the climate is dry, and there is little local runoff. Canyon cutting is accomplished by streams from the surrounding mountains. Just east of the Rocky Mountains in the northern United States and Canada is a broad area of tableland with only modest relief. The smooth, grass-covered upland is an ancient piedmont

FIG. 5.20   The ragged edge of an escarpment that is being driven back by erosion. Painted Desert, northeastern Arizona.
(Spence Air Photos.)

FIG. 5.21   A small mesa (right) and several buttes in Monument Valley, Arizona. These are detached outliers of a neighboring tableland.
(American Museum of Natural History.)

FIG. 5.22 The Grand Canyon of the Colorado River in Arizona. The portion of the canyon visible here is cut in nearly horizontal sedimentary strata. Resistant layers form the cliffs, weak strata the gentler slopes. *(National Park Service.)*

alluvial plain of unusual extent. More recently it has been trenched by streams coming out of the Rockies.

Other significant tablelands are the sandstone and lava-capped uplands of interior southern Brazil, the low somewhat cuestaform plateaus of southern Russia, and the broad, stony cuestas (hammadas) of the northern Sahara.

PLAINS WITH HILLS OR MOUNTAINS

Modes of development In contrast to tablelands, plains with hills or mountains owe their large relief to steeply sloping features that rise above the more extensive plain surface. As in tablelands, the high relief requires that tectonic action shall have raised at least part of the area above its surroundings or above baselevel, while the broad plains indicate active gradation.

There are at least two very different sequences of events that combine tectonics and gradation in such a way that plains surmounted by hills or mountains are produced. In the first, a generally mountainous area is reduced by erosion to the stage of early old age, in which only a few mountain remnants are left standing upon an erosional

FIG. 5.23   Near the western edge of the Appalachian Piedmont, numerous small monadnocks remain standing upon an erosional plain developed on crystalline rocks. This is Big Cobbler Mountain in northern Virginia. *(John L. Rich. Courtesy of the "Geographical Review," American Geographical Society of New York.)*

plain. The second sequence produces spaced mountains upon an original plain by the raising of fault blocks, the building of volcanic cones, or other localized tectonic disturbances.

Erosional varieties   Early in this chapter it was stressed that erosion of a mountainous area does not simply produce lower but still continuous mountains. Instead, the valleys widen at the expense of the mountains between them, eventually becoming very broad and merging with one another to form a low-level plain of irregular outline. For a long time, however, there may remain standing upon such a plain numerous steep-sided ridges, isolated peaks, and small groups of hills.

Mountain-studded terrain of this origin

occurs in parts of the eastern fringe of the Appalachians between Virginia and Georgia (Fig. 5.23). Glaciated varieties are found in parts of southern New England, the western Adirondacks, and in many sections of the extensive ancient-rock shield of central and eastern Canada. Similar terrain occurs in eastern Sweden and northern Finland. The most extensive areas of erosionally developed hill-studded plains are found on the hard-rock uplands of central Africa, where the remnants are often quite small and isolated. Much the same development has occurred in northeastern Brazil and in the eastern Guiana Highlands north of the Amazon plains (Fig. 5.24).

Tectonically produced varieties   Surfaces that have followed the second sequence of development are more widespread. In the majority of examples the mountains have been produced by faulting or folding, though there are a number of limited areas of plains dotted with volcanic cones.

As already suggested, the mountains, whatever their tectonic origin, are attacked by erosion as soon as they begin to appear, so that they are rarely purely tectonic forms. In many instances it is clear that the mountains that now exist have been greatly reduced from their original size. Thus the plain has expanded at the expense of the mountains, and the surface represents the result of a combination of both of the sequences of development.

One of the world's more extensive plain-and-mountain areas is the Basin and Range province, which occupies much of the southwestern United States and nearly all of northern Mexico. From southern Oregon to Mexico City this landscape of dry plains and rather small but rugged mountain ranges extends without a break and with only a moderate degree of internal variation. Most of the ranges are believed to have originated as raised and tilted fault blocks. Some of these, especially near the northwestern corner of the region, are fairly fresh and undissected. Most, however, are strongly eroded and reduced in size, much of the debris of their destruction having been deposited on the plains between them (Fig. 5.25). Some show evidence of more than one major period of tectonic disturbance. A few volcanic mountains exist, but they are numerous only at the southern end of the region, in central Mexico. In that section are hundreds of cones, ranging from cinder hillocks to the majestic and snow-capped Popocatepetl.

It cannot now be determined how smooth

FIG. 5.24 Remnant hills left standing upon an erosional plain developed on crystalline rocks in British Guiana. *(D. Holdridge. Courtesy of the "Geographical Review," American Geographical Society of New York.)*

a plain existed in the Basin and Range province before the fault blocks and cones were formed. It is clear, however, that nearly all of the individual plains there have recently been extended and smoothed by erosion of the mountains on their margins and by deposition of alluvium on their floors. Many are enclosed depressions, in the lowest parts of which are salt-covered flats or temporary saline lakes (Fig. 5.26).

Much of the Middle East, especially Iran and Afghanistan, closely resembles the Basin and Range province in topography and development. In central Asia, Tibet, and the central Andes of South America are surfaces displaying features of the same kinds but on a grander scale. The latter two areas are among the world's highest: even the basin floors stand at elevations of 10,000 to 16,000 ft, and the summits of the ranges often exceed 20,000 ft.

Because of the discontinuity and wide spacing of their peaks and ranges, plains with hills or mountains rarely offer serious hindrance to through transportation. Where conditions of soil, water, and climate are

FIG. 5.25   Deeply eroded ranges alternate with smooth basin floors in
the Mojave Desert of southeastern California. *(Spence Air Photos.)*

favorable, these plains also furnish agriculturally valuable land. Unfortunately, large
areas of this kind of terrain, such as the
Basin and Range province and the Middle

FIG. 5.26   Extensive salt flat on floor of
enclosed basin in Basin and Range province.
Clayton Valley, near Silver Peak, Nevada.
(C. D. Walcott, U.S. Geological Survey.)

East, are excessively dry. Yet the alluvial
fans, basin fillings, and occasional floodplains in these areas of dryness sometimes
provide possibilities for irrigation. Water
from the adjacent mountains may be con-
ducted to the alluvial surfaces by means of
ditches, or it may soak into the porous
alluvium where it can be reached by shallow
wells.

SELECTED REFERENCES

Atwood, W. W.: *The Physiographic Provinces of North America,* Ginn & Company, Boston, 1940.

Cotton, C. A.: *Volcanoes as Landscape Forms,* John Wiley & Sons, Inc., New York, 1952.

Fenneman, N. M.: *Physiography of Eastern United States,* McGraw-Hill Book Company, Inc., New York, 1938.

————: *Physiography of Western United States,* McGraw-Hill Book Company, Inc., New York, 1931.

Finch, V. C., G. T. Trewartha, A. H. Robinson, and E. H. Hammond: *Physical Elements of Geography,* 4th ed., McGraw-Hill Book Company, Inc., New York, 1957.

Flint, R. F.: *Glacial and Pleistocene Geology,* John Wiley & Sons, Inc., New York, 1957.

Lobeck, A. K.: *Geomorphology: An Introduction to the Study of Landscapes,* McGraw-Hill Book Company, Inc., New York, 1939.

Thornbury, W. D., *Principles of Geomorphology,* John Wiley & Sons, Inc., New York, 1954.

Wooldridge, S. W., and R. S. Morgan: *An Outline of Geomorphology: The Physical Basis of Geography,* 2d ed., Longmans, Green & Co., Ltd, London, 1959.

CHAPTER 6

The margins
of the lands

FEATURES OF THE COASTAL ZONES

That the continents end and the oceans begin at the shore line is obvious. But if the statement is changed to "the continental platforms end and the ocean basins begin at the shore line," it is no longer true. Along most continental shores the sea bottom does not drop off immediately to great depths. Instead it usually falls away gradually until it reaches depths of 400 to 600 ft and then plunges steeply to the floor of the deep-sea basin (Fig. 6.1). The shallower, gently sloping zone is a part of the continental mass both in form and geologic structure, and is called the continental shelf. Its steep outer margin,

the continental slope, is the true edge of the continent. Widths of the continental shelf vary from less than a mile to as much as 400 miles. The widest shelves are commonly found adjacent to low-lying plains on the continents (Fig. 6.2). Mountainous coasts, on the other hand, are often bordered by narrow shelves or by none at all.

As will be seen below, the shore lines of the world have, in late geologic time, repeatedly shifted their positions across the continental shelves and the lower margins of the present land areas. The existing shore lines have only recently been established.

120

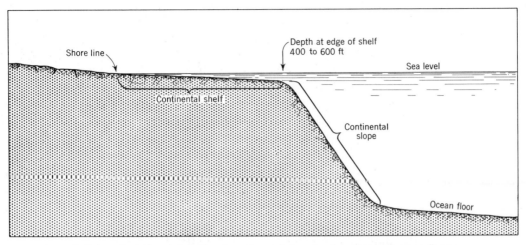

FIG. 6.1   Relation of continental shelf and continental slope to shore line and ocean floor.

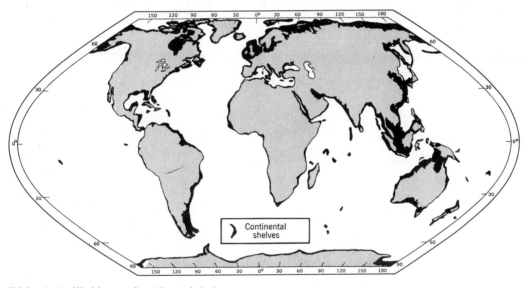

FIG. 6.2   World map of continental shelves.

CHANGES OF SEA LEVEL AND DEVELOPMENT OF SHORE LINES

Erosion and deposition by waves and currents, deposition by streams and glaciers of the adjacent lands, organic accumulations, and various tectonic happenings have all left their mark upon the features of the coastal zones. More important, however, have been large changes in the relative levels of land and sea, for it is these changes that have actively moved the shore lines about and thus greatly influenced their pattern.

A change in the relative levels of land and sea can be produced in two quite different ways. First, the land itself can be raised or lowered by crustal movement. Second, the sea surface can be raised or lowered, either by a change in the amount of water in the oceans or by a tectonic alteration of the total volume of the basins in which the oceans rest. These things have all happened frequently and on a large scale in relatively recent time, producing two kinds of changes in the position of the shore line. (*a*) If the land rose or the sea level sank, the shore line migrated seaward across the continental shelf. (*b*) If the land sank or the sea level rose, the shore line moved landward.

The changes in sea level that accompanied the formation and disappearance of the great Pleistocene ice sheets were especially

FIG. 6.3 Map of the Red Sea and its surroundings, showing the relation of its outline to major fault lines. *(After Machatschek.)*

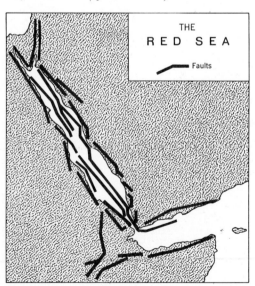

significant for the earth as a whole. Since the water that formed the glaciers originally came from the sea and was returned to the sea when the ice melted, the sea level sank as each ice sheet grew, and rose again as the ice melted. When the last glaciation was at its maximum, the sea level is believed to have been nearly 400 ft lower than it is now, thus exposing as dry land vast areas of what is now continental shelf. Thereafter the water surface rose irregularly, probably reaching its present level no more than a few thousand years ago. Tectonic raising and lowering of some coastal lands, especially in the Far North and around the Pacific rim, have occurred even more recently.

As a result of these events, the present position of the shore line has been only recently attained; indeed, in some places the shore is still shifting because of change of level of the land. The effects of these movements of the shore line may be clearly seen in the present outlines of certain coasts and in various features repeatedly encountered in the coastal zones.

Bays The majority of bays and gulfs are the result of a rising of sea level. In some instances a section of the continent has been carried below the level of the sea by warping, folding, or downfaulting. The Red Sea, Persian Gulf, and Gulf of California are major arms of the sea that occupy such structural depressions (Fig. 6.3). Some broader bordering seas, such as Hudson Bay and part of the Gulf of Mexico, may have resulted at least in part from gentler downwarping of sections of the continental margin. But most of the innumerable indentations of the coasts have been formed by the drowning of erosional topography by a rising sea level. It is not surprising to find such features so widely distributed, since the large rise of sea level during the melting of the last continental glacier was world-wide.

A general rise of sea level or a broad tectonic depression of the land permits the establishment of a new shore line upon what was previously the land surface. This new shore line assumes the position of a contour line upon the former land surface. Its outline, when first established, follows all of the wanderings of that contour line and thus reflects the form of the drowned surface.

If the submerged surface was a smooth alluvial slope, its contours were regular, and the new shore line is similarly regular. But if the surface was an erosional surface, as is more often true, its contours were probably highly irregular, and the shore line resulting from its drowning is also irregular. The sea penetrates the valleys, forming bays, while the higher divides remain above water as peninsulas or headlands. Individual embayments resulting from submergence are called drowned valleys. Those at the mouths of rivers are called estuaries.

Drowned valleys; estuaries If the gradients of the valleys drowned are very gentle, the resulting embayments reach far into the land, while the drowning of steeply pitching valleys produces only relatively short indentations. The form and pattern of the bays follow the form and pattern of the valleys that have been drowned. Thus some bays are dendritic, others are simple and parallel, and still others are highly irregular.

An especially fine example of an estuarine shore line is the Atlantic Coast of the United States in Delaware, Maryland, Virginia, and North Carolina (Fig. 6.4). There, through the drowning of a dendritic system of broad river valleys having particularly gentle gra-

FIG. 6.4 The middle Atlantic Coast of the United States exhibits a remarkably fine development of estuaries.

dients, estuaries of unusual size and length were produced.

Other strikingly estuarine coasts occur in northwestern Spain, Greece and western Turkey, western Ireland and Scotland, southern China, and southern Japan. The coasts of New England, Nova Scotia, and Newfoundland show an interesting variation on the usual estuarine pattern, an unusual complexity of outline resulting from the drowning of an irregular glaciated surface rather than a stream-eroded land (Fig. 6.5).

The extensive stretches of the world's coast lines that are not impressively estuarine are still rarely, if ever, completely free of existing or former estuaries. Most of these coasts are characterized by relatively steep-gradient valleys that yielded only small estuaries. And even these have been filled in

FIG. 6.5   The drowned glaciated shore line of Casco Bay, Maine, has many islands, rocky peninsulas, and narrow inlets.

many instances by the deposits of the swift-flowing streams. Thus, for example, the Pacific Coast of the United States, though it has but few large estuaries, abounds in sedi-ment-filled valley mouths that were formerly small bays formed by the rise of sea level.

Fiords   Several mountainous coasts of the world have large numbers of narrow, deep, and spectacularly steep-walled bays, some of which penetrate unusually far into the land. These magnificent estuaries, known by the originally Norwegian name *fiord,* are ice-scoured mountain valleys drowned since their formation (Fig. 6.6). The extreme depths found in many fiords suggest that there must

FIG. 6.6   A characteristic fiord landscape on the Norwegian coast. *(Kirk H. Stone.)*

have been glacial erosion below even the lowered sea levels of glacial times. The prin-cipal regions of fiords are the coast of Nor-way, Greenland, northern Labrador and the eastern Arctic Islands, British Columbia and southern Alaska, southern Chile, and the west coast of South Island, New Zealand (Fig. 6.7). All of these are in the higher middle latitudes, where, at least during the glacial period, many valley glaciers descended to the sea.

Cliffs and terraces   Coastal cliffs and terraces are largely the product of waves. Wherever the water on exposed coasts deepens rapidly to seaward, waves break directly against the shore, sometimes with

FIG. 6.7   The fiorded coasts of Norway, southern Chile, and British Columbia and southern Alaska are similar in pattern.

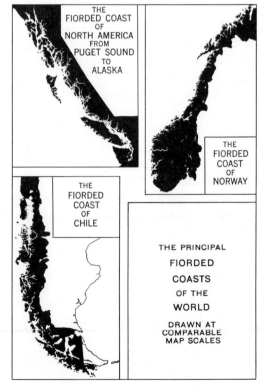

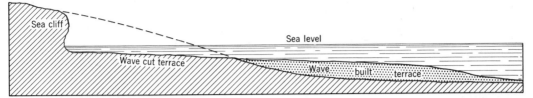

FIG. 6.8   Profile of the features on a shore line that is being subjected to wave erosion.

great force. Through this attack the shore is undercut and driven back, producing a sea cliff. Then, as the cliff is worn back, it leaves behind at its base an erosional shelf sloping gently seaward just below the sea surface. The material eroded from the cliff face is dragged out across this shelf by the return flow from the breaking waves and is deposited in deeper water at its outer edge. As the shelf is widened by erosion at its inner edge it is also extended seaward by deposition at the outer margin. In this way a marine terrace is cut and built by the waves (Fig. 6.8). Because of local inequalities in the rate of erosion, there are often many pinnacles and rocky islets left behind on the widening erosional terrace as the cliff retreats (Fig. 6.9).

In many places sea cliffs and marine terraces have been either submerged or left high and dry by changes of relative levels of land and sea. Submerged terraces are commonly hard to identify because they have been obscured by later deposition. Cliffs and terraces that have been exposed above sea level, on the other hand, are common and often prominent features of the world's coastal belts. Some coasts display a whole series of such terraces, rising like steps from the present shore. Most elevated terraces are eroded to some extent, and some have been warped by tectonic action. There is reason to believe that the world-wide changes of sea level during the Pleistocene sometimes brought the sea surface well above its present level, and

that many of the lower terraces, at elevations of less than 300 ft, were cut at those times.

Beaches and bars   On protected sections of the coast, even on exposed coasts

FIG. 6.9   A wave-cut cliff and detached rocky islets on the exposed coast of Anacapa Island, Channel Islands National Monument, California. *(Roger Toll, National Park Service.)*

that are not too frequently swept by destructive storm waves, gentle wave action tends to move sand or gravel onto the shore, forming beaches. Along a smooth and low coast, the beaches may form a continuous strip many miles in length. On irregular coasts, however, the sediment is concentrated in the bays, the projecting points often being swept clear and subjected to active erosion. Through this erosion of headlands and the accumulation of beaches in the coastal indentations, an irregular shore line is gradually straightened by wave action (Fig. 6.10).

Debris that is moved parallel to the shore by obliquely striking waves and the currents they generate continues to shift until it comes to an angle in the shore line, to the sheltered or deep waters of a bay, or to a protected position between a close-in island and the shore. At such a place it is dropped, making a ridge or embankment upon the bottom. With the aid of waves that occasionally strike them from seaward, these deposits may in time be built up to or above the water surface, forming a bar or projecting spit (Fig. 6.11).

Along coasts where shallow water causes the waves to break far from shore, long strips of sand, called offshore bars, are formed just inside the line of breakers. Such bars may

FIG. 6.10   A sandy beach has been deposited in this sheltered bay, while the headland beyond has been swept clear by wave action. Cape Sebastian, Oregon. *(Oregon State Highway Commission.)*

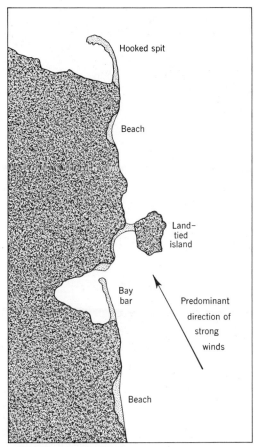

FIG. 6.11 Characteristic types and locations of bars, spits, and beaches.

touch the land at projecting points, but elsewhere they are separated from it by shallow lagoons. Occasional breaks through the bars are kept open by the scouring of tidal currents. The lagoon behind a bar is gradually filled by stream deposition and marsh growth, so that the offshore bar may eventually be joined to the mainland.

Offshore bars are unusually well developed along the south Atlantic and Gulf Coasts of the United States, where they are not far from being continuous. Many of the famous beach resorts, such as Atlantic City, Palm Beach, Miami Beach, and Galveston, are built

on these bars and are reached from the mainland by bridges or causeways. In North Carolina broad estuarine lagoons (sounds) are enclosed by an especially far-flung cordon of offshore bars, the outermost point of which is Cape Hatteras, famous for the number of ships that have been driven aground on its sandy shoals (Fig. 6.12).

Coral reefs Several types of organisms that thrive in shallow waters are able to change shore lines, largely through depositing remnants of their own structures. Most of these are only locally important because their growth is restricted to small areas of protected waters. Only the minute marine animals called corals, which can survive even on exposed coasts, achieve great significance.

The shallow waters of many tropical coasts are characterized by reefs of limestone comprised principally of the crumbled skeletal structures of colonies of corals. Most coral

FIG. 6.12 Offshore bars and sounds along the coast of North Carolina.

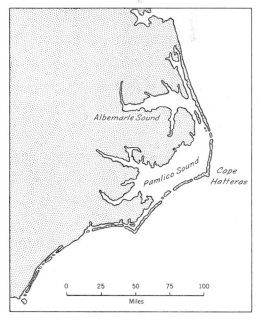

FIG. 6.13 Coral reefs and sandy islets enclose a quiet lagoon in Wake Islands, a small atoll in the central Pacific. Shallow reefs show as light-colored submerged areas ringed with white strip of heavy surf, best seen in right foreground. *(Official U.S. Navy photograph.)*

reefs form as narrow fringes along the coasts. Fringing reefs grow with such rapidity in some clear, shallow, warm waters that they build a shore line seaward in spite of wave and current erosion. Under certain conditions corals grow abundantly in shallow waters some distance from shore, and their deposits form a barrier reef which is separated from the mainland by a broad lagoon (Fig. 6.13). Of this nature is the great reef that for 1,000 miles parallels the northeast coast of Australia.

Some small reef-encircled islands, mostly volcanic, seem to have undergone slow submergence while the coral fringe about them has continued to grow. Such encircling reefs now appear at the surface as low, more or less complete coral rings, called atolls, which enclose shallow lagoons (Fig. 6.14).

Coasts and harbors There are many significant relationships between coastal characteristics and human activities, chiefly those involving navigation and the development of harbors. Clearly the configuration of the shore line and of the bottom close to shore are factors that must be taken into account in locating or improving ports or channels.

It must be kept in mind, however, that a port is a result of human need and work, rather than a feature of physical geography. The value of a harbor depends upon its own physical characteristics but even more upon whether it is located where a harbor is needed. Of course where the need for a port exists, the character of the coast may go far to determine the amount of work and money that must be expended in order to develop the necessary shelter, depth of channel, and docking facilities.

A deep and well-protected bay in a place that is well connected with a productive or populous hinterland is a resource of incalculable value. It is only natural that many significant ports have developed on estuaries and fiords or in waters sheltered by reefs, bars, or offshore islands. However, some of the most commodious and sheltered bays are of almost no value as harbors because the land behind them is unproductive, sparsely populated, or inaccessible. One example is the magnificent fiords of southern Chile, almost unused because they are backed by a wild, storm-swept, mountainous, and nearly uninhabited land.

On the other hand, some of the world's busiest ports have been developed where no natural harbor existed, because the hinterland required a shipping and receiving facility for its products and imports. The harbor of Los Angeles and to an even greater degree that of Callao, the port for Lima, Peru, are largely man-made; at both places long breakwaters have been built to protect an otherwise exposed section of coast. At London, Rotterdam, Bremen, and Hamburg, shallow estuaries have been heavily dredged to provide sufficient entrance depth, and basins that can be closed off by lock gates have been excavated to provide docking space unaffected by the excessive rise and fall of the tides.

Islands　The existence of isolated masses and bits of land surrounded by the seas, occurring sometimes in groups or strings and sometimes quite alone in midocean, has never failed to stir man's interest and curiosity. It is hard to avoid feeling that such peculiar features, strangely rising from the open sea, must have some unique and startling mode of origin. Yet this is a false notion, for the processes that produce islands are not different from those that produce high-standing features on the continental masses themselves.

Some islands, such as the British Isles, the islands of eastern Denmark, Ceylon, the Arctic Islands of Canada, Vancouver Island, and such islands off eastern North America as Prince Edward, Cape Breton, Nantucket, and Long Islands, appear to be no more than portions of the continental masses that have been isolated from the mainland by the drowning of erosional channels. The channels may well have been cut during low stands of

FIG. 6.14　How atolls are believed to develop: (a) fringing coral reefs about mountainous islands; (b) growing coral deposits keeping pace with submergence, forming encircling reef; (c) mountainous islands submerged, with only rings of coral remaining. *(V. C. Finch.)*

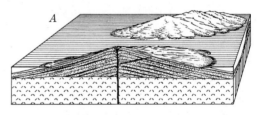

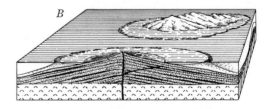

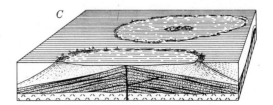

sea level in glacial times and then drowned during the postglacial rise of sea level.

Other islands, however, have come into being as the mountain peaks and ranges on the continents have, that is, by some kind of tectonic disturbance. Some are raised or tilted fault blocks. Thus originated Santa Catalina and neighboring islands off southern California, the several islands of the Gulf of California, and, in a more complex manner, the islands of Tasmania and Madagascar. But by far the greatest number of islands have originated as volcanic cones built up from the sea floor, as complex folded, faulted, and eroded masses similar to most of the continental mountain systems, or as combinations of the two. Associated as they thus are with significant tectonic activity, it is hardly surprising that so many islands are rugged and spectacular.

Isolated volcanic islands are very common, especially in the western Pacific. There the ocean floor is dotted with dozens of great cones, some of which rise above the sea surface, some of which are entirely submerged. These include not only the currently active cones, such as those of the Hawaiian Islands, but also the many more inactive, eroded

FIG. 6.15 The Marshall Islands are coral atolls which have formed about the summits of thickly clustered volcanic cones that rise more than 15,000 ft from the ocean floor in the west central Pacific. *(From "Depth Curve Chart of the Adjacent Seas of Japan." Maritime Safety Agency, Tokyo, 1952.)*

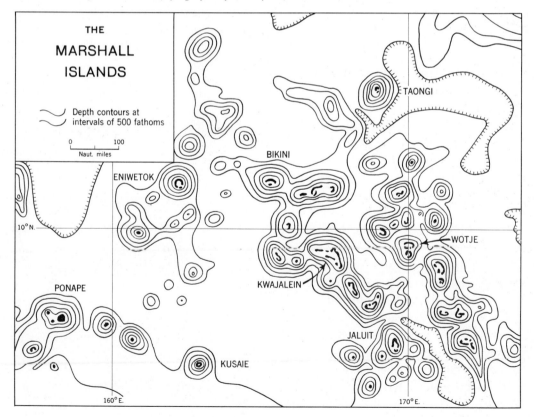

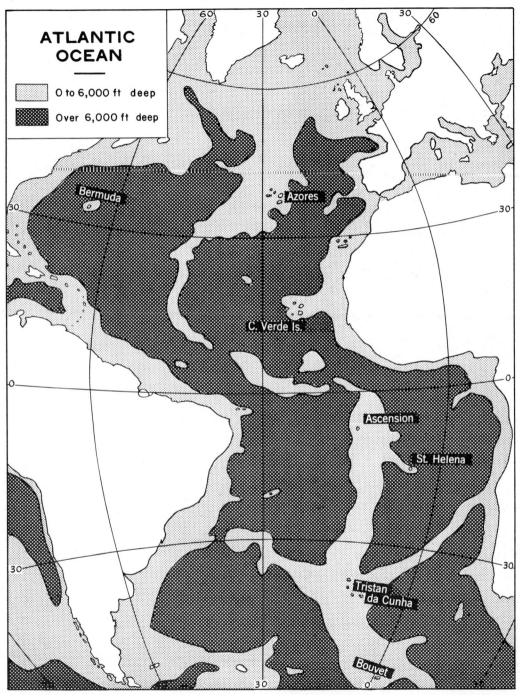

FIG. 6.16 Map of depths in the Atlantic Ocean. The Mid-Atlantic Ridge and several lesser ridges may be clearly distinguished, along with their associated islands.

cones, such as those of Tahiti, Samoa, Ponape, and Truk. As previously mentioned, some of the cones have slowly become submerged, leaving on the surface only low-lying islands or atolls that have been maintained by the continuing growth of a cap of coral atop the sinking peaks. Midway, Wake,

Bikini, and Eniwetok are of this type (Fig. 6.15). Other isolated volcanic islands occur in the Indian and Atlantic Oceans. In the Atlantic several of these, including the Azores, Ascension, and Tristan da Cunha, are cones built along the great Mid-Atlantic Ridge, the complex, faulted, structural swell,

FIG. 6.17 The Kuril Islands, stretching northeastward from Japan, are a typical island arc, with an associated trough, or deep. *(From "Depth Curve Chart of the Adjacent Seas of Japan," Maritime Safety Agency, Tokyo, 1952.)*

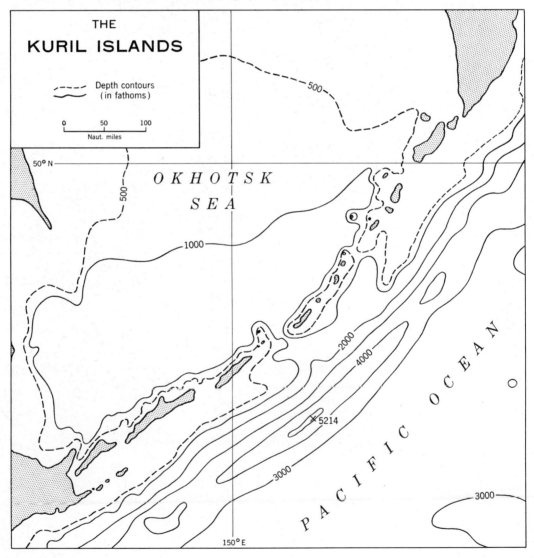

similar in size to a continental cordilleran belt, that runs almost squarely down the middle of the Atlantic Ocean Basin from north to south (Fig. 6.16).

Complex folded and faulted islands most commonly occur off the coasts of similarly structured mountainous parts of the continents. Among these are most of the islands of the Mediterranean, including Corsica, Sardinia, Sicily, and Crete, and many others, such as Borneo, Newfoundland, and Kodiak.

Many curving strings of islands, known as island arcs, festoon the borders of the continents, especially in the western Pacific. These include the lesser West Indies, the Aleutians, the Kurils, the Ryukyus, the Marianas, and such larger masses as Japan, the southern islands of Indonesia, and the eastern Philippines (Fig. 6.17). These island chains are in part volcanic and in part complex folded structures. In most instances they are bordered on their seaward side by ocean-bottom trenches of tremendous depth. They are known to be among the most active tectonic zones on earth, and appear to represent sites where deformation is proceeding actively because of lateral compression of the crust. In many respects they correspond closely to certain of the great curving continental mountain systems, such as the Himalayas, the Alps-Carpathians, and the northern Andes.

SELECTED REFERENCES

Finch, V. C., G. T. Trewartha, A. H. Robinson, and E. H. Hammond: *Physical Elements of Geography,* 4th ed., McGraw-Hill Book Company, Inc., New York, 1957.

Johnson, D. W.: *Shore Processes and Shoreline Development,* John Wiley & Sons, Inc., New York, 1919.

Kuenen, P. H.: *Marine Geology,* John Wiley & Sons, Inc., New York, 1950.

Shepard, F. P.: *Submarine Geology,* Harper & Brothers, New York, 1948.

Steers, J. A.: *The Coastline of England and Wales,* Cambridge University Press, New York, 1946.

Thornbury, W. D.: *Principles of Geomorphology,* John Wiley & Sons, Inc., New York, 1954.

Wooldridge, S. W., and R. S. Morgan: *An Outline of Geomorphology: The Physical Basis of Geography,* 2d ed., Longmans, Green & Co., Ltd., London, 1959.

CHAPTER 7

Introduction to climate; air temperature and solar energy

Man permanently occupies only the solid, or land, part of the earth's surface, not the liquid, or sea, part. Yet in a sense he does carry on his activities at the bottom of a sea—a sea of air hundreds of miles deep which surrounds the solid-liquid earth. This envelope of atmosphere is not to be thought of as something above or beyond the earth proper; it is just as integral a part of the planet as the land and water, and just as important a part of the total human habitat. Man and all other land animals, as well as the plant life from which most animals draw their sustenance,

are greatly influenced by their atmospheric environment, which varies greatly from one part of the earth to another.

The atmosphere is very largely a mixture of two gases, nitrogen and oxygen, but other minor gases in it—chief among them water vapor—are the greatest influences on the atmospheric conditions experienced by man. Thus water vapor, which on very hot, humid days may comprise as much as 4 per cent of the volume of surface air, is the source of moisture for clouds and all forms of precipitation. This same gas is the principal absorber

134

of solar energy and of radiated earth energy as well, and so it greatly influences temperature distribution over the earth.

The conditions of the atmosphere are expressed by the terms *weather* and *climate*. Weather refers to the atmospheric condition over a brief period of time, such as an individual day or week. In contrast, climate is a composite of the varieties of day-to-day weather over a considerable number of years. Among the other constituents of the earth's natural equipment, such as terrain, native vegetation, soils, water, and minerals, climate ranks high as a cause of regional variations in productive capacity. In addition climate directly affects the character of such other natural features as vegetation cover, soil, drainage, and to a lesser degree terrain.

ELEMENTS OF CLIMATE

Weather and climate are described in terms of several familiar *elements,* chief of which, in their effects on the earth's living things, are the above-mentioned temperature and precipitation. A third element, winds, while by no means equal in importance to temperature and precipitation, has risen in rank since air transport has become common. The three are the principal ingredients which comprise climate. It is their combination in varying intensities and amounts which causes climates to differ so greatly over the earth and thus leads to great differences in regional productivity and in man's use of land.

CONTROLS OF CLIMATE

But what causes the climatic elements to vary so much from one part of the earth to another and from one season to another? The answer is to be found in the operation of the climatic *controls.* Each of the climatic elements —temperature, precipitation, and winds—also functions as a control over the other elements; indeed, winds are actually far more important as a control than as an element of climate. Other climatic controls are solar energy, air masses and fronts, altitude, mountain barriers, the great semipermanent centers, or cells, of high and low pressure, ocean currents, and atmospheric disturbances of various kinds. It is these controls, themselves acting in different combinations and with variable intensities, that give rise to the areal and seasonal differences in temperature and precipitation which in turn result in the great variety of climates characterizing this planet.

Although the goal of the discussion of climates is to make clear the world pattern of climates, it is believed that a description of types of climates and their distribution over the earth will be more intelligible if it is approached through preliminary analysis of the individual climatic elements and the more important climatic controls. Such is the content of this and the three chapters which follow.

SOLAR ENERGY

DEFINITION AND DISTRIBUTION

Solar energy, which expresses its influence most directly upon temperature distribution, is the prime control of climate. So there appears to be good reason for beginning a discussion of climates with a description of solar energy—its distribution, how it heats the atmosphere, and the way it functions to produce the great variety of temperatures which characterize the different latitudes and regions of the earth.

Earlier it was pointed out that temperature acts both as an element and as a control of climate. As a *control* it affects the density and hence the weight of the air, resulting in differences in atmospheric pressure. These pressure differences in turn determine the rapidity and direction of airflow. Temperature differences, therefore, are a main cause of the earth's wind systems. Temperature of the air is also a major determinant both of the atmosphere's capacity for moisture and of its buoyancy, and hence is closely related to the processes of condensation and precipitation.

As an *element* of climate temperature is at least coequal in rank with precipitation, and its distribution over the earth is a feature of the highest geographical importance. But before temperature distribution can be understood and appreciated it is necessary to understand the distribution of solar energy and how this energy is converted into atmospheric heat.

THE SUN AS SOURCE OF ATMOSPHERIC HEAT

The sun is the single important source of heat for the earth's atmosphere. From this star, whose surface is estimated to have a temperature of about 10,000° Fahrenheit (F), energy streams outward in all directions into space.[1] The earth, over 90 million miles distant, intercepts less than one two-billionth of the sun's energy output, yet this small fractional part is responsible for maintaining the atmospheric processes. Energy from the sun, called *solar radiation* or *insolation,* is transmitted to the earth in the form of very short waves, a part of the energy being visible as light. But there are some wavelengths of solar radiation which are too short, and others that are too long, to be seen by the human eye.

FACTORS DETERMINING THE DISTRIBUTION OF SOLAR RADIATION

Disregarding for the moment the effects of an atmosphere and its clouds, the amount of solar energy, in other words, climatic energy, that any latitude on the earth's surface receives depends largely upon two factors: (*a*) the *intensity* of solar radiation, or the angle at which the rays of sunlight reach the various parts of the earth's spherical surface, and (*b*) the *duration* of solar radiation, or length of daylight.

Because an oblique solar ray is spread out over a larger surface than a vertical one, it delivers less energy per unit area. An oblique ray is weaker also because it has passed through a thicker layer of scattering, absorbing, and reflecting air (Fig. 7.1). Outside the tropics, therefore, winter sunlight is much weaker than that of summer. For example, in

[1] Throughout the book the Fahrenheit (F) scale commonly used in the United States and England will be employed to express temperature degrees, except where it is noted specifically that degrees centigrade (C) are being used.

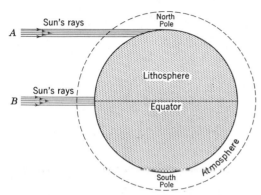

FIG. 7.1 An oblique ray, (a), delivers less energy at the earth's surface than a vertical ray, (b), because an oblique ray's energy passes through a thicker layer of absorbing and reflecting atmosphere and then is spread over a larger surface.

late December at Madison, Wisconsin, located at 43°N, the noon sun is only 23½° above the horizon, whereas in late June it has an elevation there of 70½°, and thus Madison is colder in winter. For the same reasons, the daylight period is characterized by a sun much more intense at noon than in the early morning or late afternoon hours.

As regards duration of solar radiation, it would seem to be enough to say that the longer the sun shines, i.e., the longer the day, the greater the amount of solar energy received, all other conditions being equal (following table; Fig. 7.2). Thus it is quite understandable that in the middle latitudes summer temperatures are much higher than those of winter; it is not only because in summer the sun's rays are less oblique but also because days are much longer in summer.

Since on any one day both the length of day and the angle of the sun's rays are equal all along any parallel of latitude, all parts of a parallel (allowing for differences in the transparency of the atmosphere) receive identical amounts of solar energy in a whole year as well as on any day. Similarly, different parallels receive unlike amounts of solar radiation, the annual amount decreasing from equator to poles. Thus if solar energy were the only control of weather and climate, all places in the same latitude would have identical climates. Although all such places certainly are not identical in climate, the strong temperature resemblances within latitude belts testify to the dominant, even though not exclusive, rank of sun control.

Earth and sun relations   The rotation and revolution of the earth and the inclination and parallelism of its axis were discussed in Chapter 1. It remains to be analyzed how these earth motions and axis positions act to produce the changing lengths of day and varying angles of the sun's rays, which in turn are the causes of the seasons.

The equinoxes: spring and fall   Twice during the yearly period of revolution, on March 21 and September 23, the sun's noon rays are directly overhead, or vertical, at the equator (Fig. 7.2). At these times, therefore, the circle of illumination, marking the position of the sun's tangent rays, passes through both poles and consequently cuts all the earth's parallels exactly in half. One-half of each parallel (180°) consequently is in light

Extremes in Length of Day for Different Latitudes (in hours and minutes)

Latitude (degrees)	0	10	20	30	40	50	60	66½
Longest day	12:00	12:35	13:13	13:56	14:51	16:09	18:30	24:00
Shortest day	12:00	11:25	10:47	10:04	9:09	7:51	5:30	0:00

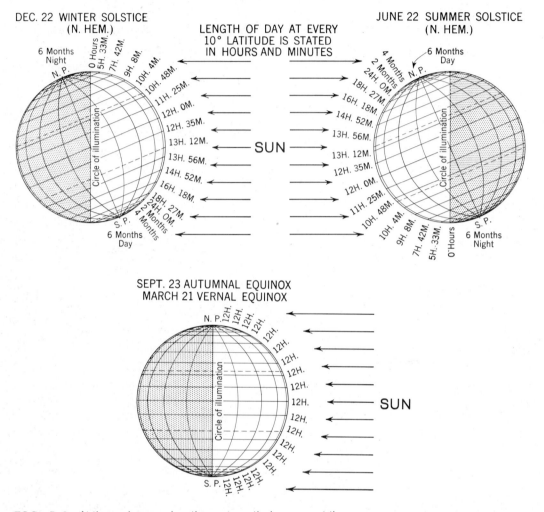

FIG. 7.2 At the equinoxes, when the sun's vertical rays are at the equator, the circle of illumination cuts all the parallels in half, and days and nights are equal in length over the entire earth. At this time insolation decreases regularly from equator to poles (Fig. 7.4b). At the times of the solstices the sun's vertical rays have reached their greatest poleward migration. The circle of illumination cuts all the parallels (except the equator) unequally, so that days and nights are unequal in length except at latitude 0° (Fig. 7.4c, d).

and the other half in darkness at these times. Since the path described by any point on the earth's surface during the period of rotation is coincident with its parallel of latitude, days and nights are equal (12 hr each) over the entire earth. Because of this fact the two dates March 21 and September 23 are called the *equinoxes*. (Equinox is derived from Latin words meaning equal night.) At these times the maximum solar energy is received in equatorial latitudes; the solar energy received diminishes regularly toward either pole, where it becomes zero.

The solstices; summer and winter On June 22 the earth is approximately midway in its orbit between the equinoctial positions, and the North Pole is inclined 23½° toward the sun (Fig. 7.2). As a result of this axial inclination, the sun's rays are shifted northward the same number of degrees, so that the noon rays are vertical at the Tropic of Cancer (23½°N), and the tangent rays in the Northern Hemisphere pass over the pole and reach the earth 23½° of latitude beyond it, at the Arctic Circle (66½°N.). In the Southern Hemisphere the tangent rays do not reach the pole but terminate at the Antarctic Circle, 23½° short of it. Thus while all parts of the earth north of the Arctic Circle are experiencing constant daylight, similar latitudes in the Southern Hemisphere (poleward from the Antarctic Circle) are entirely without sunlight. On June 22 all parallels, except the equator, are cut unequally by the circle of illumination, those in the Northern Hemisphere having the larger segments of their circumferences toward the sun so that days are longer than nights. These longer days, plus a greater angle of the sun's rays, make for a maximum receipt of solar energy in the Northern Hemisphere at this time. Summer, with its associated high temperatures, is the result, and north of the equator June 22 is known as the *summer solstice*. In the Southern Hemisphere at this same time, all of these conditions are reversed, nights being longer than days and the sun's rays relatively oblique, so that solar radiation is at a minimum and winter conditions prevail.

On December 22, when the earth is in the opposite position in its orbit from that of June 22, it is the South Pole that is inclined

23½° toward the sun. The latter's noon rays are then vertical over the Tropic of Capricorn (23½°S), and the tangent rays pass over the South Pole to the Antarctic Circle 23½° beyond (66½°S). Consequently, south of 66½°S there is constant light, while north of 66½°N there is no sunlight. All parallels of the earth except the equator are cut unequally by the circle of illumination, with days longer and sun's rays more nearly vertical in the Southern Hemisphere. This, therefore, is summer south of the equator but winter in the Northern Hemisphere (winter solstice), where opposite conditions prevail.

Effects of the atmosphere upon incoming solar energy The total effect of the atmosphere upon a beam of sunlight passing through it is to reduce its intensity by amounts varying with latitude, the seasons, and cloudiness (Fig. 7.3). The atmosphere weakens solar

FIG. 7.3 Only about one-half (51 per cent) of the incoming solar radiation passes through the atmosphere and heats the earth's surface. Another 14 per cent is absorbed by the atmosphere. Some 35 per cent of the solar energy is scattered and reflected back to space, and thus has no effect on heating either the earth's surface or its atmosphere.

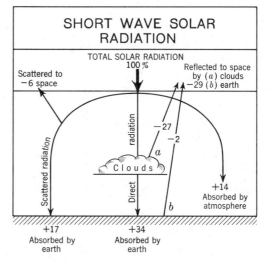

energy through (*a*) selective scattering, chiefly of the short waves of blue light, by very small obscuring particles, (*b*) diffuse reflection of all wavelengths by larger particles, such as cloud droplets, and (*c*) absorption of selected wavelengths, chiefly by water vapor concentrated in the lower strata of the atmosphere. The scattering and reflecting processes operate to send a part of the solar radiation they effect back to space, but some of it reaches the earth's surface as diffuse daylight.

Quantitatively, it is estimated that about 35 per cent of the solar radiation reaching the outer limits of the air layer is returned to space by scattering and reflection from clouds, small dust particles, and molecules of air, and by direct reflection from the earth's surface. This has no part in heating either the earth or its atmosphere. Fourteen per cent of the solar radiation is absorbed directly by the atmosphere, most of it by the water vapor. The remaining 51 per cent reaches the earth's surface either as direct sunlight or as diffuse daylight, is absorbed by it, heats it, and eventually heats the atmosphere as well.

Thus only some 65 per cent of the solar radiation (14 per cent absorbed by the atmosphere directly, and 51 per cent absorbed by the earth's surface) is available for heating the atmosphere. Also, and equally significant, the atmosphere receives several times as much energy from the heated earth's surface as it does from direct absorption of solar radiation.

DISTRIBUTION OF SOLAR RADIATION
OVER THE EARTH'S SURFACE

As the previous discussion has indicated, the belt of maximum solar radiation swings back and forth across the equator during the course of a year, following the shifting rays of the sun, with the two variables angle of sun's rays and length of day largely determining the amount of solar energy received at any time or place.

Distribution from pole to pole   Assuming a cloudless sky, solar radiation *for the year as a whole* is highest at the equator and diminishes with regularity toward the poles; and the Northern and Southern Hemispheres share equally in the annual amounts of solar energy received (Fig. 7.4). This distribution has important climatic consequences. Chief of these is that average air temperatures for the year are highest in the tropics, or low latitudes, and decrease toward the poles.

At the time of the *equinoxes,* disregarding again the effects of clouds, the latitudinal distribution of solar radiation is similar to that for the year as a whole. There is a maximum of solar radiation at the equator and a minimum at each pole. This fact also has important climatic implications. For it is in the equinoctial seasons of spring and fall, when the Northern and Southern Hemispheres are receiving approximately equal amounts of solar energy, that temperature conditions in the two hemispheres are most nearly alike. Similarly, pressure, wind, and precipitation conditions, and as a result the over-all weather situation, are more in balance to the north and south of the equator than at other times. Finally, world temperature, pressure, wind, and precipitation-distribution patterns for spring and fall bear close resemblances to those for the year as a whole.

At the time of the two *solstices* when the sun's noon rays are vertical 23½° poleward from the equator and the length of day increases toward one pole, the latitudinal distribution of solar radiation is very asymmetrically developed. The summer hemisphere receives two to three times as much as the winter hemisphere (Fig. 7.4).[2] Latitudinal distribution of solar radiation at the surface of the earth shows a broad maximum in the belt of latitude that extends from about 30 to about 40°, while latitude 60° receives as much as or more than the equator. It is not surprising, therefore, that the highest surface-air temperatures in summer occur over the land masses of the lower middle latitudes (30°–40°) and not at the equator.

During the course of a year the zone of maximum solar radiation shows a total latitudinal displacement of more than 60° (Fig. 7.4c, d), which must have important effects upon seasonal temperatures, rainfall, pressure, and winds. It is significant also that the latitudinal solar-radiation gradient (the rate of change in solar radiation) is much steeper in the winter hemisphere than in the summer hemisphere.

The characteristics of solar-radiation distribution at the times of the solstices, which are the extreme seasons of summer and winter, provide the basic explanations for many of the earth's larger features of weather and climate. (*a*) Marked north-south migration of the temperature, wind, and precipitation belts follows a similar migration of solar-radiation

[2] By *summer hemisphere* is meant the hemisphere that has summer. Thus the Northern Hemisphere would be the summer hemisphere in July, and the Southern Hemisphere would be the summer hemisphere in January.

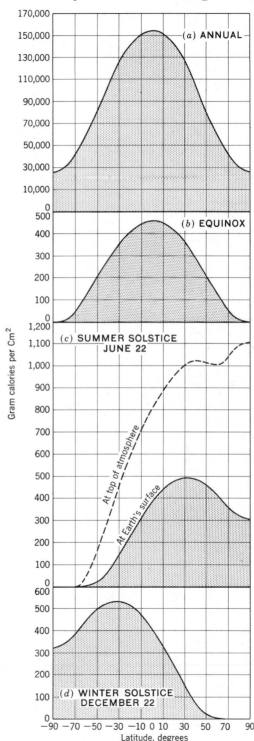

F I G . 7 . 4 Latitudinal distribution of the maximum values of solar energy at the earth's surface. For the year as a whole and at the two equinoxes, solar energy is symmetrically distributed in the Northern and Southern Hemispheres. There is a maximum in equatorial latitudes and there are minima at the North and South Poles. At the solstices solar energy is very unequally distributed, with the summer hemisphere receiving two to three times the amount of the winter hemisphere.

belts. (*b*) Warm-to-hot summers occur in the lower middle latitudes where solar radiation reaches a near maximum for the summer hemisphere. (*c*) There are much steeper temperature gradients in the winter hemisphere than in the summer hemisphere, the temperature gradients paralleling solar-radiation gradients. (*d*) Greater storminess and weather variability occur in the winter hemisphere.

Annual distribution of solar radiation for representative latitudes The yearly solar-radiation patterns (curves) for the different latitudes can be arranged in three general groups, those for low, middle, and high latitudes (Fig. 7.5). (*a*) In the low, or tropical, latitudes between the Tropics of Cancer and Capricorn, solar radiation is high and varies little throughout the year. This accounts for the constant year-round heat of the tropics. Since during the course of a year all regions between the two tropics are passed over twice by the vertical rays of the sun, the annual solar-radiation curve for low latitudes contains two weak maxima and two slight minima. (*b*) The middle-latitude curve, on the other hand, has a single maximum, but as in the tropics, solar radiation at no time declines

to zero. The great seasonal contrasts in solar radiation are reflected in similar large seasonal contrasts in temperature. (*c*) The regions poleward from the Arctic and Antarctic Circles also have but one maximum and one minimum period of solar radiation. But unlike the other latitudes there is a portion of the year when direct sunlight is completely absent. For this reason, the high-latitude, or polar, solar-radiation curve does decline to zero. Also, seasonal contrasts in solar radiation are marked, and temperature contrasts are strong.

HOW SOLAR RADIATION HEATS THE EARTH'S SURFACE AND ATMOSPHERE

HEATING AND COOLING LAND AND WATER SURFACES

Thus far the discussion has been concerned largely with the latitudinal distribution of solar energy, the single important source of atmospheric heat. Now the complexities of *how* the heating of the atmosphere occurs will be explored.

Sun energy is in the form of such short wavelengths that only relatively small amounts (around 14 per cent, as we have seen) can be absorbed directly by the earth's atmosphere, chiefly by the water vapor in it. Three to four times as much gets through to the earth's surface and is absorbed by it and heats it because the solid-liquid surface is capable of absorbing the short-wave solar energy more readily than the atmosphere is. Thus the heated earth's surface becomes a radiator of energy.

Because the earth's temperature is lower than that of the sun, earth radiation is composed of longer wavelengths and so is much more readily absorbed by the atmosphere

FIG. 7.5 In the very low latitudes close to the equator the amount of solar energy received is large and varies little throughout the year. In the middle and higher latitudes there are large seasonal differences in the receipt of solar energy.

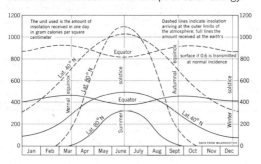

than short-wave solar radiation. As a consequence the atmosphere receives most of its heat *indirectly* from the sun and *directly* from the earth's surface, which has served to convert the solar energy into more readily absorbable earth radiation. It is obviously necessary, therefore, to understand how different kinds of earth surfaces react to solar energy and the contrasting temperatures that they acquire as a result, before specific discussion of heating and cooling the atmosphere is begun.

The greatest contrasts in temperature are between land and water surfaces, although land surfaces of different shades (snow, light sand, green fields, and forests) also will differ in temperature by reason of their unlike reflection and absorption of solar energy.

Land and water contrasts   For a number of reasons a land surface without snow heats (and cools) more rapidly than a water surface even when both receive similar amounts of solar energy. Most importantly, the fluid character of water causes vertical and horizontal currents, tides, and waves to distribute the energy received from the sun throughout a large mass. Similarly, when a water surface begins to cool, the surface water becomes heavier and sinks, to be replaced by warmer, lighter water from below. Both kinds of distribution make for slower temperature change in water than on the solid land surface.

A supplementary, although less important, factor is that water is more transparent than land. The sun's rays are able to penetrate a water body to considerable depths, and in this way also to distribute energy throughout a somewhat larger mass. On the other hand, the opaqueness of land concentrates the sun energy close to the surface, which results in comparatively rapid and intense heating. This

concentration likewise permits the land area to cool more rapidly than a deeply warmed water body.

Also of some significance is the fact that the specific heat of water is higher than that of land. In other words, it requires only one-third to one-half as much energy to raise a given volume of dry earth by one degree as it does an equal volume of water.

Thus it becomes evident that land-controlled, or continental, climates should be characterized by large daily and seasonal extremes of temperature, becoming alternately hot and cold, whereas ocean-controlled, or marine, climates should be more moderate, with only small seasonal and daily temperature changes.

HEATING AND COOLING THE ATMOSPHERE

Now that there has been discussion of the distribution of solar energy over the earth, the contrasting reactions of land and water surfaces to this solar energy, and the fact that the air receives most of its energy directly from the earth's surface and only indirectly from the sun, it is appropriate to proceed with an analysis of the processes involved in heating and cooling the atmosphere.

Absorption of solar radiation   As indicated previously, the earth's atmosphere is capable of absorbing only about 14 per cent of the short-wave solar energy that enters it. Moreover, while most of the absorption occurs in the more humid lower atmosphere, it takes place well above the immediate surface layer. As a consequence this absorption is not very effective in heating the air very close to the ground. This is evident from the fact that on a clear winter day the air may remain bitterly cold in spite of a bright sun.

Conduction   The solid earth (without a snow cover), being a much better absorber of solar radiation than air, attains a higher temperature during the daylight hours. But when two bodies of unequal temperature are in contact with one another, energy in the form of heat passes from the warmer to the colder object until they both attain the same temperature, a process called *conduction*. By conduction, therefore, the layer of air resting upon the warmer earth becomes heated. Yet air is a poor conductor, so that heat from the warmed layer in contact with the earth's surface is transferred very slowly to those above, unless there is some air movement.

Heating of the air by conduction is primarily a daytime and a summer process. An opposite process, cooling by conduction, occurs under opposite conditions. That is, just as a warm earth on a summer day heats the air layer next to it by conduction, so a cold land surface on a winter night, chilled through energy losses to space by earth radiation, cools the air by conduction. But in general, conduction is a relatively unimportant factor in heating and cooling the whole atmosphere.

Earth radiation   The surface of the earth without a snow cover readily absorbs short-wave solar energy and is heated by it. As a consequence the heated earth becomes a

FIG. 7.6   The greenhouse effect of the earth's atmosphere. The glass in the roof and sides of the greenhouse, like the atmosphere, is relatively transparent to the short-wave solar energy but relatively opaque to the long-wave earth radiation.

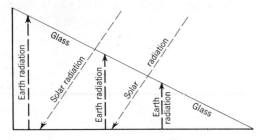

radiating body giving off heat in the form of long-wave earth radiation. In this the atmosphere is importantly involved, for while it is able to absorb only about 14 per cent of the short-wave solar radiation, it can absorb up to 90 per cent of the long-wave earth radiation. The atmosphere thus acts like a pane of glass in a greenhouse or automobile, letting through much of the incoming short-wave solar energy but greatly retarding the escape of the heat, or long-wave earth radiation. This is called the *greenhouse effect* of the atmosphere (Fig. 7.6). Its total influence on climate is to maintain surface-air temperatures considerably higher than they otherwise would be, and to prevent great extremes in temperature between day and night. The fact that it is chiefly the atmosphere's water vapor which is effective in absorbing earth radiation is illustrated by the rapid night cooling in deserts, where the dry air and cloudless skies permit a rapid escape to space of heat radiated from the earth.

Radiation of heat from the earth's surface upward through the atmosphere toward space is a continuous process. During the daylight hours and up to about midafternoon, however, more energy is received from the sun than is radiated from the earth, with the result that surface-air temperatures usually continue to rise. But during the night, when receipts of solar energy cease, a continued loss of energy through earth radiation results in a cooling of the earth's surface and a consequent drop in air temperature.

Being a better radiator than air, the ground indeed becomes cooler than the air above it during the night. When this happens, the lower layers of atmosphere lose heat by radiation to the colder ground as well as upward toward space. This process is particularly important during the long nights of winter when, if the skies are clear and the air is dry, the loss of heat is both rapid and long-continued.

If a snow cover mantles the ground, cooling is even more pronounced, for most of the incoming solar radiation during the short day is reflected by the snow and thus does not heat the earth's surface. At night the snow, which is a poor conductor of heat, allows little energy to come up from the soil layer below to replenish that lost by radiation from the top of the snow surface. As a result, the snow surface becomes extremely cold, and then so does the air layer resting upon it.

Water, like land, is a good radiator, but as has been indicated, the cooled surface waters keep constantly sinking to be replaced by the warmer water from below. Extremely low air temperatures over water bodies are therefore impossible until they are frozen over, after which they act like a land surface.

Humid air or a cloudy sky tends to prevent rapid earth radiation, so that air temperatures remain higher and frosts are less likely on humid nights, especially when a cloud cover prevails. In contrast, there are authentic cases in the dry air and under the cloudless skies of Sahara, of day temperatures of 90° having been followed by night temperatures slightly below freezing. When clouds cover the sky, all the earth radiation is completely absorbed at the base of the cloud sheet, which reradiates a part of it back to the earth so that cooling of the earth is retarded. Water vapor likewise absorbs and reradiates outgoing terrestrial energy, but not so effectively as liquid or solid cloud particles.

Warming the atmosphere by heat of condensation A large amount of the solar energy which reaches the earth's surface is consumed in evaporating water (changing it into a gas). This converted solar energy consequently is contained in the atmosphere's water vapor in latent or potential form. When condensation occurs and the water vapor is returned to the liquid or solid state this latent energy is again released into the atmosphere and heats it. This heat of condensation is a principal source of heat energy for the atmosphere.

TRANSFER OF HEAT BY CURRENTS
IN THE ATMOSPHERE

The heat acquired by the atmosphere by absorption of solar energy, conduction and radiation processes, and condensation is transferred from one part of the atmosphere to another by vertical and horizontal currents.

Vertical transfer Vertical transfer of heat results from convectional (vertical) currents, mechanical turbulence, and eddy motions in the atmosphere. When surface air is heated, it expands in volume and consequently becomes less dense. Hence it is forced upward by the surrounding colder, denser air which at the surface flows toward the warm source. Such circulation is called a *convectional system*. Warm surface air, expanded and therefore less dense, is like a cork that is held under water, i.e., unstable and inclined to rise. Vertical circulation, whether by thermal convection, turbulence induced by rough terrain, or eddy currents, is the most important method of distributing the heat acquired by the surface air through the higher layers of the atmosphere.

Horizontal transfer Horizontal transfer of heat, which is accomplished by winds, is called *advection*. For the earth as a whole this is the most important means of heat transfer. Advection by winds causes many of the earth's day-to-day weather changes, as well as the storminess of winter climates in the middle latitudes. For instance, in the Northern Hemisphere middle latitudes a south wind usually means unseasonably high temperatures, as almost everyone who lives there knows. In this case the wind acts as the conveyer of heat from lower latitudes where solar radiation is greater and higher temperatures are normal. Such an importation of southerly warmth in winter results in mild weather, with melting snow and slushy streets. In summer, several days of south wind may result in a heat wave, with maximum temperatures over 90°.

In a similar way, north winds from colder, higher latitudes, or from the cold interiors of continents in winter, bring lower temperatures. These cold importations are particularly effective where there are no mountain barriers to block the wind movement. In central eastern North America where lowlands prevail, great masses of cold polar air pour down over the Mississippi River Valley at irregular intervals, occasionally carrying severe freezing temperatures even to the margins of the Gulf of Mexico. Large-scale horizontal transfer of temperature conditions likewise may result from winds moving on-shore from large bodies of water.

HEAT BALANCE IN THE ATMOSPHERE

Since the mean temperature of the earth as a whole gets neither colder nor warmer, it is clear that the heat lost by the earth through radiation to space is identical in amount with the energy received from the sun. But this balance does not hold for individual latitudes. In the low latitudes, equatorward from about 37°, the incoming solar energy exceeds the outgoing earth energy, whereas poleward from latitude 37° exactly the reverse is true. This means there would be a constant increase in the temperatures of low latitudes and a constant decrease in the temperatures of the middle and higher latitudes if there were not a continuous transfer of energy from low to high latitudes of the earth. But this transfer is accomplished by the winds and the ocean currents. In fact, in the unequal latitudinal distribution of solar and terrestrial radiation is to be found the ultimate cause for the earth's atmospheric circulation and for much of its weather.

AIR TEMPERATURE

TEMPORAL DISTRIBUTION: MARCH OF TEMPERATURE

The average temperature of any month, season, year, or even long period of years, is determined by using as a basic unit the *mean daily temperature*, which is the average of the highest and the lowest temperatures recorded during the 24-hr period.

The *daily march, or cycle, of temperature*, obtained by plotting the temperature for each hour of the day, chiefly reflects the balance between incoming solar radiation and outgoing earth radiation (Fig. 7.7). From about sunrise until 2:00 to 4:00 P.M., when energy is being supplied by incoming solar radiation faster than it is being lost by earth radiation, the daily temperature curve usually rises (Figs. 7.7, 7.8). Conversely, from about 3:00 P.M. to sunrise, when loss by terrestrial radiation exceeds receipt of solar energy, the temperature curve usually falls.

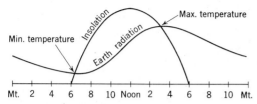

FIG. 7.7 The march of incoming solar radiation and of outgoing earth radiation for the daily 24-hr period at about the time of an equinox, and their combined effects upon the time of daily maximum and minimum temperatures.

In marine locations the daily temperature curve is relatively flat in appearance, there being only a modest difference between day and night. By contrast, in continental, or land-controlled, climates the amplitude of the daily temperature curve is much greater. Important modifications of the symmetrical daily temperature curve are frequently imposed by the presence of a cloud cover which obstructs both incoming and outgoing radiation, or by the importation of temperature by winds.

The *annual march, or cycle, of temperature,* obtained by plotting the mean temperature for each month, reflects the increase in insolation (and hence heat accumulated in the air and ground) from midwinter to midsummer and the corresponding decrease from midsummer to midwinter. Usually the reaching of temperature maxima (and minima) lags 30 to 40 days behind the periods of maximum (and minimum) insolation. This seasonal temperature lag may be even greater over oceans and along windward coasts in middle latitudes, where August may be the warmest month and February the coldest. Normally, marine locations have annual temperature curves, just as they have daily curves, with a much smaller amplitude or range than those of continental locations.

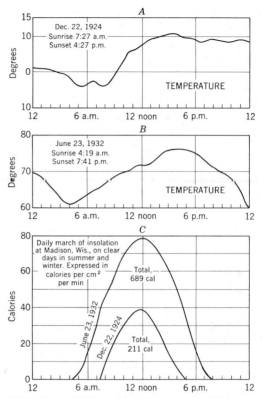

FIG. 7.8 Daily march of temperature (a, b) and of insolation (c) on clear days in winter and summer at Madison, Wisconsin. The total solar energy recorded was 3¼ times as great on June 23 as on December 22. Note that temperature lags behind insolation. South winds prevented normal night cooling on December 22.

GEOGRAPHICAL DISTRIBUTION OF TEMPERATURE

Vertical decrease with altitude Numerous observations made during mountain, balloon, and airplane ascents have shown that under normal conditions there is a general decrease in temperature with increasing elevation. The rate of decrease is not uniform, varying with time of day, season, and location, but the average is approximately 3.6°

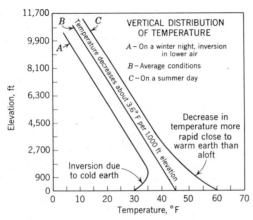

FIG. 7.9

for each 1,000-ft rise (Fig. 7.9). The fact that air temperature generally is highest at low elevations close to the earth's surface and decreases with altitude is a clear reflection of the fact that most of the atmospheric heat is received directly from the earth's surface and only indirectly from the sun.

Inversions   *Temperature inversions* are said to exist when the temperature *increases* with distance from the earth instead of decreasing. Such reversed temperature conditions can exist in the lowest layer of the atmosphere next to the earth's surface, or they can be found at altitudes of several thousand feet above the surface.

Surface inversions   Surface temperature inversions, one of the commonest and most readily observed kinds, originate from cooling of the lowest layers of air at night when, as described earlier, the land surface cools more rapidly than the air. The lowest air layer is chilled by radiation and by conduction of the heat of the air to the adjacent cold ground. This air layer thereby becomes colder than the air farther removed from the earth's surface (Fig. 7.9).

Local, diurnal, surface (ground) inversions of a few score or hundred feet in depth are well-known nighttime phenomena of the cooler seasons. Ideal conditions for these inversions are (*a*) long winter nights, which have a relatively long period when outgoing earth radiation exceeds incoming solar radiation, (*b*) a clear sky, under which loss of heat by terrestrial radiation is rapid and not retarded by a cloud cover, (*c*) cold, dry air that absorbs little earth radiation, (*d*) calm air to keep much mixing from taking place and thus to help the surface stratum become very cold by conduction and radiation, and (*e*) a snow-covered surface, which, owing to reflection of solar energy, heats little by day and, being a poor conductor, retards the upward flow of heat from the ground below the snow cover. Some of the deepest, most extensive, and most persistent surface inversions are those which prevail over the snow-covered northern parts of North America and Eurasia in winter. A very close relationship also exists between surface temperature inversions and frost and fog, since the same conditions are favorable for all.

During a surface temperature inversion, when the coldest, densest air is at the surface, the air is stable or nonbuoyant, that is, not inclined to rise. Such a condition, therefore, is opposed to the formation of precipitation.

Above-surface inversions   Inversions also occur in the free atmosphere well above the earth's surface. They are usually a result of the settling and warming of air in a large semistationary anticyclone (high-air-pressure system). Such above-surface inversions act to hinder the upward movement of air currents, and consequently they are opposed to the formation of rainfall. Some of the most extensive and well-developed above-surface inversions are found in the eastern and central parts of the great subtropical anticyclones and their trade-wind circulations, and these regions characteristically have dry climates. (These regions will be considered in detail in the next chapter.)

Surface inversions and air drainage Although surface temperature inversions are common over flattish land surfaces, they are most perfectly developed in low spots or topographic depressions. This results from the fact that the cold surface air, because of its greater density, moves downslope into the low areas where it collects in the form of pools (Fig. 7.10). This downslope movement of cold air is known as *air drainage*. It is well known that the first frosts in fall and the last in spring occur in bottomlands, and that on a clear, cold night valleys and depressions experience the lowest temperatures.

Frost and its distribution Frost is simply a temperature of 32° (freezing temperature) or below. The period between the last killing frost in spring and the first in fall is known as the growing season. Thus throughout the middle latitudes frost is most serious as a menace to crops in spring and fall, or at the beginning and end of the growing season; in subtropical areas such as Florida and California midwinter frosts are critical because of the active growth of sensitive crops during their normally mild winters (Fig. 7.11).

Ideal conditions for killing frost are those which favor rapid and prolonged surface cooling, namely, importation of a mass of dry, cool, polar air, followed by a calm, clear night during which the temperature of the surface air is brought below the freezing point through radiational cooling. With the air temperature already low but still above freezing, the following loss of heat by earth radiation is all that is required to reduce the temperature of the surface air below freezing. If the late afternoon temperature of the cool,

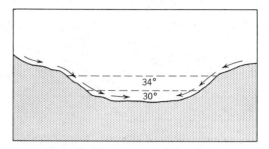

FIG. 7.10 Cold surface air, because it is denser, tends to settle in lower places. This drainage of the cold, dense air into depressions makes frost and fog more common in low places than on adjacent slopes.

northerly air is not much over 40°, and skies are clear and air calm, killing frost is likely during the following night. But even when conditions are generally favorable for a killing frost over an extensive area, the destructive effects upon plant life are usually local and patchy in distribution. This is chiefly a matter of terrain irregularities and air drainage, with most frost damage restricted to the lower lands. This is why sensitive crops such as fruit and vegetables are commonly planted on slopes rather than in valley bottoms.

Protection against killing frost For small-scale vegetable gardeners or fruit growers the simplest and most effective means of protection against frost is to spread over the crop some nonmetallic covering such as straw, paper, or cloth. Such a covering tends to retard the heat loss by radiation from the ground and the plants. The function of the cover is not to keep the cold out but the heat in. But this method is not suitable for protecting extensive orchards, so in such places as the valuable citrus groves of California and Florida small oil heaters are commonly used to prevent a bad freeze. Such heaters, well distributed among the fruit trees, are kept burning for several hours during those night

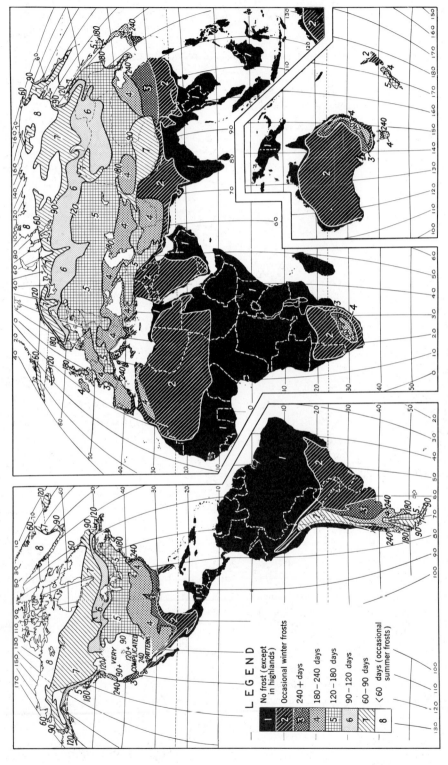

LEGEND

No frost (except in highlands)
1   Occasional winter frosts
2   240+ days
3   180 – 240 days
4   120 – 180 days
5   90 – 120 days
6   60 – 90 days
7   < 60 days (occasional summer frosts)
8

FIG. 7.11   Average length of the frost-free period, or growing season, in days. Note that there are extensive areas in the tropics where frost is unknown except at high elevations. *(From Great Soviet World Atlas, vol. 1.)*

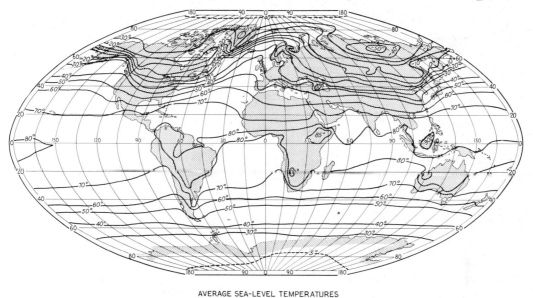

AVERAGE SEA-LEVEL TEMPERATURES
(After Shaw, Brunt and Others)
JANUARY

FIG. 7.12

hours when the lowest temperatures are to be expected.

Horizontal distribution of temperature over the earth; isothermal maps Tem-

perature distribution over the earth is represented on maps by *isotherms*, lines connecting places with the same temperature (Figs. 7.12, 7.13). All points on the earth's surface

FIG. 7.13

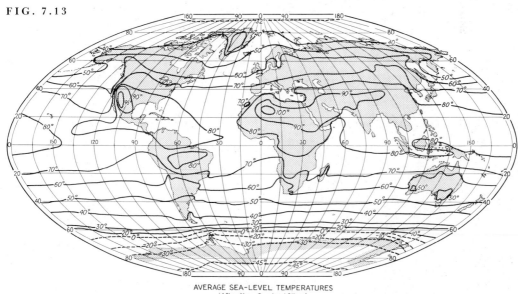

AVERAGE SEA-LEVEL TEMPERATURES
(After Shaw, Brunt and Others)
JULY

through which any one isotherm passes have identical average temperatures. In Figs. 7.12 and 7.13 temperatures of all locations have been reduced to the temperatures that would prevail if the locations were at sea level, by use of the formula which indicates an average vertical change of about 3.6° in temperature for each 1,000-ft change in altitude. If the temperatures recorded by widely distributed stations in a great variety of locations were not so reduced to eliminate the effects of altitude, the complications in the isotherms caused by hills and mountains would make the maps so confusing that the general world patterns of temperature distribution would be difficult to observe.

One very conspicuous feature of the temperature maps is that the isotherms have a strong east-west alignment, roughly following the parallels of latitude. This is not surprising, given the fact that, except for differences in the transparency of the atmosphere, all places in the same latitude receive identical amounts of solar energy. This east-west course of the isotherms simply illustrates that solar energy is the single most important control of the broadscale temperature distribution over the earth.

WORLD-WIDE FEATURES OF ANNUAL TEMPERATURE DISTRIBUTION

As already indicated, for the year as a whole the highest average temperatures are in the low latitudes where the largest amounts of solar energy are received; the lowest average temperatures are in the vicinity of the poles, the regions of least solar energy. Within a broad belt some 40° wide in the tropics, or low latitudes, the temperature differences in a north-south direction are small and the

thermal conditions are relatively uniform. It is chiefly in those latitudes poleward from 20°–25° N and S, chiefly the middle and higher latitudes, that the average annual temperatures decrease rapidly toward either pole.

Isotherms tend to be straighter and also more widely spaced in the Southern Hemisphere where oceans predominate. The greatest deviations from east-west courses are where the isotherms pass from continents to oceans. This is caused by the contrasting heating and cooling properties of land and water surfaces and by the effects of ocean currents. Next to solar energy, land and water distribution is the most important control of temperature distribution. Cool ocean currents off the coasts of Peru and northern Chile, southern California, and southwestern Africa cause equatorward bending of isotherms. Similarly, warm currents in higher latitudes cause isotherms to bend poleward, a condition most marked off the coast of northwestern Europe.

January and July average temperatures   For the earth in general, January and July are the months of seasonal extremes of temperature, and the temperature maps for these two months (Figs 7.12, 7.13) illustrate significant features of seasonal temperature distribution.

(*a*) From a comparison of the two maps it is obvious that there is a marked north-south shifting of the isotherms, and thus temperature belts, between July and January, following the north-south migration of sun's rays and the belt of maximum solar energy. (*b*) This shifting is much greater over continents than over oceans because of the greater seasonal extremes of temperature over land masses. (*c*) The highest temperatures in both January and July are over land areas, and much the lowest temperatures in January are over Asia and North America, the largest land masses in the middle and higher latitudes. (*d*) In the Northern Hemisphere the January isotherms bend equatorward over the colder continents and poleward over the warmer oceans, whereas in July exactly the opposite condition prevails. (*e*) No such seasonal temperature contrasts between land and water are to be found in the Southern Hemisphere, for there large land masses are absent in the higher middle latitudes. (*f*) The lowest temperatures in January are over northeastern Asia, the leeward side of the largest land mass in higher middle latitudes. The next lowest temperatures are over Greenland and North America. (*g*) North-south temperature gradients (rates of horizontal temperature change), like solar-energy gradients (Fig. 7.4), are steeper in winter than in summer. Steep gradients, represented by close spacing of the isotherms, are particularly conspicuous over the Northern Hemisphere continents in January.

Annual range   The difference between the average temperatures of the warmest and coldest months is the *annual range of temperature.* The largest annual ranges are over the Northern Hemisphere continents, which become alternately hot in summer and cold in winter (Fig. 7.14). Ranges are never large (*a*) near the equator, where insolation varies little, or (*b*) over large water bodies, which explains why ranges are everywhere small in the middle latitudes of the Southern Hemisphere. In general, they increase toward the higher latitudes, with the increase much more marked over the continents than over the oceans.

Air temperature and sensible temperature   Correct air temperature can be obtained only by an accurate thermometer properly exposed. The instrument must not be in the sun; otherwise it receives energy not only from the surrounding air but also from the absorption of solar energy. It also should be protected against direct radiation from the ground and adjacent buildings.

Sensible temperature is the sensation of temperature that the human body feels, as distinguished from actual air temperature re-

FIG. 7.14   Average annual ranges of temperature are smallest in low latitudes and over oceans. They are largest over continents in the middle and higher latitudes.

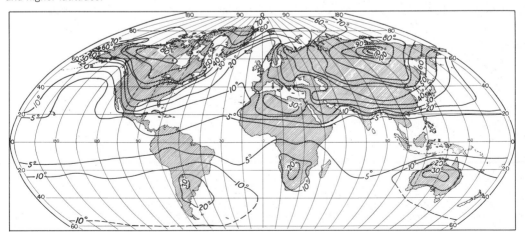

corded by a properly exposed thermometer. Unlike a thermometer, which has no temperature of its own, the human body is a heat engine, generating energy at a relatively fixed rate when at rest. Anything, therefore, that affects the rate of loss of heat from the body affects physical comfort. Air temperature, of course, is one important factor, but so also are wind, humidity, and sunlight. Thus a hot day that is humid is more uncomfortable than an equally hot day that is dry, since loss of heat by evaporation is retarded more when the air is humid. A hot day with a good breeze feels less oppressive than a still hot day because of increased evaporation. A windy cold day feels uncomfortable because the loss of heat is speeded up by greater evaporation. A sunny day in winter feels less cold than it actually is, owing to the body's absorption of solar energy. Cold air containing moisture particles is particularly penetrating because the skin becomes moist and evaporation results, and further loss of heat results from contact with the cold water. Because of all this sensitiveness to factors other than air temperature, the human body is not a very accurate thermometer. This should always be remembered in considering world, regional, and local temperatures and their effects on human beings.

CHAPTER 8

The circulation of the atmosphere: winds and pressure

CLIMATIC IMPORTANCE OF WINDS AND ATMOSPHERIC PRESSURE

The film of air which envelops the solid-liquid earth is in motion almost everywhere at all times. Such movement, when it is in a direction essentially horizontal to the earth's surface, is known as wind. Air is set in motion by differences in its density which cause variations in the weight or pressure of the atmosphere at the same altitude.

As climatic elements affecting living things on the earth's surface, atmospheric pressure and winds are of small importance compared with temperature and precipitation. This is especially true of pressure. Winds do affect sensible temperatures and rates of evaporation, and winds of high speed may be genuinely destructive. Nevertheless, the fundamental reason why winds and pressure are considered in this book is that they are essential keys to an understanding of temperature and precipitation distribution over the earth. The basic importance of atmospheric pressure is that pressure differences generate winds. And the fundamental and *very important* climatic functions of winds are (*a*) the maintenance of a heat balance between the high and low latitudes, in spite of a constant low-latitude excess and high-latitude deficiency of radiant energy, and (*b*) the transport of water vapor from the oceans to the lands where the water vapor may condense and fall as rain.

PRESSURE DIFFERENCES AND THEIR ORIGINS

The downward pressure (weight) of the air is measured by a barometer. This weight at sea level is balanced against the weight of a column of mercury 29.92 in., or 762 mm (millimeters), in length having the same cross-sectional area. The more air pressure, the higher the mercury rises in the tube. Until about 1914 it was customary to report pressure in units of length (inches, millimeters, or centimeters of mercury). Since then a new measuring unit, called the *millibar* (*mb*), has come into general use by the weather services of the world. Since $\frac{1}{10}$ in. of mercury is equivalent to 3.4 mb, sea-level atmospheric pressure may be expressed as 29.92 in., 760 mm, or 1013.2 mb.

Any map representing atmospheric pressure at sea level shows at once that pressure is not uniform over the earth but varies with latitude and also from one region or locality to another. The variations can be classified in two general types of pressure systems: (*a*) high-pressure systems, called *anticyclones* or *highs,* and (*b*) low-pressure systems, called *cyclones, depressions,* or *lows.*

At present there is no simple and adequate explanation for the average annual or seasonal arrangement of high- and low-pressure systems over the earth, nor for the moving cells of high and low pressure that appear on the daily weather map. Some highs and lows appear to have their origin in temperature characteristics of the air. Thus, cold air being denser and heavier than warm air, it is not surprising for low air temperatures sometimes to be the cause of high pressure and for high temperatures to result in low pressure. Examples of high-pressure systems produced by low surface temperatures are the extensive highs over central and eastern Eurasia and northern North America in winter. Similarly, heat-induced lows are to be found over such superheated locales as the Pakistan–northwestern India area and the

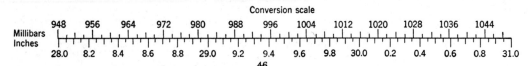

Conversion scale

| | 948 | 956 | 964 | 972 | 980 | 988 | 996 | 1004 | 1012 | 1020 | 1028 | 1036 | 1044 |
Millibars
Inches
| | 28.0 | 8.2 | 8.4 | 8.6 | 8.8 | 29.0 | 9.2 | 9.4 | 9.6 | 9.8 | 30.0 | 0.2 | 0.4 | 0.6 | 0.8 | 31.0 |

46

southwestern United States in summer (Figs. 8.3, 8.4).

More numerous and widespread, however, are pressure systems, both high and low, whose immediate and direct cause is not surface-temperature differences. Their origin appears to be associated instead with mechanical processes involving such factors as centrifugal force, surface friction, and the blocking effects of highlands which lie athwart the paths of extensive and deep air streams.

DISTRIBUTION OF ATMOSPHERIC PRESSURE

Vertical distribution Since air is very compressible, there is a rapid decrease in air weight or pressure with increasing altitude. The lower layers of the atmosphere are most compressed, or densest, because the weight of all the layers above rests upon them. For the first few thousand feet above sea level the rate of pressure decrease is about 1 in., or 34 mb, of pressure for each 900 to 1,000 ft. As higher altitudes are reached, the air rapidly becomes much thinner and lighter, so that at an elevation of 18,000 ft. one-half the atmosphere by weight is below the observer, although a rarefied atmosphere extends to a height of several hundred miles.

Horizontal distribution at sea level Just as temperature distribution is represented by isotherms, so atmospheric pressure distribution is represented by *isobars,* that is, lines connecting places having the same atmospheric pressure at a given elevation. On the isobaric charts here shown (Figs. 8.3, 8.4), all pressure readings have been reduced to sea level to eliminate the effects of altitude on pressure. Most pressure-distribution charts represent sea-level pressures, although the need for understanding upper-air flow has in recent years caused the development of pressure charts for higher levels, usually for about 10,000 ft (750 mb) and 18,000 ft (500 mb).

Where isobars are closely spaced, there is a rapid horizontal change in pressure in a direction at right angles to the isobars. The rate and direction of the change is called the *pressure gradient.* Where isobars are widely spaced, the pressure gradient is weak.

The arrangement of average sea-level pressures is reasonably well generalized and portrayed by both the idealized isobaric chart (Fig. 8.1) and the meridional profile of pres-

FIG. 8.1 Arrangement of zonal sea-level pressure. Except in the higher latitudes of the Southern Hemisphere, the pressure zones, or belts, are in the nature of cells of low or high pressure arranged in latitudinal bands.

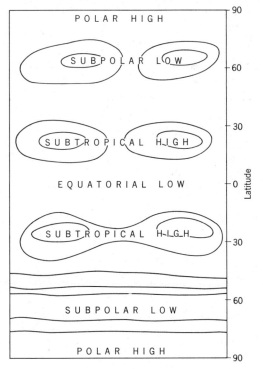

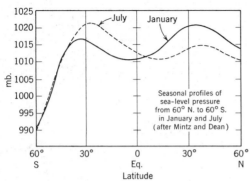

F I G . 8 . 2   Profiles of sea-level pressure from
60°N to 60°S averaged for all longitudes, at the
time of the extreme seasons. Equatorial low,
subtropical highs, and subpolar lows are
conspicuous features. Note the seasonal
north-south movements of the pressure belts,
following the sun.

sure (Fig. 8.2). Both figures suggest that
pressure, averaged for all longitudes, is
arranged in zones resembling belts. The so-
called belts are more accurately described as
centers, or cells, of pressure, arranged in
latitudinal bands. The belted arrangement is
more conspicuous in the relatively homogeneous Southern Hemisphere, where oceans
prevail. This suggests that two features of the

great Northern Hemisphere continents—their
highlands which obstruct the free flow of the
atmosphere and their great seasonal temperature changes—have much to do with the
origin and arrangement of pressure cells.

The most noteworthy features of the generalized world pattern of sea-level pressure
can be derived from Figs. 8.1 and 8.2. (*a*)
The dominant and key element is the series
of high-pressure cells which form irregular
belts of high pressure at about 25°–30° N
and S. These are the subtropical highs. Their
origin is not fully understood, but certainly it
is mechanical or dynamic, not thermal. (*b*)
Between the belts of subtropical high pressure is the equatorial trough of low pressure.
(*c*) Poleward from the subtropical highs,
pressure decreases toward either pole, with
minima being reached in the vicinity of
65° N and S. At these latitudes are the subpolar centers, or troughs, of low pressure.
Their origin is not so clear, but it is due
more to mechanical than to thermal causes.
(*d*) Poleward from about latitude 65° data are
so scanty that the pattern of pressure distribu-

F I G . 8 . 3

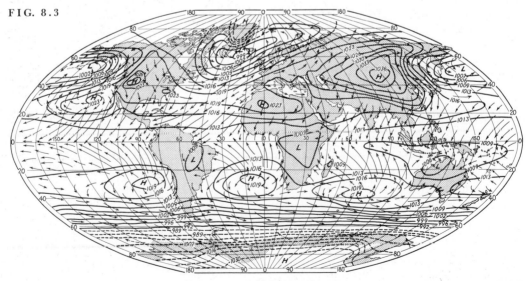

AVERAGE SEA-LEVEL PRESSURES AND WINDS
JANUARY

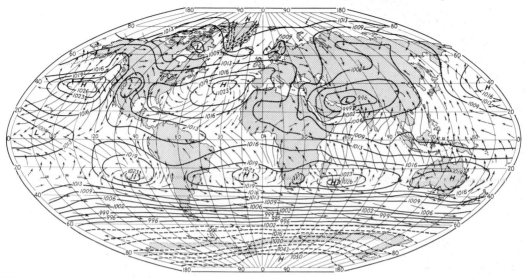

FIG. 8.4   AVERAGE SEA-LEVEL PRESSURES AND WINDS
JULY

tion is not well known. It is generally assumed that fairly shallow surface highs of thermal origin occupy the inner polar areas.

If one were to inspect a weather map of the earth for a single day, the above-described arrangement of zonal surface pressure would not be so evident. This would suggest that the generalized cells and zones of surface pressure are, partly at least, in the nature of statistical averages of complicated day-to-day systems of moving highs and lows.

Sea-level pressure distribution in January and July, the extreme seasons Figures 8.3 and 8.4 illustrate some of the features of seasonal pressure distribution which are of the greatest significance climatically. (*a*) Pressure belts and cells, like those of temperature, migrate northward with the sun's rays in July and southward in January. This is most readily observed in Fig. 8.2, which shows the meridional profiles of pressure. In general, pressure is higher in the winter, or cold, hemisphere. (*b*) The oceanic subtropical highs are best developed over the eastern sides of the oceans and tend to be weaker toward the western sides. (*c*) The subpolar low in the Southern Hemisphere is very deep, i.e., characterized by very low pressure, and forms a continuous circumpolar trough in both January and July, but the subpolar low in the Northern Hemisphere consists of individual pressure cells which are much more seasonal in character, being strongest in winter. (*d*) In January a strong thermal cell of high pressure develops over the cold continent of Eurasia, a weaker one over smaller and less frigid North America. In July these same continents, now warm, develop weaker thermal lows.

RELATION OF WINDS TO PRESSURE

Large-scale vertical and horizontal movements of air are required to correct the unbalanced distribution of energy which results from latitudinal inequalities in the amount of incoming solar, and outgoing earth, radiation.

Wind and the pressure gradient As

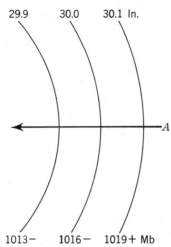

29.9   30.0   30.1 In.

A

1013−   1016−   1019+ Mb

FIG. 8.5   Pressure gradient is the rate and direction of pressure change. Gradient is represented by a line drawn at right angles to the isobars.

noted previously, air is set in motion by differences in air density which result in horizontal differences in air pressure. Wind, therefore, represents nature's attempt to correct pressure inequalities. The rate and direction of pressure change, or pressure gradient, largely determines the speed and general direction of the wind. There are two fundamental principles which control the relationship between pressure and winds:

1. The *rate* of airflow, or speed of the wind, depends upon the steepness of the pressure gradient (rate of pressure change). When the gradient is steep, with isobars closely spaced, airflow is rapid. When the gradient is weak, with isobars widely spaced, the wind is likewise weak. Calms prevail when pressure differences over extensive areas are almost, or quite, nil.

2. The *direction* of airflow is from high to low pressure, or down the gradient (Fig. 8.5). This is just as natural as the well-known fact that water, following the law of gravitation, runs downhill. Because of earth rotation,

however, the actual flow of air from high to low pressure is very oblique, or indirect.

Deflection by earth rotation   On a nonrotating earth, air set in motion by pressure differences would simply flow along the pressure gradient at right angles to the isobars. But on a rotating earth where meridians and parallels are constantly changing direction, winds have an apparent deflection from the gradient direction so that they cross the isobars at an oblique angle. Over land surfaces, where friction is relatively great, the surface winds make an angle with the isobars of 20 to 40°. Over the oceans, where friction is much less, the angle may be as low as 10°, and in the free atmosphere several thousand feet above the earth's surface, winds nearly parallel the isobars, the angle being as low as 1 to 3°.

In the Northern Hemisphere earth rotation causes all winds to have an apparent deflection to the right of the gradient direction; in the Southern Hemisphere the apparent deflection is always to the left (Fig. 8.6). This rule will not appear to be true when tested, however, unless it is kept in mind that one must always face in the direction the wind is blowing in order to observe the proper deflection. Deflective force of earth rotation increases with increasing latitude, i.e., toward either pole; only at the equator is it absent.

Wind direction   Winds are always named by the direction from which they come. Thus a wind from the south, blowing toward the north, is called a south wind. The wind vane points toward the source of the wind. *Windward* refers to the direction from which a wind comes, *leeward* refers to that toward which it blows. Thus a windward coast is one along which the air is moving onshore, while on a leeward coast winds move offshore. When a wind blows more frequently

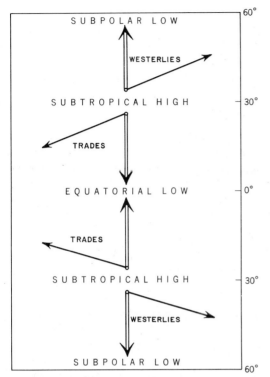

FIG. 8.6 Apparent deflection of the planetary winds on a rotating earth. Double-line arrows indicate wind direction as it would be developed from pressure gradient alone. Solid-line arrows indicate the direction of deflected winds.

from one direction than from any other, it is a *prevailing wind.* On the daily weather map wind arrows fly with the wind.

Cyclonic and anticyclonic circulations
As indicated earlier, sea-level-pressure patterns are commonly cellular in character and appear on an isobaric chart as systems of closed isobars. Such a system of closed iso-

bars with the lowest pressure at the center is a cyclone. When the highest pressure is at the center, such a system is an anticyclone. In a cyclone, or low-pressure system, the airflow is from the margins toward the center. It is a *converging-wind system.* The deflective force of earth rotation causes the converging air to move anticlockwise north of the equator and clockwise south of it. In an anticyclone air flows from the center toward the margins, so that it is a *diverging-wind system,* clockwise in the Northern Hemisphere and anticlockwise in the Southern (Fig. 8.7).

FIG. 8.7 A much idealized representation of the earth's surface winds. Airflow is from the east in the low latitudes and from the west in the middle latitudes.

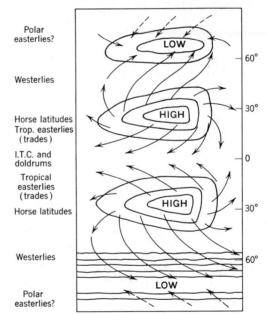

THE EARTH'S SURFACE WINDS[1]

Zonal pattern From the meridional profile of pressure (Fig. 8.2) or from the idealized sketch showing arrangement of pressure belts (Fig. 8.1), the principal elements of the

earth's zonal surface-wind system can be readily visualized (also Fig. 8.7). From the

[1] The term *surface wind* refers to the lower few thousand feet of the atmosphere.

subtropical highs at about 25°–30° N and S surface winds flow both from north and south toward the low-pressure trough near the equator. Earth rotation deflects these two air streams into oblique easterly winds appropriately designated as the *tropical easterlies*. They are also known as the *trade winds:* northeast trades north of the equator and southeast trades to the south of it.

Poleward from the subtropical high-pressure ridge in each hemisphere, winds flow downgradient toward the subpolar lows. They are turned by earth rotation so that they have a general west-to-east movement. These are the middle-latitude *westerlies:* southwest in the Northern Hemisphere and northwest south of the equator.

Poleward from about 65°, where weather observations are few, the nature of the surface-wind system is uncertain. It seems probable, however, that easterly winds prevail.

To summarize zonal surface winds, there is a predominance of easterly winds in the low latitudes, or tropics, and a prevalence of westerly winds in the middle latitudes.

Between the converging trades, in the vicinity of the equatorial trough of low pressure, is a zone of variable and weak winds. This transition belt between the two trades has various names: *intertropical convergence zone* (ITC), *doldrums,* and *equatorial belt of variable winds.* Here, in some seasons and over extensive longitudes, equatorial westerly winds are in evidence. At other times and places here, easterly flow prevails.

In the intermediate area between the diverging trades and middle-latitude westerlies, fairly coincident with the crests of the subtropical highs located at about 25°–30° in each hemisphere, is still another belt of weak and variable winds, the *horse latitudes.*

Seasonal contrasts   The concept of a simple, zonal arrangement of winds as previously described is a satisfactory introduction to surface winds. It is not, however, adequate for portraying a number of features of the atmospheric circulation which have important climatic significance, such as seasonal surface winds. For instance, a somewhat more realistic representation of the surface winds in the extreme seasons, winter and summer, is shown by Figs. 8.3 and 8.4. Here a zonal belted arrangement of winds is not so conspicuous. More prominent are the spiraling cyclonic and anticyclonic circulations around individual cells of low and high pressure. Most striking are the large systems of divergent anticyclonic circulation around the subtropical high-pressure cells. These systems dominate in both January and July. The equatorward branches of anticyclonic circulation are the tropical easterlies, or trade winds; the poleward branches are the middle-latitude westerlies. Close observation of Figs. 8.3 and 8.4 reveals a north-south shifting of the wind systems, comparable to such shifting of temperature belts, following the seasonal course of the sun.

Notable in *January* are the well-developed converging cyclonic circulations around the expanded and deepened subpolar cells of low pressure over the North Atlantic and North Pacific Oceans. Equally important winter climate features are the anticyclonic circulations around the seasonal cells of high pressure over the cold land masses of Eurasia and North America. These diverging-wind systems are the *winter monsoons.* A well-developed center of low pressure with converging cyclonic circulation is conspicuous over the heated continent of Australia, south of the equator.

In *July* the cyclonic circulations over the North Atlantic and North Pacific are weaker, but over heated Asia and North America there are extensive cyclonic circulations with converging winds developed around low-pressure cells. These are the well-known *summer monsoons.*

Zones and areas of average horizontal divergence and convergence   From the preceding analysis of the surface winds, it becomes clear that there are certain zones and areas where the surface winds converge, or tend to meet along a line or at a center. There are others where the winds diverge, or move away from a common line or center of origin. Where surface winds converge, there has to be an escape of the air through upward movement, a condition which favors condensation, the development of storms, and associated clouds and precipitation. By contrast, where winds diverge, there must be a downward movement of air from aloft (subsidence) to compensate for the divergent surface flow. Since such subsidence heats and dries the air, divergence and subsidence are opposed to the development of storms and to the formation of clouds and precipitation (Fig. 8.8).

Divergence and subsidence   Some prominent and best developed of all the zones of subsidence and divergence are the zones of divergence associated with the subtropical anticyclones located at about 25°–30° north and south of the equator. These zones are not continuous around the earth, for the oceanic cells of high pressure are strongest toward the eastern sides of the oceans. There subsidence is best developed and deserts are conspicuous features of the adjacent lands. Toward the western sides of the oceans where the subtropical anticyclones, and thus divergence and subsidence, are weaker, humid climates are likely to prevail. Surface divergence is likewise strong in the winter anti-

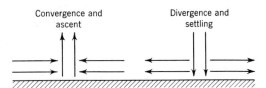

FIG. 8.8   Where surface winds flow toward each other, or converge, there is a resulting upward movement of air. Where surface winds move apart, or diverge, there must be a settling or subsidence of the air.

cyclones over northern and eastern Asia and over northern North America.

Convergence and ascent   Most prominent of all the extended lines of wind convergence is that located between the Northern Hemisphere trades and the Southern Hemisphere trades in the general vicinity of the geographic equator, the previously mentioned intertropical convergence zone (ITC).

There are other zones of convergence associated with the subpolar troughs, or cells, of low pressure where the westerlies flowing poleward from subtropical latitudes meet air of polar origin. These zones appear to be less continuous both areally and temporally than the ITC. Much of the convergence appears to occur in the individual moving cyclonic storms which are numerous in these latitudes, especially over the oceans. Seasonal areas of convergence, associated with thermally induced lows, are to be observed over southern and eastern Asia and interior North America in July.

SPECIFIC SURFACE WINDS AND THEIR CHARACTERISTICS

Tropical easterlies, or trade winds   The easterly winds which move obliquely downgradient from the subtropical anticyclones toward the equatorial trough of low pressure, roughly between latitudes 20°–25° and 5°–10° in each hemisphere over the oceans, probably got their other name, trade winds, from their prevailingly fair weather and steadiness of flow (Fig. 8.7). Yet, the trades are now known to be neither as uniformly steady in direction and speed nor as full of fair weather as was formerly thought.

Over the eastern parts of the oceanic trades, where the subtropical anticyclone and its subsidence are strong, storms are few, winds steady, cloud and rainfall meager, and fair weather prevails. But in the western parts, where the anticyclone and the accompanying subsidence are weaker, atmospheric disturbances are more numerous, the trades less constant, and cloud and rainfall more prevalent (Fig. 8.9).

There are likewise important weather contrasts within the trade winds in a north-south direction. Toward their poleward margins, which are close to the centers of the subtropical highs where subsidence is strong, the trades are characterized by dry weather and much sunshine (Fig. 8.9). Here the air is said to be stable, for it lacks buoyancy, that is, it is disinclined to rise, and is opposed to the formation of rainbringing storms. But very gradually as the trades move equatorward and westward from their source in the subtropical highs, they are importantly modified in ways which create an atmospheric environment more favorable for the development of clouds and rainfall. One such modification occurs as the winds, in passing over great expanses of tropical ocean, take on large additions of moisture through evaporation. A second modification of great climatic significance is a consequence of the trade winds having left a region of strong divergence and subsidence in the subtropical anticyclones and gradually approaching the equatorial trough of low pressure where horizontal convergence and lifting, and so instability of the air, are characteristic. Here atmospheric disturbances are more common, convectional overturning of the air easier, and clouds and rainfall more abundant. Thus it is that the trades are likely to be dry, fair-weather winds in their poleward and eastern oceanic parts, while their western and equatorward sections are characterized by more weather disturbances, cloud, and precipitation.

But even in these rainier parts of the tropical easterlies or trades the air ordinarily is not so buoyant and unstable as it is in equatorial latitudes close to the ITC, or where equatorial westerlies prevail. As a consequence, in the absence of highlands, the total annual rainfall is not excessive.

Winds of the intertropical convergence zone   Winds are very complex in the vicinity of the equatorial trough of low pressure, which in the mean is located close to the geographic equator but in the extreme seasons may shift 10 to 15° to the north and south over the continents (Fig. 8.7). Air movement is usually light, and it is variable both in speed and direction. Calms are frequent.

FIG. 8.9   The circulation pattern around a subtropical anticyclone with general areas of stability and instability shown. The eastern end of the cell is much more stable than the western. The poleward parts of the trades are more stable than the equatorward parts.

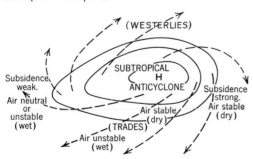

At some times and places airflow is from the west (equatorial westerlies), at other times and places from the east. As a rule this region between the trade winds is characterized by much horizontal convergence and associated rising air, so that the atmosphere is buoyant and unstable. Only slight lifting is required to trigger off strong vertical air currents, resulting in cumulonimbus clouds of great height, capable of producing heavy, showery rains. Convergence and ascent of air cannot be continuous, however, for all days are not rainy. Probably, therefore, the convergence and lifting are concentrated in the numerous weak disturbances which infest these areas close to the ITC.

Winds of the subtropics   The latitudes from 25 to 30° are close to the centers of great anticyclonic circulations around zonally arranged cells of high pressure. The poleward branch of this anticyclonic circulation is the middle-latitude westerlies; the equatorward branch is the tropical easterlies or trades. Thus these latitudes—the subtropics, or horse latitudes—are the transition area between the diverging surface trades and westerlies. As noted earlier, such divergence must be accompanied by a slow settling of the air, or subsidence, and both divergence and subsidence are opposed to the formation of clouds and precipitation. So the centers of the subtropical anticyclones are characterized by much fair weather and meager rainfall.

Like the equatorial trough of low pressure, the centers of the subtropical anticyclones are characterized by light winds coming from a variety of directions, and by frequent calms. However, the two regions are quite unlike in their general weather conditions, the former being a region of horizontal convergence, numerous atmospheric disturbances, and much showery rainfall, the latter an area of horizontal divergence, few disturbances, and generally fair weather.

In reality the horse latitudes are not altogether similar in weather throughout (Fig. 8.9). Toward the western margins of each oceanic anticyclone there is less atmospheric subsidence than in the center and eastern parts, so that while the latter are characteristically dry, the western parts have a moderate amount of cloud and precipitation. This is how it develops that the eastern parts of the subtropical oceans and adjacent (western) parts of continents have dry and subhumid climates, while the western parts of subtropical oceans and their bordering land areas have humid climates.

The variable westerlies of middle latitudes   The stormy westerlies of the Northern and Southern Hemispheres move obliquely downgradient from the centers of subtropical high pressure to the subpolar lows. They are located from roughly 35°–40° to 60°–65° (Fig. 8.7). Here the airflow is highly variable in speed and direction. At times, especially in the winter, the westerlies blow with gale force; sometimes mild breezes prevail. Although the winds are designated as westerlies, westerly being the direction of most frequent and strongest winds, they do blow from all points of the compass.

The variability of these winds in both direction and strength is largely the result of the procession of storms—cyclones and anticyclones—which travels from west to east in these latitudes. The storms, with their local systems of converging and diverging winds, tend to disrupt and modify the general westerly air currents. Moreover, on the eastern sides of Asia, and to a lesser degree North America, the continental wind systems called the monsoons tend to modify the westerlies, especially in summer. It is in the Southern

Hemisphere, where in latitudes 40°–65° land masses are largely absent, that the stormy westerlies can be observed at their maximum and least interrupted development. Over these great expanses of ocean, winds of gale strength are common in summer as well as winter. The westerlies of the Northern Hemisphere, where the great land masses with their seasonal pressure reversals cause the wind systems to be much more complex, are considerably less boisterous in summer than in winter.

The poleward margins of the westerlies near the subpolar troughs of low pressure are particularly subject to great surges of cold polar air in the winter season. A sinuous line of discontinuity known as the *polar front* separates the cold, dry, polar air from the warmer and more humid mass coming from the subtropics as westerlies and is the zone of origin for a great many middle-latitude cyclones and anticyclones. It follows, therefore, that the poleward margins of the westerlies are more subject to stormy, variable weather than are the subtropical margins. The polar front and the accompanying belt of storms migrate with the sun's rays, retreating poleward in summer and advancing equatorward in winter, so aperiodic storm control of weather in the middle latitudes

should be most pronounced in the winter season.

Winds of the polar regions As previously indicated, the few and poorly distributed aerological observations in the higher latitudes beyond about 65° make an adequate description of the polar wind systems impossible at this time, but would appear to indicate that wind from an easterly direction generally prevails.

THE GENERAL CIRCULATION OF THE ATMOSPHERE

Up to this point atmospheric circulation in the lower atmosphere has been emphasized. But some features of climatic distribution, especially as it is related to precipitation, are affected by the airflow at higher elevations as well. The topic of general circulation, including both high-level and low-level winds, will be briefly considered at this point so that some of the larger distribution features of world weather and climate may be better understood. It must be borne in mind, however, that important elements of the general circulation remain controversial.

The necessity for a general circulation of the atmosphere to compensate for the un-

FIG. 8.10 Schematic representation of the general circulation. In both the low and the high latitudes the atmospheric circulations resemble that of a convectional system, with the surface flow moving toward lower latitudes; the opposite prevails aloft. In the middle latitudes the circulation is more complex, and its features are not so well understood. In general, this intermediate region appears to be a meeting place of contrasting air streams from high and low latitudes.

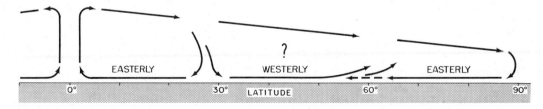

equal distribution of solar energy over the earth between poles and equator has been described earlier. It has also been said that winds and ocean currents are the means by which the excess of energy received in the tropics is carried to the deficit regions farther poleward. One might, then, readily conceive of the atmospheric circulation as being in the form of a gigantic convectional system with a direct meridional flow, aloft from warm equator to cold poles, at the surface from cold poles to warm equator. But on the rotating earth, with its surface composed of continents and oceans with contrasting frictional and heating properties, such a simple direct convectional circulation between equator and poles could not exist. The one that actually prevails is much more complex, so much so that no acceptable unified theory of the general circulation now exists.

In its simplest form, the atmospheric circulation between equator and poles is usually represented as broken down into three smaller meridional circulations, tropical, middle-latitude, and polar (Fig. 8.10). In the low latitudes equatorward from about 30°, and also in the high latitudes poleward from about 65°, the evidence suggests circulations which resemble that of a convectional system. In both there is, on the average, an oblique movement of air equatorward at the surface and poleward aloft. Deflective force of earth rotation causes the surface winds to be easterly (trades and polar easterlies) and those at higher levels to be westerly. Such a circulation requires an upward movement of air in equatorial latitudes and likewise in the vicinity of latitude 60°. Similarly, there is a settling of the upper air both in subtropical latitudes and near the poles.

It is principally in the middle latitudes (35°–60°) that the nature of the circulation pattern is most complex and controversial.

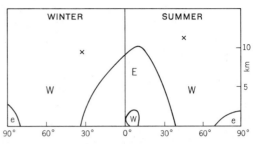

FIG. 8.11 A pole-to-pole cross section of the planetary winds up to about 8 or 9 miles above the earth's surface. E = tropical easterlies, or trades; W = westerlies; x = average location of the jet stream; w = the somewhat doubtful belt of equatorial westerlies; e = polar easterlies. *(From Flohn.)*

Here, apparently, much of the necessary north-south heat exchange occurs in the form of irregular invasions of cold polar air moving equatorward and of warm surges of tropical air moving poleward. In these latitudes, both at the surface and aloft, the air movement is prevailingly from the west, but wind and weather are both highly variable, a result of the frequent, alternating passage of cyclones and anticyclones, accompanied by shifts in wind direction and marked changes in temperature. These cyclones and anticyclones are associated with the alternating thrusts of cold and warm air, which in turn accomplish the required heat exchange. It is significant, also, that only in the middle-latitude cell of meridional circulation do the surface winds flow poleward, and hence in an opposite direction from those of a convectional circulatory system, in contrast to those of the polar and tropical cells on either side. Because of this, there is a zone of divergence on the equatorial side of the middle-latitude westerlies, as well as a zone of frequent convergence in their other parts, a fact that has important consequences in weather and climate.

The preceding analysis and Fig. 8.11 show

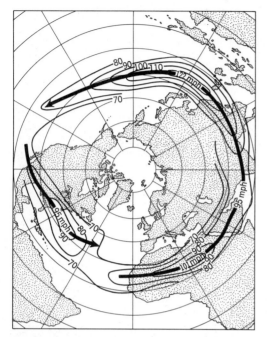

FIG. 8.12 Jet-stream map for January in the Northern Hemisphere, showing average positions and speeds in miles per hour at an elevation of about 35,000 ft. *(From Namias.)*

that a west-to-east circulation prevails throughout most of the earth's atmosphere. This westerly flow is often obscured at the earth's surface, of course, by the frictional effects of terrain irregularities and by numerous atmospheric disturbances in the form of storms. Also, there are at least two important exceptions to this general west-to-east movement of the earth's atmosphere. The first and principal one is the east-to-west flow in most of the low latitudes. The tropical easterlies, or trades, of these latitudes may reach heights of about 6 miles near the equator. Poleward from the equator they decline rapidly in depth until they cease to exist at about 30° N and S Lat (Fig. 8.11).

The jet stream, upper-air waves and surface weather A relatively spectacular feature of the atmospheric circulation, whose existence has been made known only recently,

is the jet stream (or streams). The jet resembles a meandering fast-flowing river. It travels at speeds of 100 to 150 miles per hour, moving from west to east at elevations of 20,000 to 40,000 ft (Fig. 8.12). Its position shifts north and south with the seasons, but its average location is between 30 and 40°. Even though the jet stream and the high-level westerly winds of which it is a part are essentially zonal (east-west) in character, they do develop north-south oscillations, or waves, of enormous length.

It is known that the jet stream and these waves are closely associated with surface weather conditions. For example, the waves on the jet are directly related to the horizontal expulsion of great masses of polar and tropical air. When the jet stream is unusually sinuous, these north-south thrusts of air masses are strong and frequent. During such periods storms are numerous and weather is very changeable in the middle latitudes. Less variable and stormy conditions prevail when the jet is characterized by few and weaker oscillations. Well-developed middle-latitude cyclones extend upward into the jet-stream waves, and may have their origin in these waves. At least such storms intensify when they are positioned underneath the jet, and the jet stream appears to have the effect of steering the cyclonic disturbances across the earth's surface. It seems reasonable, therefore, that cyclonic rainfall should be concentrated underneath the jet stream.

TERRESTRIAL MODIFICATIONS OF THE SURFACE WINDS

Some effects of the earth's surface upon surface winds which have been mentioned incidentally in the previous discussion can now be usefully amplified.

Latitudinal shifting of the wind belts

Because of the parallelism and inclination of the earth's axis, the sun's vertical noon rays shift during half the annual period of revolution from 23½° N (summer solstice) to 23½° S (winter solstice), a total of 47°, as noted previously. But the belt of maximum solar energy actually undergoes a latitudinal shift of 60 to 70°. Following this north-south migration of solar energy comes a similar shift in temperature belts, largely sun-controlled, and in pressure and wind belts, in part thermally induced. The north-south shifting of wind belts is by no means so simple a thing as it may appear to be from this description, for it varies in amount and rapidity from one part of the earth to another because of the variations in the earth's surface. Over the oceans and along coasts where the latitudinal shift of winds is more readily observable, the total migration is not great, usually not much over 10 to 15°. Over continents, on the other hand, where seasonal temperature changes are greater, the total latitudinal shift of winds, as well as pressure, is also greater. In general, there is a lag of a month or more behind the sun. But the time lag is considerably less over land than over oceans.

Latitudes affected by more than one wind belt The north-south shifting of the wind belts is especially significant in those latitudes lying between two wind systems having unlike weather conditions, as for example, between a converging and a diverging system. Such latitudes are encroached upon by one of the contrasting wind systems and its weather conditions at one season, by the other wind system and its weather at the opposite season. Two such latitudes will be noted (Fig. 9.12).

1. Latitudes 5 to 15° north and south of the equator lie between the equatorial convergence zone (ITC) with its unstable air, numerous atmospheric disturbances, and abundant rainfall, and the subtropical zone of divergence and subsidence where stable air and few disturbances result in meager rainfall. These latitudes experience weather associated with the ITC and its disturbances at the times of high sun (summer); but in the season of low sun (winter) the fair, dry weather of the divergence zone of the subtropical anticyclones and their trade winds prevails. A wet summer and a dry winter are the results. This seasonal variation in weather is not so conspicuous along the eastern side of a continent where the anticyclone is weaker and the air less stable.

2. Latitudes 30 to 40° are located between the dry subtropical anticyclones and the middle-latitude westerlies with their numerous rainbringing cyclones. Drought associated with anticyclonic subsidence and divergence is characteristic of summer, while in winter there is adequate precipitation from cyclonic storms in the westerlies. This seasonal rainfall variation in latitudes 30°–40° is confined largely to the eastern side of oceans and the adjacent western side of continents where the subtropical anticyclone is well developed and the air stable.

Monsoon winds Winds which reverse their direction of flow during the course of a year and prevailingly blow from land to sea in winter and from sea to land in summer are called *monsoon winds*. Commonly this seasonal reversal of wind direction in a monsoon is attributed to the unequal heating of land and water surfaces.

In *winter*, for example, a large continent in middle latitudes is colder than the surrounding sea surface, so that the air over the land is colder and denser and the atmospheric pressure higher (Fig. 8.3, eastern Asia). As a consequence there is a flow of surface air from land to sea. Because this winter monsoon originates over a cold land mass, it is dry, cold, and stable and therefore resists upward movement which might result in cloud and precipitation.

In *summer*, by contrast, the land air is warmer and less dense than that over the sea, with atmospheric pressure lower over the land. As a consequence surface air flows from sea to land (Fig. 8.4, eastern Asia). This summer monsoon originates over the sea, and usually over relatively warm waters. Thus its humidity content is high, with the consequence that it provides an atmospheric environment favorable for the development of atmospheric disturbances capable of producing cloud and rainfall. The following illustrates the above-described causation sequence of monsoon systems:

Winter—land cold with high pressure—surface winds from land to sea.

Summer—land warm with low pressure—surface winds from sea to land.

Monsoon winds are climatically significant chiefly because of their effects upon temperature and precipitation conditions of those parts of continents where they prevail.

Ideally, monsoons should produce a climate characterized by seasonal extremes of both temperature and precipitation, with winters that are cold and dry and summers that are warm and wet. Actually, the effects, as well as the origin and nature, of monsoon winds have been greatly simplified in the preceding description. For example, much of the seasonal wind reversal to be observed in *tropical* lands—well exemplified in southern Asia, northern Australia, and tropical Africa —is more a consequence of the latitudinal shifting of wind belts following the sun

than it is the unequal heating of land and water (Figs. 8.3, 8.4). It is chiefly the monsoons of middle latitudes, such as those in eastern Asia and in eastern North America, that owe their origin to land-water thermal contrasts.

Moreover, neither the winter nor the summer monsoons consist of a steady, uninterrupted flow of air. Both are infested with a variety of atmospheric disturbances which interrupt the onshore and offshore flow of air and at times even reverse its direction. These are the same atmospheric disturbances which produce the abundant summer, and the more modest winter, precipitation in the monsoon currents. Spells of weather are characteristic of both monsoons.

Land and sea breezes   Like monsoons, land and sea breezes are wind reversals that have their origins in the unequal heating of land and water surfaces. But these wind reversals have a daily periodicity, not the seasonal one of the monsoons. At night the land's greater coolness results in an offshore breeze; by day the heated land causes the wind to flow onshore. Universally the effects of the sea breeze are felt for only a few miles inland, and this only in the warmer seasons of middle latitudes. Along tropical coasts the daily sea breeze is not limited to any season. Modest temperature and rainfall effects are produced by the sea breeze. Along coasts high daytime temperatures may be appreciably reduced by the cooler sea or lake air moving onshore. It is believed, also, that the sea breeze may have some generating effect on thunderstorm activity, thereby increasing the total precipitation along littorals (coastal regions).

CHAPTER 9

Precipitation

WATER VAPOR, OR HUMIDITY

Only in the invisible, or gas, form is water an integral part of the atmosphere; it is then referred to as water vapor or as humidity. The water vapor in the atmosphere varies in quantity from place to place and also from time to time, but always comprises only a small part of the total atmosphere. If all of the water vapor in the air were condensed to the liquid form and evenly distributed over the earth as rain, it would form a layer only about 1 in. deep. Nevertheless, water vapor is by far the most important gas in the atmosphere as far as weather and climatic phenomena are concerned, for several reasons. (*a*) The amount of moisture in the air is *directly* related to precipitation possibilities. (*b*) The more water vapor in the atmosphere, the more *stored-up* energy available for the growth of atmospheric disturbances which produce rainfall. (*c*) Water vapor is the chief absorber of both solar radiation and energy radiated from the earth, and therefore regulates temperature. (*d*) The relative amount of water vapor affects the human body's rate of cooling and hence its feeling of heat and cold, i.e., the sensible temperature.

Evaporation-condensation cycle and sources of water vapor The water vapor in the air is derived from water in the liquid or solid form through the process of *evaporation*. In reverse, *condensation* occurs when water vapor is changed to the liquid or solid state to form clouds. The condensed water or ice may then fall on the earth's surface as *precipitation.* Among the several gases of the air, only water vapor condenses to form a liquid (water) or a solid (ice) within the range of atmospheric temperatures.

The principal source of atmospheric humidity is the oceans which cover nearly 71 per cent of the earth's surface. By winds the water vapor evaporated from the oceans is carried in over the continents. Indeed, most of the continental precipitation is derived from moisture from over the oceans. However, a portion of the atmosphere's humidity is derived from evaporation which occurs over the continents—evaporation from the moist soils, the vegetation cover, and from inland bodies of water.

The evaporation-condensation-precipitation cycle is constantly in progress as water vapor is added to the atmosphere by evaporation and removed by condensation-precipitation (Fig. 16.3). Over the oceans evaporation exceeds precipitation; over the continents precipitation is in excess of evaporation. But these differences are equalized by (*a*) the discharge of rivers and glaciers into the oceans, and, to a much greater extent, by (*b*) the transfer of land-evaporated moisture seaward in the great streams of continental air.

Latent energy in water vapor   Energy in the form of heat is required to change ice (solid) into water (liquid), and water into water vapor (gas). The unit of heat energy, the calorie (cal), is the amount of heat required to raise the temperature of a gram (g) of water one degree centigrade (c). It takes 79 cal to convert 1 g of ice into 1 g of water at freezing temperature. A much greater quantity of heat, 607 cal, is required to evaporate 1 g of water (change it to water vapor) at freezing temperature. Thus, water vapor must contain more potential energy than water or ice. This energy stored up in water

vapor is called *latent heat.* For the most part it is transformed solar energy which has been used in the process of evaporation.

If energy is consumed in the process of evaporation, then, conversely, energy in the form of heat must be released into the atmosphere when water vapor is condensed into the liquid or solid state to form clouds. This latent heat of condensation furnishes one of the principal ways in which the atmosphere is heated. On a cloudy night when condensation is in progress, the liberated heat acts to retard the normal night cooling. The heat of condensation is likewise a principal source of energy for the growth and development of storms, especially thunderstorms, hurricanes, and other tropical disturbances. Thus it plays an important role in causing precipitation and in determining its distribution.

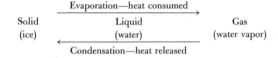

Atmospheric humidity   The amount of water vapor that air can hold depends almost wholly upon air temperature. Air that is warm is able to contain much more water vapor than air that is cold. Moreover, *capacity,* the maximum amount of water vapor that a given volume of air can hold at a given temperature, *increases at an increasing rate* as the temperature rises. This is made clear by the following table and by Fig. 9.1. Thus, if the temperature of 1 cu ft of air is increased by 10°F, from 30 to 40°, the moisture capacity is advanced only 1 grain, while a similar 10° increase from 90 to 100° increases the capacity 5 grains. So it is evident that the warm air of the tropics has a far greater moisture capacity than has the cold air of the subarctic and polar regions. Likewise, warm summer air is able to contain much more water vapor than cold winter air is. These facts have important climatic implications, for they help to explain the meager precipitation of the polar regions compared with the abundant rainfall of equatorial latitudes, as well as the greater precipitation in summer than in winter over the middle-latitude continents.

Distribution of humidity　The water-vapor content of the air (expressed as specific humidity, absolute humidity, or vapor pressure) normally is highest near the earth's surface and decreases rapidly upward. Such a vertical distribution is to be expected since the earth's surface is the source of the atmosphere's humidity and temperatures normally are higher at low elevations. Half the water vapor in the air lies below an altitude of 6,500 ft.

In a north-south direction, or along a meridian, water-vapor content is highest in the low latitudes near the equator and decreases poleward (Fig. 9.2). This also is associated with temperature distribution. As a general rule, winds arriving from tropical latitudes, especially from oceanic sources, contain an abundance of water vapor, and so

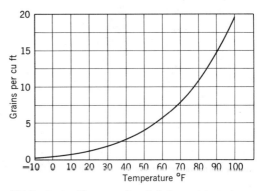

F I G . 9 . 1　The capacity of air to contain water vapor not only increases as the temperature of the air rises, it increases at an increasing rate.

are conducive to large-scale condensation and precipitation. By contrast, air derived from cold polar sources and some continental areas is low in water-vapor content and hence too dry to yield much precipitation.

Relative humidity　*Relative humidity* refers to the amount of water vapor in the air (absolute or specific humidity) compared with the greatest amount that the air could contain at the same temperature (its capacity). Relative humidity is always expressed in the form of a fraction, ratio, or percentage. For example, air at 70° has the capacity of containing 8 grains of water vapor per cu ft. If it

Maximum Water-vapor Capacity of 1 Cu Ft of Air at Varying Temperatures

Temperature, degrees Fahrenheit	Water vapor, grains	Difference between successive 10° intervals, grains
30	1.9	
		1.0
40	2.9	
		1.2
50	4.1	
		1.6
60	5.7	
		2.3
70	8.0	
		2.9
80	10.9	
		3.8
90	14.7	
		5.0
100	19.7	

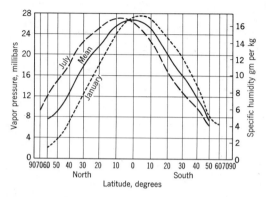

FIG. 9.2 Zonal distribution of the water-vapor content of the air. Specific humidity is highest in the vicinity of the equator and decreases toward the poles. There is a northward displacement in July and a southward displacement in January because of the shift of temperature belts. Specific humidity at each latitude is higher in summer than in winter. *(From Haurwitz and Austin.)*

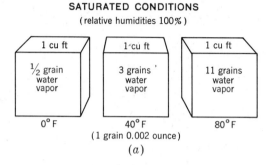

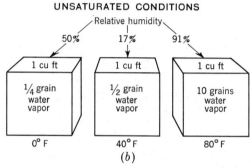

FIG. 9.3 Absolute and relative humidity.

actually does contain 6 grains, then it is only three-fourths saturated, and its relative humidity is 75 per cent. When the relative humidity reaches 100 per cent the air is said to be saturated.

The relative humidity of an air mass can be altered in two ways, (*a*) by a change in the amount of the water vapor in the air, or (*b*) by a change in the temperature of the air and hence its capacity. The following table shows how air which is saturated (relative humidity 100 per cent) at 40° acquires successively lower relative humidities simply by

an increase of its temperature, the water-vapor content remaining unchanged. Various humidity relationships are also illustrated by Fig. 9.3*a* and *b*. Figure 9.3*a* shows the changing capacity for water vapor of a cubic foot of air under three different temperature conditions. Figure 9.3*b* shows the same cubic-foot samples as Fig. 9.3*a*, but with varying relative humidities.

Since relative humidity is an important

Temperature, degrees Fahrenheit	Absolute humidity, grains	Relative humidity, per cent saturated
40	2.9	100
50	2.9	71
60	2.9	51
70	2.9	36
80	2.9	27
90	2.9	20

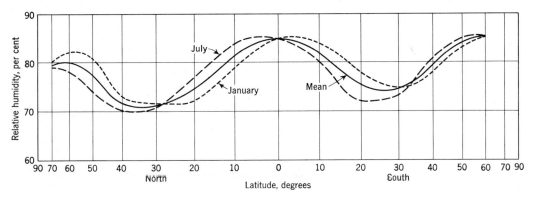

FIG. 9.4 Zonal distribution of relative humidity. Note that the north-south distribution of relative humidity is quite different from that of specific humidity (Fig. 9.2).

determinant of the amount and rate of evaporation, it is critical in determining the rate of moisture and heat loss by plants and animals, including human beings. Consequently it importantly affects the sensible temperature and therefore human comfort. Relative humidity is also closely related to the development of clouds and precipitation. Air that is close to the saturation stage requires only a minimum amount of cooling to bring about condensation and the formation of clouds. On the other hand, air with low relative humidity requires a large amount of cooling in order to form clouds and cause rainfall. In desert regions the relative humidity is usually so low that only rarely is the air cooled enough for rain clouds to form.

Meridional distribution   There is a strong maximum of relative humidity near the equator, from which there is a decline poleward to minima located at about 25° N and S (Fig. 9.4). Subsidence of deep air masses at these latitudes of the subtropical anticyclones is the cause of the reduced relative humidity. Here are located some of the earth's most extensive deserts. Poleward from the subtropics, the relative humidity again increases as the temperature declines, and a second pair of maxima are located in the higher middle latitudes (about 60° N and S). During the daily period of 24 hr, relative humidity of air near the ground is everywhere usually highest in the cool early-morning hours and lowest in the warm midafternoon.

CONDENSATION

Origin   If nonsaturated air is subjected to progressive cooling and its capacity for moisture thereby reduced, a temperature is eventually reached at which the air is saturated with moisture (relative humidity 100 per cent), even though the total amount of

water vapor has remained unchanged. This critical temperature is called the *dew point*. If the air is then cooled below the dew point, the excess water vapor, over and above what the air can contain at this lower temperature, forms as minute globules of water (if the tem-

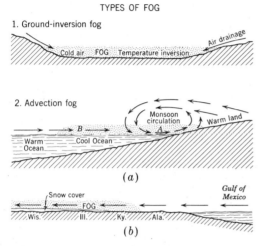

FIG. 9.5 Common types of fog and ways in which they form.

perature is above 32°) and possibly tiny ice crystals (if below 32°). When this has happened, condensation has taken place. As an example, air with a temperature of 80° and containing 8 grains of water vapor per cu ft has a relative humidity of 73 per cent (table, p. 173). If this air is gradually cooled and its capacity for water vapor thus lowered, it eventually reaches its dew point, 70°, the temperature at which it is saturated. Further cooling results in condensation and the release of latent heat, the varying amount of condensation that occurs at the different temperatures reached reflecting the changing water-vapor capacity of the air. It bears repeating that an equivalent cooling of warm air and of cold air does not result in the same amount of condensation (table, p. 173).

Most large-scale condensation, including the formation of all precipitation, is a consequence of the reduction of air temperature below the dew point. When the relative humidity of any mass of air is high, only a slight amount of this cooling is required before the dew point is reached and condensa-

tion begins. Condensation, therefore, depends upon two variables: (a) the amount of cooling, and (b) the relative humidity of the air.

Surface condensation   The temperature of shallow layers of surface air may be lowered below the dew point, resulting in condensation, by direct cooling through conduction and radiation of heat to a cold earth surface or by the mixing of two air masses having unlike temperatures and humidities. Appreciable rainfall probably never results from these cooling processes; rather, such forms of condensation as dew, white frost, and fog are the consequences. In a description of world climates such surface condensation is not of great importance.

Fog   Fog, by far the most climatically important of the several forms of surface condensation, can develop in a variety of ways. One of the commonest types of land fog, known as *radiation* or *ground-inversion* fog, results from the cooling, by radiation and conduction processes, of shallow layers of quiet air overlying a chilled land surface (Fig. 9.5). Clear nights with little wind favor the development of such fog. Also, it is most prevalent and becomes deepest in valleys and depressions where, as a result of air drainage, the colder, heavier air collects. Being characteristic of the cooler night hours, radiation fog is usually short-lived, for it tends to dissipate with sun heating during the day. But in the vicinity of large industrial cities where sulfurous condensation nuclei are numerous, it is likely to be more persistent, as well as denser. Such a combination of smoke, automobile exhaust fumes, and fog is known as *smog*.

Another very common kind of fog is the *advection fog* which develops in moving, rather than quiet, air. Fogs of this kind are formed in mild, humid air as it moves over a colder surface and is chilled by radiation and conduction (Fig. 9.5). They are very common over oceans, especially in summer, along seacoasts and the shores of large inland lakes, and over middle-latitude land surfaces in winter. They are particularly prevalent in the vicinity of cool ocean currents. In the interiors of continents advection fogs are commonly associated with a poleward flow of mild, humid air from low latitudes over a cold and snow-covered surface. In general, advection fogs are less local in development than the simple radiation type, and they tend to persist for longer periods of time. Thus days as well as nights may remain shrouded by them.

Distribution of fog. Generalization about fog distribution is not easy. Yet without much doubt fog is more common over oceans than over continents, and it is more frequent over oceans in middle and higher latitudes than over those in the tropics. On the continents the coastal areas have the greatest number of days with fog. In the United States fog days are most frequent along the Pacific Coast and the North Atlantic seaboard and over the Appalachian Highlands. The least foggy area is the dry interior of the western country.

Condensation in the free atmosphere: clouds and associated precipitation Of incomparably greater climatic importance than surface condensation in the form of dew, white frost, and fog is cloud condensation occurring well above the earth's surface, for all of the earth's precipitation originates in clouds. Clouds of great vertical thickness, capable of yielding moderate or abundant precipitation, are the product of one atmospheric process almost exclusively, viz., cooling as a result of expansion in upward-moving, thick air masses.

When air rises, no matter what the cause, it expands because there is less weight of air upon it at the higher altitudes. For example, if a mass of dry air at sea level rises to an altitude of about 18,000 ft, the pressure upon it is reduced by one-half, and consequently its volume is doubled. Thus 1 cu ft of sea-level air would occupy 2 cu ft if carried to that altitude. To make room for itself as it ascends and gradually expands, this air has to displace other air. The work of displacing the surrounding air requires energy, and this necessary energy is taken out of the rising air mass in the form of heat, resulting in a lowering of its temperature. Conversely, when air descends from higher altitudes, it is compressed by the denser air at lower levels. Work is done upon it, and its temperature consequently is raised. It is obvious, therefore, that rising air cools, while descending air is warmed. This is spoken of as *adiabatic temperature change.*

The rate of cooling resulting from the ascent of dry or nonsaturated air—the *dry adiabatic rate*—is constant and is approximately 5.5° per 1,000-ft change in altitude. This rate of cooling of ascending air is considerably greater than the normal rate of temperature decrease with increasing elevation (about 3.6° per 1,000 ft) called the *lapse rate.* These two rates, the adiabatic rate and the lapse rate, should be clearly distinguished as being very different things, for one represents the cooling of a rising and therefore moving mass of air, while the other represents the change in air temperature that would be recorded by a thermometer carried up through the atmosphere by a balloon or airplane.

It bears repeating that this process of cooling, by expansion within rising air currents, is the only one capable of reducing the temperature of thick and extensive masses of air below the dew point. It is the only process, therefore, which is capable of producing condensation on such a large scale that abundant precipitation results. There is no doubt that nearly all the earth's precipitation is the result of expansion and cooling in rising air currents. The direct result of cooling due to ascent is clouds.

Conditions affecting the buoyancy of air Since nearly all of the earth's precipitation originates in thick clouds that are a consequence of cooling in ascending air, the conditions which promote or hinder such upward movement are of prime importance.

Stability As previously suggested, when air resists vertical movement and tends to remain in its original position it is said to be *stable*. Normally an air mass is most stable when dry and colder air underlies warmer air. The denser air below the lighter air makes upward movement difficult. Thus, in highly stable air abundant precipitation is less likely to occur. However, even stable, nonbuoyant air may be forced to rise, cool, and produce cloud and rainfall, as when an air stream is obstructed by mountains or hills or when two air streams converge and come into conflict.

Atmospheric stability is promoted in at least two ways. If an air mass is chilled at its base through loss of heat by radiation and conduction to a cold underlying surface, the density of the lower air is increased, and so the stability is also increased (Fig. 9.6). A surface temperature inversion, therefore, is an instance of stability. Another way a mass of air can develop stability is by subsiding and spreading laterally (horizontal divergence). This process of stabilization occurs in high-pressure anticyclonic systems.

Instability When air does not resist upward vertical displacement but, on the contrary, has a tendency to move upward from its original position, a condition of *instability* prevails. In such buoyant air upward vertical movement is made easy, and clouds and precipitation are likely. Instability is characteristic of warm, humid air in which there is a rapid vertical decrease in temperature, i.e., a steep lapse rate, and humidity.

Instability is developed in an air mass when it is warmed and humidified in its lower layers by moving over a warm earth's surface

FIG. 9.6 Atmospheric stability and instability. When the lapse rate exceeds the abiabatic rate, instability prevails. When the reverse is true, the air is stable.

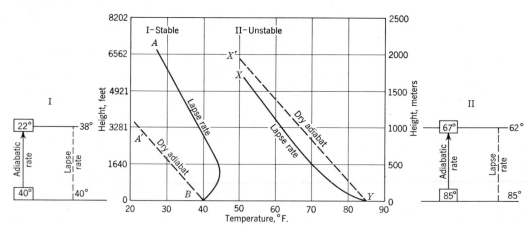

(Fig. 9.6). Instability is likewise promoted in a thick air mass when it is forced to rise. Hence the air in any converging-wind system, such as a cyclonic storm, is likely to become unstable. Or again, when humid air that is originally mildly stable is forced to rise over mountain barriers or over colder wedges of air, the resulting condensation may add so much heat to the ascending air that it becomes buoyant and unstable. Then it continues to rise with accompanying heavy precipitation. Precipitation occurring in unstable, buoyant air is likely to be heavy and showery in character, and usually is associated with thick cumulus clouds (Fig. 9.7). Unstable air will continue to rise until it reaches air layers having temperature and density similar to its own.

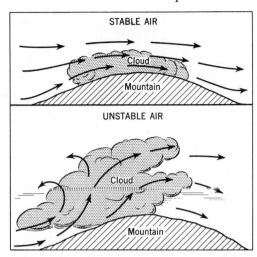

FIG. 9.7 Cloud formation in the forced ascent of air which is stable in one case and unstable in the other. In stable air, which is nonbuoyant, the clouds are not so thick in a vertical dimension, and the resulting precipitation will probably be lighter.

PRECIPITATION

FORMS

Although all precipitation originates in clouds, by no means do all clouds yield precipitation. This is because the condensed water or ice particles which form clouds are too small to fall to the earth's surface. To produce precipitation the myriad of tiny cloud droplets must be forced to combine to form drops of sufficient size and weight to reach the surface.

Rain, which is much the commonest and most widespread form of precipitation, results from cloud condensation in ascending air at temperatures either above or below freezing (Fig. 9.8). Some of the earth's rain certainly originates as ice and snow particles formed at temperatures below 32°, which subsequently melt as they fall through the warmer atmosphere closer to the earth's surface.

The most common form of solid precipitation is snow. Its fundamental form is the intricately branched, flat, six-sided crystal which occurs in an almost infinite variety of patterns. Numbers of these crystals matted together comprise a snowflake. Snow must develop from condensation taking place at temperatures below freezing, and on the average it takes about 1 ft of snow to yield as much water as 1 in. of rain.

Data on the amount and distribution of snowfall are very scant for much of the earth. Snow occasionally falls near sea level in subtropical latitudes, but it does not remain on the ground; farther equatorward it is not recorded at low elevations. A winter snow cover durable enough to last for a month or more does exist at low elevations in the interior and eastern parts of Eurasia and North America poleward from about 40°.

ALTITUDE IN FEET

35,000

CIRRUS
Entirely of Ice Particles

30,000

CIRROCUMULUS
"Mackerel Sky"
Ice Particles

CIRROSTRATUS
Ice Particles Form Halos Around
Sun and Moon, Which Usually Foretell Rain
or Snow Within 24 Hours

25,000

Anvil Head

20,000

ALTOCUMULUS
"Wool-Pack" Clouds, Bumpy

CUMULONIMBUS
Violent Vertical Currents

15,000

ALTOSTRATUS
High, Gray Sheet Clouds
Often Followed by Rain or Snow; Windy

10,000

STRATOCUMULUS
Rough, Bumpy

NIMBOSTRATUS
Storm Clouds

5,000

RAIN   SNOW

CUMULUS
Fair Weather Clouds

RAIN, HAIL AND
SQUALL WINDS

STRATUS
High Fog, "Low Ceiling"

FIG. 9.8 Very generalized representation of the forms and elevations of the principal cloud types.

In low and middle latitudes a *permanent* snow cover is characteristic only of elevated areas, with the height of the snow line, or limit of perpetual snow, declining poleward. Thus in the deep tropics permanent snow is usually found only at elevations over 15,000 ft, but at 60°N in Norway snow remains on the ground throughout the year at an elevation of about 3,500 ft.

Sleet and hail are other forms of solid precipitation. They occur only very occasionally and are restricted in their distribution; thus their total climatic significance is minor. Sleet is frozen raindrops. Hail, which falls almost exclusively in the violent thunderstorms to be described in the next chapter, is ice lumps which are larger than sleet.

PRECIPITATION CLASSIFIED BY CAUSES OF AIR ASCENT

Since almost all precipitation originates in ascending air which is cooled by expansion, it is essential, for an understanding of precipitation distribution over the earth, to be familiar with the causes for the ascent of thick and often extensive masses of air. Therefore three principal kinds of atmospheric lifting and their associated precipitation will be noted. But it should be emphasized that none of these three ordinarily exists in pure form: most precipitation is a consequence of the combined effects of more than one type of atmospheric lifting.

Orographic precipitation Even a hasty observation of a precipitation map of the earth shows that many areas of above-average precipitation are coincident with highlands (Plate 1). This is at least partly the result of the forced ascent of air currents whose course is obstructed by hills or mountains. In addi-

tion, convectional updrafts caused by strong solar heating along some mountain slopes increase precipitation in highlands. Since water vapor is largely concentrated in the lower layers of the atmosphere, even the modest upthrust of air masses caused by a highland of moderate elevation may be sufficient to induce important rainfall effects. Rainfall produced this way is called *orographic precipitation*. Noteworthily, it is concentrated on the windward side of a highland where the lifting effect on the approaching winds is concentrated; the lee side where the air is descending and warming is much drier (Fig. 9.9).

Convectional precipitation *Convectional precipiation* is associated with strong vertical updrafts of air and with the towering cumulonimbus thunderstorm clouds which the updrafts produce. Such rapidly ascending air currents are likely to develop when humid air containing much latent heat is subjected to strong surface heating. Such a condition often prevails on a hot summer afternoon when the earth's surface has become unusually warm through solar heating. The heated surface air expands, becomes less dense, and, like an inflated toy balloon, is inclined to move upward.

Strongly heated surface air creates a general environment favoring such convectional overturning of the atmosphere, so it is not surprising that this type of precipitation is most

FIG. 9.9 Precipitation conditions on windward and leeward slopes of highlands.

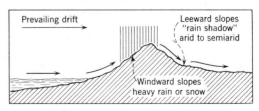

common in tropical latitudes, and that there, as well as in the middle latitudes, it is concentrated in the warmer months of the year and the warmer hours of the day. Yet it has been observed that much convectional rainfall does not have the distribution which would be expected if widespread surface heating were the single cause. Instead, the convectional activity is organized in character and appears to develop only in certain areas. One favored area is the vicinity of highlands, where orographic effects supplement those of surface heating. More common is the moving area of organized convectional activity associated with an extensive atmospheric disturbance in which a general horizontal convergence of air streams lifts the air and increases its instability.

Convectional overturning has a cellular pattern of local ascending and descending air currents which are small in horizontal dimensions. Consequently the cumulonimbus clouds marking the tops of the ascending warm currents, while very thick in a vertical direction, are not areally extensive, and are frequently isolated and distinct, with patches of clear sky between. Therefore convectional rainfall is usually in the form of locally heavy showers which do not last long. Long-con-

tinued, steady rains falling from a uniformly gray overcast are not characteristic.

Horizontal convergence in extensive atmospheric disturbances   In any zone or area of horizontal wind convergence an upward movement of air must occur, with consequent cooling. In the heart of the tropics, where the converging air streams usually are similar in temperature and density, the upward movement of air is commonly in the form of vertical convective currents which result in showery rainfall. But outside the tropics horizontal wind convergence usually produces a conflict between air masses of contrasting temperature and density, with the cooler, denser air providing an obstacle over which the warmer, lighter air is forced to ascend (Fig. 9.10). The boundary between such unlike air masses is called a *front.*

Some of the most commonly occurring convergence areas of the earth are those associated with the great variety of extensive, moving atmospheric disturbances, one such disturbance being the cyclonic storm of middle latitudes. In parts of the earth atmospheric disturbances are so numerous that for a month or a year their paths can appear on mean-pressure and mean-wind charts as average lines of horizontal wind convergence.

FIG. 9.10   The origin of precipitation along a front. Here the warmer and less dense air cools because of expansion as it ascends over a wedge of cooler, denser air.

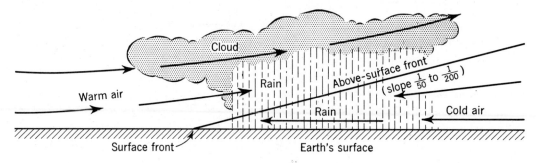

The zone of convergence between the trades (ITC) and the zones of convergence in the North Atlantic and North Pacific lows in winter may be partly of such origin.

Since in middle-latitude cyclones and along their fronts the air commonly rises obliquely over mildly inclined surfaces of colder air, the cooling of the rising air is less rapid than in vertical convectional currents. As a result, precipitation in cyclones is characteristically less showery and heavy than convectional rainfall, and is inclined to be steadier and longer-continued. The dull, gray, overcast skies and prolonged precipitation which result in some of the most unpleasant weather in the cooler months in middle latitudes are usually associated with cyclonic storms; and most of the long-lasting, mild winter precipitation of lowlands in the middle latitudes is cyclonic or frontal in origin. But by no means is all the precipitation in a convergent system of the mild and prolonged kind, for not infrequently there is enough initial upthrust of air along a front to make it so unstable that intermittent showery rain may result.

IMPORTANT CHARACTERISTICS OF PRECIPITATION

Even an incomplete description of the precipitation of a region requires taking note of at least three features: (*a*) the annual amount of precipitation, (*b*) the seasonal distribution of the annual total, and (*c*) its dependability, or conversely, its variability.

Amount   It is estimated that if the total annual rainfall were spread evenly over the earth's surface, it would form a layer about 39 in. deep. Actually precipitation is distributed very unevenly, for there are extensive areas that receive less than 5 in. and there are a few spots that receive over 400 in. (Plate 1).

Seasonal distribution   The seasonal distribution of precipitation is as important as amount. The fact that Omaha, Nebraska, receives 30 in. of rainfall annually is no more significant than the fact that 17 in. (58 per cent of the annual total) falls during the warm months from May to August and only 3 in. (11 per cent) falls during the cold period from November to February. Seasonal distribution of precipitation is of greatest importance in the middle latitudes where the winter is a dormant season for plant growth imposed by low temperatures. In the tropics where frost is practically unknown except at higher elevations, rainfall is effective for plant growth no matter what time of year it falls. In the middle latitudes, however, only the part of the annual precipitation which falls during the frost-free season is effective, so that in severe climates it is desirable to have a strong concentration of rainfall in the warmer months when plants can use it.

Variability   Data on the dependability or reliability of the annual or seasonal precipitation express its variability as well, and are scarcely less important than those concerned with amount and seasonal distribution (Fig. 12.1).

Variability of precipitation may be defined as the deviation from the mean computed from 35 years or more of observations. In humid climates the annual variability is usually not greater than 50 per cent on either side of the mean; i.e. the driest year can be expected to have about 50 per cent of the normal value, the wettest year 150 per cent. In dry climates these values vary between about 30 and 250 per cent. Thus it is a general rule that variability increases as the amount of rainfall decreases. Variability of

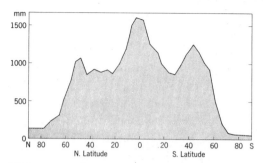

FIG. 9.11   Zonal distribution of precipitation. The amount for any latitude represents the average for all longitudes. *(From Brooks and Hunt.)*

precipitation must be taken into consideration when agricultural plans are made, for it must be expected that there will be many years when the precipitation is less than the average. In semiarid and subhumid climates where crop raising normally depends on a small margin of safety from failure, rainfall variability is of utmost concern. Moreover, the agriculturist in such regions must bear in mind that negative deviations from the mean are more frequent than positive ones; that is, a greater number of dry years are compensated for by a few excessively wet ones. In dry climates and other climates as well, variability of seasonal and monthly rainfall amounts is even greater than that for annual values.

DISTRIBUTION OF PRECIPITATION

Average annual precipitation amounts A glance at Plate 1 makes it obvious that the distribution of annual precipitation is very complicated. No simple explanation for this will suffice, but fundamentally two things are involved. They are (1) the nature of the air itself, especially its varying humidity and stability, and (2) the distribution over the earth of influences on vertical movement of the air, which include (*a*) the principal zones of horizontal convergence and divergence, (*b*) atmospheric disturbances, (*c*) thermally induced convectional overturning, and (*d*) highland barriers. The nature of the air as regards its moisture content is chiefly determined by its place of origin: maritime or continental, as well as tropical or high-latitude. Some of the controls, for example the zones of horizontal convergence and divergence, are relatively zonal (having an east-west alignment) in their influence. Others, like the distribution of land and water and of highlands, operate to modify zonal controls.

Zonal features of annual rainfall distribution Some of the most fundamental facts about world rainfall distribution may be presented in the form of a meridional profile of the precipitation means for the different parallels. Such a profile is shown in Fig. 9.11. It suggests the existence of a strong primary maximum of rainfall amounts in the vicinity of the ITC. Belts of lower rainfall are characteristic of subtropical latitudes, where anticyclonic diverging-wind systems and vertical subsidence are relatively strong. Poleward from the subtropics rainfall increases again so that secondary, or lower, maxima are indicated for latitudes 40°–50° N and S. These are the middle-latitude convergences with their numerous cyclonic storms. Poleward from about 50°–55° precipitation declines sharply; minima of 10 in. and less characterize the very high latitudes where low temperatures, low moisture content, and subsidence are characteristic (Fig. 9.12).

Nonzonal features of annual rainfall distribution An analysis of Plate 1 and of Fig. 9.13, which attempts to generalize the features of precipitation on a hypothetical continent, reveals that precipitation amounts

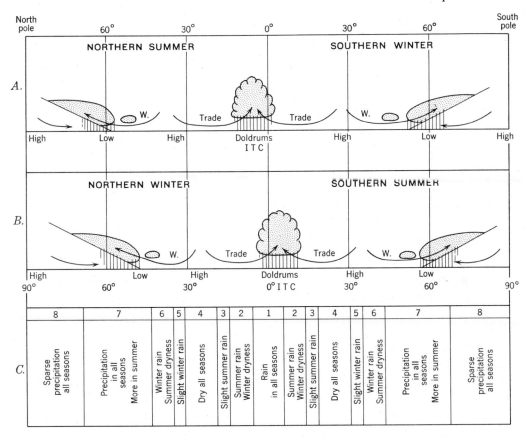

FIG. 9.12   Schematic cross section through the atmosphere along a meridian, showing the main zones of horizontal convergence and ascent, and of divergence and subsidence, together with associated precipitation characteristics: (a) during the Northern Hemisphere summer; (b) during the Northern Hemisphere winter; (c) zones of precipitation. It must be emphasized that many nonzonal features of precipitation distribution cannot be adequately represented on this type of diagram. *(From Sverre Petterssen, Introduction to Meteorology, 2d ed., McGraw-Hill Book Company, Inc., New York, 1958.)*

vary not only in a latitudinal direction, or zonally, but also longitudinally. Thus the typical areas with below-average precipitation (arid, semiarid, and subhumid) are asymmetrically developed in the tropics and subtropics, for such areas are concentrated in the western and central parts of the large land masses. These are the regions of strong horizontal wind divergence and vertical subsidence associated with the stable eastern end of the subtropical anticyclones. Cool ocean currents along the tropical and subtropical west coasts serve to intensify the aridity.

In the middle latitudes the dry and subhumid low-rainfall areas are located toward

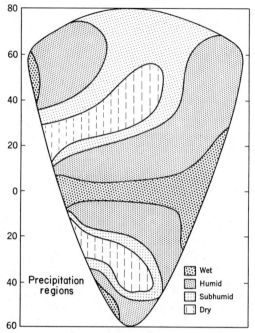

FIG. 9.13 The distribution, on a hypothetical continent, of the four great moisture regions, based largely upon annual amounts of precipitation. *(From Thornthwaite.)*

the centers of the continents, which are farthest removed from the oceanic sources of moisture supply.

Abundant rainfall conditions extend across the entire breadth of the continents in the low latitudes close to the equator, with somewhat heavier precipitation characterizing the eastern and western oceanic margins. This equatorial zone of abundant rainfall is less wide in the western part of a continent, where the subtropical anticyclone is strong, than in the east, where the anticyclone is weaker, the coastal waters are warmer, and the tropical easterly winds are onshore. In the large middle-latitude continents humid conditions are to be found both to the east and the west of the drier continental interiors.

Variations in seasonal distribution Total precipitation in oceanic areas is not only greater than over the lands but is also less seasonal in concentration. Land masses, with their tendency to strong summer heating, associated thermal convection, and onshore summer winds, are likely to have more of their annual precipitation concentrated in summer. Over large land masses in middle and higher latitudes the cold-season anticyclone with its diverging winds also makes for dry winters.

In the vicinity of the equator where the ITC prevails at all seasons, rainfall not only is abundant but also falls throughout the year; i.e., there is no dry season (Figs. 9.12, 9.14, 9.15). Farther away from the equator, from about 5°–10° out to 15°–20°, rainfall becomes more seasonal as it decreases in amount, with a marked dry period in the low-sun season, or winter. The high-sun period, or summer, is wet (Figs. 9.12, 9.15). This sequence of high-sun rainfall and low-sun drought is associated with the latitudinal shifting of the zones of convergence and divergence following the sun (Figs. 9.12, 9.15). These latitudes are affected by the ITC at the time of high sun, but feel the effects of the subtropical anticyclone and divergence at the time of low sun. This area of winter drought does not extend to the east side of the continent where the subtropical anticyclone is weaker.

In the subtropical, or lower middle, latitudes at about 30°–40° are areas, restricted to the western side of the continents and usually of limited extent, where summer is the season of precipitation deficiency and winter is wet (Fig. 9.15). Here, because of latitudinal migration of pressure and wind systems following the sun, the stable eastern limb of a subtropical anticyclone controls the weather in summer, and cyclones associated with the middle-latitude convergence zone prevail in winter (Figs. 9.12, 9.15).

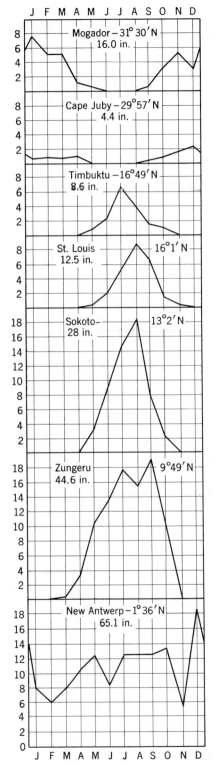

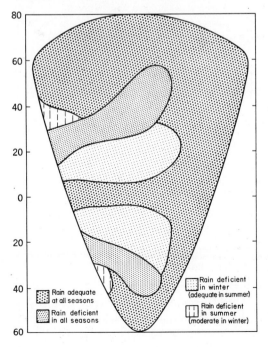

FIG. 9.14 The change in the features of the annual rainfall profiles in tropical latitudes, from the equator to about 30°N, in Africa. The stations are arranged according to latitude, with Nouvelle-Anvers (New Antwerp) closest to the equator.

In the middle latitudes poleward from about 40° there is usually no dry season, some precipitation falling at all times of the year (Fig. 9.15). Yet this is not to say that all seasons have equal amounts. It is in the interiors of the great continents that the seasonal precipitation maximum and minimum are most emphatic and most consistent. Here summer, with its warmer air of higher moisture content, is usually the wettest season. As explained earlier, the drier winter is related to the lower temperatures and the anticyclonic wind system of that season.

FIG. 9.15 Seasonal rainfall distribution on a hypothetical continent. *(From Thornthwaite.)*

CHAPTER 10

Atmospheric disturbances; air masses and fronts

INTRODUCTION

The climate in a locality or region is a generalization of the day-to-day weather prevailing there. And the weather of an area is closely identified with the air masses which prevail there and with the atmospheric disturbances, known commonly as storms, which develop there.

Those areas which experience almost exclusively one type of air mass are likely to

have relatively uniform weather. Such areas are the central Sahara in summer and the upper Amazon River Basin at all times of the year. But much of the earth's surface is affected by more than one air mass, and this causes changeable weather. In some parts of the earth the change from control by one air mass to control by another is largely seasonal in effect, while in others, especially the middle latitudes, rapidly shifting air masses with striking temperature and humidity contrasts may produce highly changeable weather even within a short period of a few days.

The zone of contact between unlike air masses, where air streams of contrasting temperature and humidity converge, is called a front, as stated earlier. These frontal zones of converging air are the breeding area for atmospheric disturbances of various kinds.

Consequently it is along air-mass boundaries, or fronts, that weather changes are concentrated and much of the earth's precipitation is developed.

Thus some understanding of air masses, fronts, and atmospheric disturbances and the relationship between them is essential to an appreciation of the world pattern of climates the discussion of which follows this chapter.

AIR MASSES AND FRONTS

ORIGIN, DEVELOPMENT, AND MOVEMENT

An air mass is defined as an extensive body of air whose temperature and humidity characteristics are relatively uniform in horizontal directions. An air mass develops whenever the atmosphere remains in contact with an extensive and relatively uniform area of the earth's surface for a sufficiently long period for the properties of the air to become similar to those of the surface. These areas where air masses develop are called *source regions.*

The earth's principal source regions occur where the surface is relatively uniform and where, in addition, the wind system is a divergent one. In regions of convergence unlike temperatures are brought close together, so that thermal contrasts are great. Anticyclonic circulations, therefore, provide the most ideal source-region conditions. The snow-covered arctic plains of Canada and Siberia in winter, large areas of tropical ocean, and the hot, arid Sahara in summer are good examples of source regions.

As a rule air masses do not remain in their source regions but sooner or later move out to invade other areas whose weather they in turn affect. Moreover, the moving air itself is affected by its new surface environment, so that it slowly changes in character.

When air streams of unlike temperature converge, as they do in low-pressure centers, fronts are usually present. In the tropics, however, where air temperatures are relatively uniform, genuine density fronts are infrequent even in the presence of wind convergence.

When air masses having different temperature and humidity characteristics come together, they do not mix freely with each other. They tend, rather, to maintain a fairly distinct sloping boundary surface between them, the warmer and therefore less dense air mass being forced aloft over the wedge of colder air (Fig. 10.1). This sloping surface is called either a front or a *surface of discontinu-*

FIG. 10.1 Three-dimensional representation of an atmospheric front.

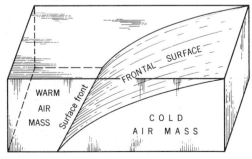

ity. Where a surface of discontinuity, or front, in the free atmosphere intersects the earth's surface, a *surface front* is formed.

Surface fronts are not lines but rather zones varying from 3 to 50 miles in breadth, which usually bring observably marked changes in temperature and humidity as they pass. Indeed, the location of fronts and the nature of the contrasting air masses on either side of them are of great importance in weather forecasting, for along fronts a great many storms and associated weather changes originate.

It is unusual for a front to remain very long in a stationary position. Usually one of the unlike air masses it separates is more active than the other and advances into the latter's domain. As a consequence the position of the front is shifted. When the warmer air mass is more aggressive and advances against the cold air, there is an active upward movement of the lighter warmer air over the wedge of colder denser air (Fig. 10.2). This is a *warm front*. When the colder air is the aggressor, it underruns the warmer air and forces it upward. This is a *cold front.* How the two differ in their effects on weather will be considered in later discussion of middle-latitude cyclones.

CLASSIFICATION OF AIR MASSES

Any classification of air masses must be based primarily upon the characteristics of their source regions. For this reason air masses are designated by the name or abbreviated name of the source region. The source regions fall naturally into two great groups: those of high latitudes, or polar regions (*P*), and those of low latitudes, or tropical regions (*T*). It is largely in the high and the low latitudes that there are large areas of relatively homogeneous surface conditions and relatively light air movement.

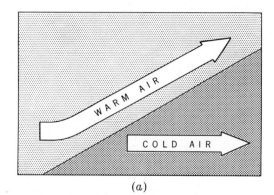

(a)

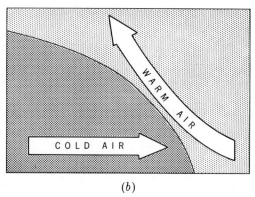

(b)

FIG. 10.2   (a) A warm front; (b) a cold front. *(U.S. Weather Bureau.)*

The middle latitudes are the scene of intense interaction between the polar and tropical air masses and generally lack the uniform conditions essential to a source region (Figs. 10.3, 10.4).

The air-mass classification may be further refined by dividing both the polar (*P*) and the tropical (*T*) groups into continental (*c*) and maritime (*m*) subgroups. This results in four main types of air masses: polar continental (*cP*), polar maritime (*mP*), tropical continental (*cT*), and tropical maritime (*mT*). The types correspond generally to moisture and temperature differences. Thus polar air masses are characteristically colder than tropical air masses, while maritime air is usually more humid than continental air.

All of these four main air-mass types may

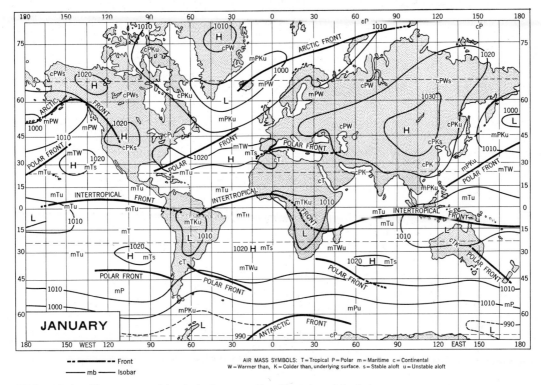

FIG. 10.3   Air masses and fronts in January. *(From Haurwitz and Austin.)*

FIG. 10.4   Air masses and fronts in July. *(From Haurwitz and Austin.)*

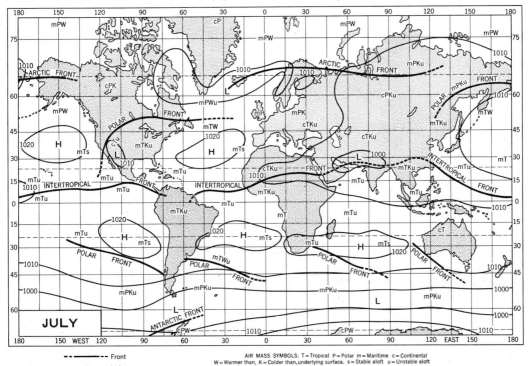

be modified in important respects as they move away from their source regions and travel over parts of the earth's surface which are unlike their source regions (Figs. 10.3, 10.4). The air mass will become actually or potentially more buoyant and unstable, and so inclined to rise and produce rain, (*a*) when it is warmed at the base by passing over a warm land or water surface (Figs. 10.3, 10.4, symbol k), (*b*) when it is humidified from below while passing over a water surface as a consequence of large-scale evaporation from the water, or (*c*) when it is forced to rise as a result of wind convergence, as in a cyclonic system (symbol u). Nonbuoyancy and stability, on the other hand, result when the air mass is (*a*) cooled from below as it travels over a cooler surface (symbol w) or (*b*) when it subsides or sinks as a consequence of wind divergence (symbol s), as in an anticyclone. These principles of air-mass

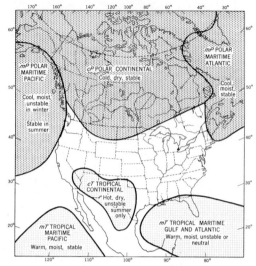

FIG. 10.5   North American air masses and their source regions.

modification will be used later in describing world climates and their temperature and precipitation characteristics (Fig. 10.5).

ATMOSPHERIC DISTURBANCES

FUNCTION AS MODIFIERS OF TEMPERATURE AND GENERATORS OF PRECIPITATION

An atmospheric disturbance may be thought of as an extensive wave, eddy, or whirl of air existing within any of the earth's great wind systems. As observed on a daily weather map of the earth through their isobar and wind patterns, these disturbances are characteristically so numerous and widespread that they tend to obscure the lineaments of the general atmospheric circulation. The circulation is somewhat analogous to a river so full of minor whirls and eddies that it is difficult to distinguish the main current.

Atmospheric disturbances are of great im-

portance to weather and climate because many of them are accompanied by cloud and precipitation. In fact atmospheric disturbances cause a great deal of the earth's precipitation and have important temperature effects as well. They travel in the general direction of the wind system in which they exist, so that in some latitudes they move from west to east and others from east to west.

TRAVELING CYCLONES AND ANTICYCLONES OF MIDDLE LATITUDES

Of principal importance in producing the frequent, erratic, day-to-day weather changes characteristic of middle and high latitudes are the moving cyclones and anticyclones which fill the westerly wind belts. In these parts of the world the fickleness of the weather is proverbial, so it is not surprising that weather-forecasting services are most necessary and, indeed, best developed here.

No two disturbances are exactly alike, and storms differ from region to region, so that the generalizations concerning cyclones and anticyclones which follow must not be expected to fit any particular storm in all respects.

Nature and size   Cyclones, the low-pressure disturbances commonly called lows or depressions, and anticyclones (highs) are chiefly characteristic of the regions of air-mass conflict within the belts of westerly winds, and consequently are best known in latitudes 30°–70°.

These disturbances are represented on surface weather maps by series of closed concentric isobars, roughly circular or oval in shape (Figs. 10.6, 10.7). In the cyclone the lowest pressure is at the center, and pressure increases toward the margins; in the anti-

FIG. 10.6   A model cyclone (Northern Hemisphere) showing arrangement of isobars, wind system, warm and cold air masses, and surface fronts.

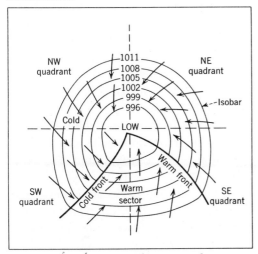

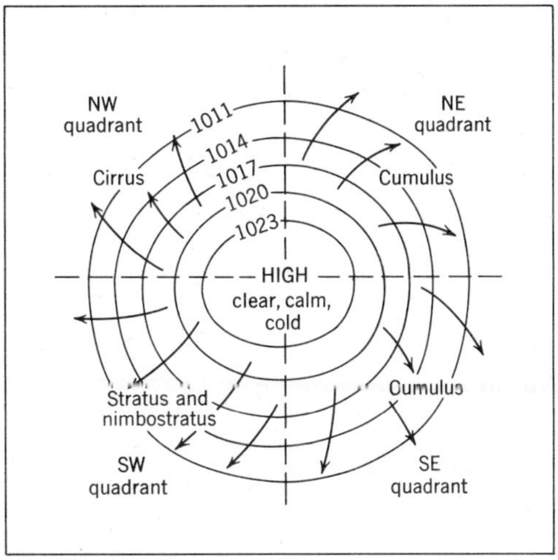

cyclone the pressure is highest at the center and decreases outward. No definite difference in pressure distinguishes lows from highs; pressure difference between them is entirely a relative thing.

Normally there is a pressure difference of 10 to 20 mb, or several tenths of an inch, between the center and the circumference of a low. In highs the pressure difference between center and margins is likewise variable, but commonly it is somewhat less than in lows. It is a general rule that both cyclones and anticyclones are less well developed, have smaller internal differences in pressure and weaker pressure gradients, and travel more slowly in summer than in winter.

There are great variations in the size of these storms, but on the whole they spread over huge areas, sometimes as large as one-third of the United States, or 1 million square miles, although most of them are smaller. Diameters of 500 to 1,000 miles are common. Such storms are extensive rather than intensive.

Direction and rate of movement   Cyclones and anticyclones in middle latitudes

FIG. 10.7   A model anticyclone (Northern Hemisphere).

wind eastward
maximum movement of air - warm front

are carried along in a general west-to-east direction by the system of westerly winds in which they exist. That is not to say, however, that storms always move due eastward. To be sure, they follow different routes, just as they vary in concentration from region to region. But in spite of these vagaries in direction the general eastward progress is maintained. It is easy to understand, therefore, why a weather forecaster in the middle latitudes bases his prediction upon weather conditions to the west, rather than on those to the east, of his station. The storms to the east already have passed; those to the west are approaching.

Cyclones and anticyclones vary in rate of movement both with the season and with individual storms; in general the highs are somewhat slower than the lows. In the United States cyclones move eastward across the country at velocities averaging 20 miles an hour in summer and 30 miles an hour in winter; in winter a well-developed low characteristically requires 3 to 5 days for the transcontinental journey across the United States. In summer, when the whole atmospheric circulation is slowed down and storm speeds are reduced, the contrasts between cyclones and anticyclones are less pronounced. As a consequence, warm-season weather is less changeable, and atmospheric disturbances are less vigorous.

Just as temperature, pressure, and wind belts shift poleward in summer and equatorward in winter, following the seasonal movements of the sun's rays, so also do the storm tracks. This helps to explain why there are fewer and weaker storms over the lower middle latitudes in summer than in winter.

Origin   It is very likely that middle-latitude cyclones have more than one type of origin. Many such storms appear to have

their beginnings as wavelike disturbances along air-mass fronts, i.e., where winds of contrasting temperature and density converge. Consequently, regions of strong horizontal temperature contrasts and of air-mass convergence favor cyclonic development. Also most, if not all, fully developed middle-latitude cyclones appear to extend upward from the surface and make connection with an upper-level trough in the high westerlies and the jet stream they include. This seems to suggest that cyclone origin is associated with disturbances on the jet stream, although the precise nature of the connection is not clear, as indicated in the earlier discussion of the jet stream. As stated then, it is certain that cyclones strengthen underneath the jet, and their courses appear to be steered by it.

There appear to be at least two quite different types of anticyclones. The rapidly moving cold anticyclone is essentially a mass of cold polar air (cP) which originates over a cold surface in higher latitudes. This anticyclone is the product of heat transfer by conduction and radiation processes from the air to the cold surface. Understandably such anticyclones are chiefly a phenomenon of the middle and higher latitudes and are most common and intense over continents in the winter season. The slowly moving warm anticyclone is especially characteristic of the subtropics and poleward margins of the tropics, and of the lower middle latitudes in summer (cT and mT). Its origin is not well understood.

Structure of a model cyclone   A cyclonic storm frequently begins as a wave or indentation along a surface front (Fig. 10b). As the frontal wave deepens the storm grows in size and intensity, and extensive cloud and precipitation areas develop. The six stages shown in Fig. 10.8 illustrate the life history

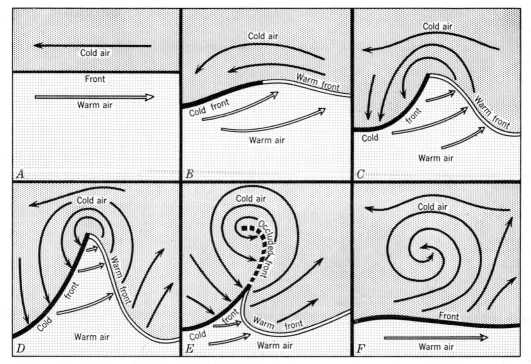

FIG. 10.8 Six stages in the life cycle of a frontal-wave cyclone: (b) shows the beginning of a small horizontal wave along the front. In (c) the wave development has progressed to the point where there is a definite cyclonic circulation with well-developed warm and cold fronts. (d) shows a narrowed warm sector as the more rapidly advancing cold front approaches the retreating warm front. In (e) the occlusion process is occurring, the cyclone has reached its maximum development, and the warm sector is being rapidly pinched off. In (f) the warm sector has been eliminated; the cyclone is in its dying stages, and is represented by only a whirl of cold air. *(U.S. Weather Bureau.)*

of a cyclone. A prime feature of such a disturbance is the fact that wind, temperature, cloud, and precipitation are not the same throughout it.

Normally a cyclone is made up of two contrasting air masses. To the south and southeast there is a poleward tongue of warm, humid, southerly air which originated in lower latitudes (Fig. 10.9). Enveloping this warm tongue of tropical air on its western, northern, and eastern sides are colder, drier, polar air masses. The zone of conflict between the tropical and polar air is

the front. Along most parts of this front the less dense tropical air is ascending over a mildly inclined wedge of polar air. This lifting of the warm air is the cause of many of the clouds and much of the precipitation in the storm. That part of the extended front lying *ahead,* or east, of the advancing tongue of warm air is the warm front, while that to the rear, or west, of the warm air is the cold front. In the later stages of the cyclone the cold front overtakes the warm front, resulting in a narrowing, and eventually a pinching out, of the tongue of warm air at the sur-

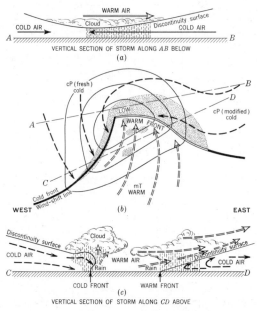

FIG. 10.9   Structure of a model cyclone:
ground plan (b) and vertical sections (a and c) of a
fully developed wave cyclone in the middle
latitudes of the Northern Hemisphere.

face. The cyclone then becomes a whirl of
cold air and the storm is said to be *occluded*
(Fig. 10.8).

Wind systems   Unlike the violent and
destructive winds of tornadoes and hurricanes, the winds in middle-latitude cyclones
and anticyclones are usually only moderate
in speed. Of much greater importance than
the speed, anyway, is the horizontal direction and vertical nature of the air movement.

Wind system of the cyclone   As previously
stated, the cyclone is a converging system of
surface winds with the lowest pressure at the
center, in which, because of the deflective
force of earth rotation, the winds cross the
isobars at an oblique angle, forming an in-
ward spiral which in the Northern Hemisphere has a counterclockwise rotation. (Figs.
10.6, 10.10).

To the converging movement of air much

of the weather in a cyclone can be attributed.
It is convergence, as previously indicated, that
leaves the air in the cyclone only one way
to escape, through upward movement, and
makes the storm a region of *ascending* air,
with all of the favorable implications this
has for the development of clouds and
precipitation.

The nature of the ascent itself is of great importance because throughout much of the cyclone the upward movement of air is not the
rapid vertical ascent that occurs in a thunderstorm. The ascent is rather a slower gliding of
warmer air up over a mildly inclined wedge
of colder, denser air. Thus the resulting
clouds are not likely to be the towering
cumulus type; instead extensive sheets of
flattish cloud forming a uniformly gray overcast are the rule.

*Changes in wind direction with the passage
of a cyclone*   Because the cyclone's wind
system is a converging one, the winds to the
east, or front, of the storm's center must be
easterly, while to the rear, or west, of the
center the airflow must be from the west.
Easterly winds in middle latitudes, therefore,
often foretell the approach from the west of a
cyclonic storm with its accompanying cloud
and rain; westerly winds, by contrast, indicate the retreat of the storm center and the
coming of clearing weather.

If the cyclone center passes to the north of
a weather station, placing the observer in the
southern parts of the storm, the wind shift
from easterlies on the front to westerlies on
the rear will be accompanied by a southerly
flow of air (Fig. 10.11). Under these conditions weather will be relatively warm, the
cloud and precipitation may be less persistent,
and in winter rain is as likely as snow. But
when the storm center travels south of the
station northerly winds are characteristic,

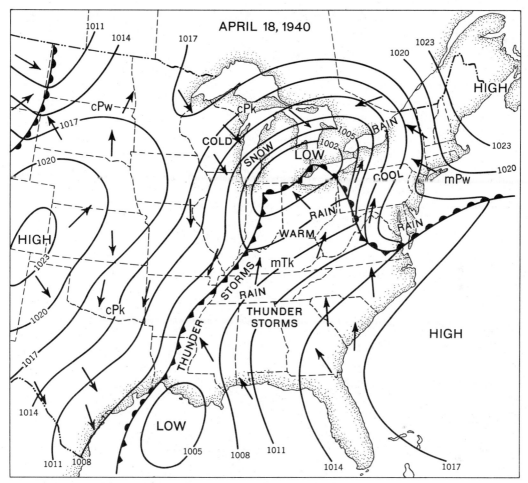

FIG. 10.10 A well-developed wave cyclone over eastern United States. This weather-map representation should be compared with the ground plan of the model cyclone in Fig. 10.9.

temperatures are relatively low, the cloud cover (deck) more lasting, and snow is more common.

Wind system of the anticyclone The anticyclone's wind system is opposite in all respects to that of the cyclone: pressure is highest at the center, so surface winds flow outward, or diverge, from the center, and there must be a compensating downward, or subsiding, movement of air to feed the surface flow (Figs. 10.7, 10.12). (Earth rotation

causes this diverging flow to have something of a clockwise whirl in the Northern Hemisphere.) This slow subsidence in an anticyclone is as important as ascent of air is in a cyclone. Subsidence causes anticyclonic air to be stable and nonbuoyant, so that above-surface temperature inversions are developed and the whole environment becomes opposed to precipitation.

Precipitation in cyclones and anticyclones As the preceding discussion has suggested, cyclones and anticyclones are as unlike in precipitation as in their wind systems, cyclones being much more favorable for it because with their upward movement of air, cooling by expansion occurs and cloud and rain result. By contrast, the divergence and subsidence in an anticyclone operate to make it an area of generally fair weather. It should be remembered, to be sure, that not all cyclones are rainy, for the rising air in them may be too dry to permit abundant condensation.

Most of the precipitation that falls on lowlands in middle latitudes owes its origin either directly or indirectly to cyclonic storms. Although in the warmer months much of the rainfall may be showery and convective in nature, a large part of even this precipitation is organized in character and occurs in association with cyclonic systems.

Since in a cyclone, as previously stated, warm and less dense air commonly glides up over a mildly inclined wedge of cooler, denser air, cooling of the lifted air is not very rapid, with the consequence that much cyclonic rainfall is moderate in its rate of fall. But because the cyclone is extensive, and the slow

lifting of the warm air is thereby widespread, its precipitation is likely to be of relatively long duration and to cover a wide area. Fairly steady precipitation is as typical of cyclonic weather as the dull, gray, uniformly overcast skies from which the rain falls.

However, the likelihood of precipitation and its nature and origin are not the same in all parts of a cyclone. In general the eastern, or front, half where convergence is greater is cloudier and rainier than the western, or rear, half. In winter lows, snow is more common in the colder northern and northeastern parts than in the warmer southern parts.

The most extensive area of general precipitation is usually found in association with the above-surface warm front. As Fig. 10.9 shows, here, to the east, northeast, and north of the storm center, warm southerly air flows up over a gently inclined wedge of colder air and widespread cloud and precipitation are the result. Along the cold front, usually positioned to the south and southwest of the storm's center, is a second region of active air ascent with accompanying precipitation. Here cold northwesterly air underruns the warm southerly air and lifts it. But here, because the sloping surface of the cold air is steeper than along the warm front, the rise of the warm air is more rapid. As a consequence cold-front precipitation is likely to be somewhat more vigorous but of shorter duration than precipitation along the warm front. However, where the air to the rear, or west, of the cold front is from maritime sources, as it is along west coasts in middle latitudes, showery rainfall in the cool, moist polar air may extend for some distance to the rear of the surface cold front. In the warmer months thunderstorms may occur along both fronts, but they are more common and likely to be stronger along the cold front.

FIG. 10.11 Veering and backing wind shifts as a cyclonic storm approaches and passes an observer.

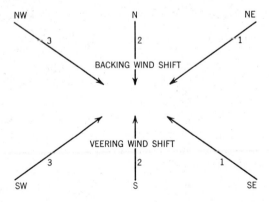

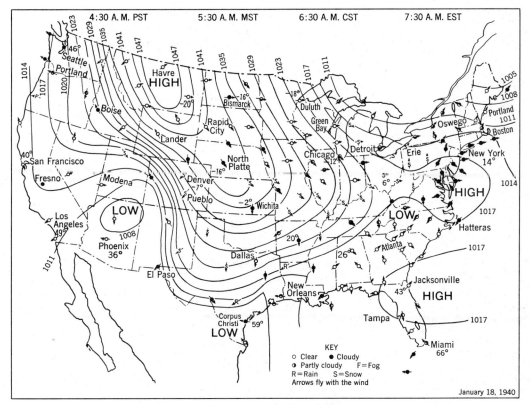

FIG. 10.12 A well-developed cold anticyclone in winter. This cold anticyclone moved into the United States from the arctic plains of Canada as a mass of cold, stable, polar continental (*cP*) air. St. Joseph, Missouri, experienced a minimum temperature of 21° below zero, Galveston, Texas, on the Gulf of Mexico a minimum of 15° above zero. Such southward thrusts of polar air are essential elements of the moisture-balancing and of the heat-balancing mechanisms of the earth. *(U.S. Weather Bureau.)*

During the warmer seasons some showery convective rainfall may also occur within the warm sector of southerly airflow to the south of the cyclone center, where it is not associated with either a warm or a cold front (Fig. 10.9).

Temperatures associated with cyclones and anticyclones Simple rules of wide application are difficult to make concerning the temperature effects of cyclones and anticyclones. Yet some generally applicable statements may be made on these effects.

Since anticyclones develop in both cold polar air and warm subtropical air, they may bring either very cold or very hot weather. Indeed the coldest weather in winter and the hottest in summer are usually associated with anticyclones. Also, the anticyclone is characteristically accompanied by clear skies, which adds to its tendency to produce seasonal temperature effects. During the long winter nights in middle latitudes the lack of clouds permits a rapid loss of heat from the earth; thus a cold anticyclone at such times

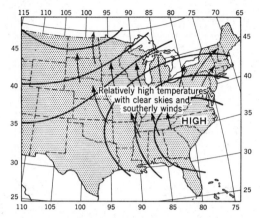

FIG. 10.13 Illustrating a warm anticyclone which is relatively stagnant over southeastern United States. Such a weather-map condition produces unseasonably warm weather over the central and eastern parts of the country.

may cause subzero temperatures (Fig. 10.12). But the same clear skies in summer, when days are relatively long, permits of strong solar heating, so that at this time a warm anticyclone of subtropical origin is accompanied by high daytime temperatures (Fig. 10.13).

By contrast, the cloud cover which usually accompanies a cyclone tends to reduce night cooling in winter and daytime heating

FIG. 10.14 Characteristic arrangement of isotherms in a winter cyclone over the central and eastern United States in winter.

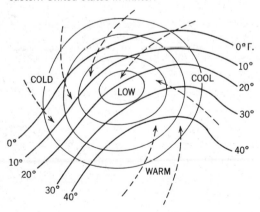

in summer, so that less extreme temperatures prevail. However, since the cyclone is composed of unlike air masses, temperatures may vary greatly in different parts of an individual storm. Where northerly winds prevail (*cP* air) as they do to the northeast, north, and west of the cyclone center, relatively low temperatures are to be expected (Fig. 10.14). Where the air flow is from the south (*cT* or *mT* air) as is commonly the case to the south of the storm center, relatively high seasonal temperatures are the rule.

MIDDLE-LATITUDE WEATHER IN GENERAL

The very essence of middle-latitude weather, which to a high degree is under the control of a procession of eastward-moving cyclones and anticyclones, is its irregular, or aperiodic, changeability. The *averages* of such weather elements as temperature and precipitation for a month or a year give a very atypical and lifeless picture of the climate unless supplemented by use of the daily weather map where the various weather episodes induced by cyclones and anticyclones are represented. Especially in the colder months weather variability reaches peak strength (Figs. 10.15, 10.16, 10.17). Nor is it absent in summer, although it is weaker and sun control producing regular diurnal

FIG. 10.15 Barograph and thermograph traces showing the approach and retreat of a middle-latitude cyclone.

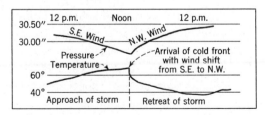

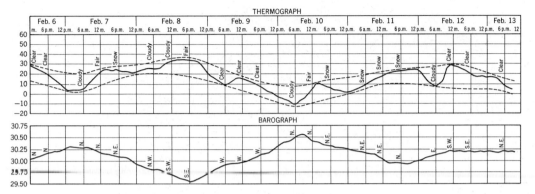

FIG. 10.16   Barograph and thermograph traces of a week of winter
weather at a middle-latitude station. Note the marked pressure changes
indicating the passage of well-developed cyclones and anticyclones with their
contrasting air masses. The temperature belt (as bounded by the dashed lines)
rises as pressure falls and sinks when the pressure rises. *(From Ward.)*

change is very important then. It should also
be repeated that the weather conditions of
cyclones and anticyclones described above
are idealized, and individual storms vary
greatly in the weather patterns they produce.
For instance, cyclonic weather is by no
means identical in various parts of the middle
latitudes. Even within the United States,
cyclones produce relatively different weather
patterns along the Pacific Coast from

those they produce over the interior and
eastern parts.

**Cyclone tracks and their concentra-
tions**   All parts of the middle latitudes, as
well as those parts of tropical and high latitudes which border the middle latitudes,
are affected by moving cyclones and anticyclones, but not to the same degree.
Cyclones, for example, cross some extensive
areas more frequently than others, and as a

FIG. 10.17   Barograph and thermograph traces of a week of summer
weather at a middle-latitude station. Note the relatively flat barograph curve
indicating weak cyclonic-anticyclonic control. Regular daily temperature
changes induced by sun control are more conspicuous than those
nonperiodic changes associated with the contrasting air masses of cyclones
and anticyclones. *(From Ward.)*

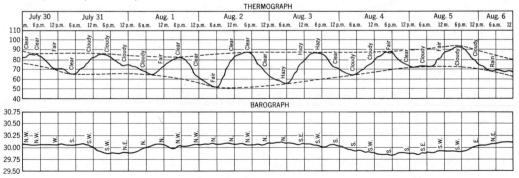

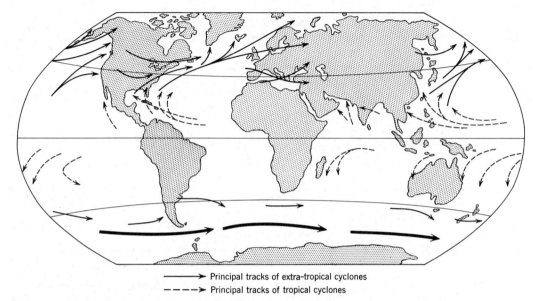

————————▶ Principal tracks of extra-tropical cyclones
- - - - - -▶ Principal tracks of tropical cyclones

FIG. 10.18 Showing, in greatly simplified form, the principal regions of cyclonic-storm concentration in both middle and low latitudes.
(From Sverre Petterssen, Introduction to Meteorology, 2d ed., McGraw-Hill Book Company, Inc., New York, 1958.)

consequence weather in the former areas is more variable.

Figure 10.18 shows in a generalized fashion the principal cyclonic tracks of the earth. In observing them, it should be remembered that the weather effects of such extensive disturbances are felt well beyond the path of their centers.

The United States and adjacent parts of Canada have the distinction of being the world's continental area with the most cyclonic activity. This may be because North America east of the Rocky Mountains is a region of numerous well-developed fronts resulting from the clash of polar and tropical air masses which move freely across extensive lowlands from arctic to tropical latitudes. All parts of the United States east of the Rockies, except possibly peninsular Florida, have an abundance of cyclonic weather. But it is in the northeastern parts of the United States

and adjacent sections of Canada, where there is a distinct bunching of cyclone tracks, that cyclonic disturbances are most numerous in North America.

TROPICAL WEATHER DISTURBANCES

THE APERIODIC WEATHER ELEMENT IN THE TROPICS

Not until recently has it been appreciated how importantly large atmospheric disturbances affect the weather and climate of the tropics. Earlier it was assumed that the diurnal and seasonal course of the sun controlled the weather in the low latitudes to an unusual degree and so produced the regularity that is monotonous compared with the variety and irregularity of weather characteristic of middle latitudes. But while the effect of weather disturbances is not so marked in the tropics as in

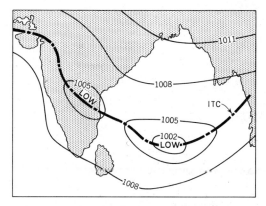

FIG. 10.19 Weak tropical disturbances of the summer period in southern Asia. Such disturbances are responsible for much of summer precipitation in this region.

the middle latitudes, it is by no means absent. Unfortunately, however, the variety of disturbances which produce the modest aperiodic weather changes in the tropics are not yet satisfactorily understood, and discussion of them must reflect this fact.

WEAK TROPICAL DISTURBANCES AND THEIR WEATHER CONSEQUENCES

Most of the extensive tropical disturbances appear to be relatively mild (Fig. 10.19). Their organized pressure and wind systems are frequently difficult to distinguish on the daily surface-weather map, and some exist only as above-surface phenomena. Numerous, very weak disturbances appear to be concentrated in the vicinity of the ITC, where they may move in either an easterly or a westerly direction, depending on the general direction of airflow. Others are characteristic of the deep trade winds, where they move in a general east-to-west direction. The temperature effects of such tropical disturbances are small and usually a consequence of their production of increased cloudiness, which in turn reduces the amount of incoming solar energy.

Because they involve air convergence, these tropical disturbances do produce clouds and precipitation, most of it of a showery nature falling from cumulonimbus clouds, and this is their principal climatic effect. The progress of most weak tropical disturbances can indeed be best detected by the moving areas of organized cloud and rainfall which they generate.

SEVERE TROPICAL DISTURBANCES: THE HURRICANE OR TYPHOON

In addition to these numerous weak disturbances, which are responsible for much of the weather and rainfall in the low latitudes, there are very likely disturbances of all degrees of intensity there. Certain it is that there are a few of a much more violent nature, and that the most violent of all is the *hurricane,* or *typhoon* (Fig. 10.20). These severe vortex storms, however, are of much less climatic significance than the weak disturbances, for

FIG. 10.20 A West Indies hurricane, with the barograph trace of this storm as recorded at Miami, Florida.

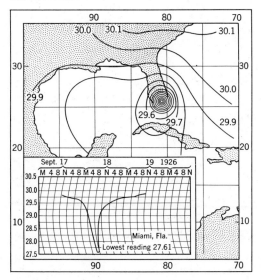

they are far less frequent and characteristic of much more restricted areas. Moreover, since hurricanes originate and mature only over the sea, the land areas that feel their concentrated effects are mostly only coasts and islands.

Differences from middle-latitude cyclones   The violent and destructive hurricane resembles a middle-latitude cyclone in having a central area of low pressure, a converging vortex system of winds, and a relatively widespread area of clouds and rain. But it also differs in a number of respects. (a) The isobars of the hurricane are more symmetrical and more nearly circular. (b) Pressure gradients are much steeper, so that winds are stronger. Wind speeds in the storm must reach at least 75 miles an hour for it to be a genuine hurricane. (c) Rains are inclined to be more torrential and somewhat more evenly distributed about the center. (d) Temperature distribution around the center is relatively similar in every direction. Cold and warm sectors and surface fronts are absent. (e) There are no sharp wind shifts within the violent parts of the storm. Instead, the winds develop a perfect spiral whirl, with strong, vertically ascending currents around the center, or core. (f) The storms are most numerous in the warm months of late summer and fall, rather than in winter, and where frequent may give rise to a fall maximum of rainfall. (g) Each has a relatively calm, rainless center of descending air 5 to 30 miles in diameter, called the *eye* of the storm. (h) This tropical cyclone has no anticyclone companion.

Although variable in size, the hurricane is smaller than the cyclone of middle latitudes, having a diameter of about 100 to 400 miles. But its winds may reach such destructive speeds as 90 to 130 miles per hour, resulting in tremendous damage to shipping and coastal

settlements, and loss of life by drowning is by no means rare. A considerable part of this loss of life and property is due to two things: great avalanches of sea water piled up and driven onshore by the gale winds, and excessive rainfall and resulting floods that accompany the storm.

Origin and concentration   There is no generally accepted theory of the origin of hurricanes. But it is clear that they develop only over warm water, probably 82° or higher. Summer and fall, when they are most numerous, is the period when the ITC is farthest from the equator. Many apparently have their beginnings as weak disturbances which subsequently mushroom into the intense and dreaded hurricane.

Severe tropical cyclones appear to occur occasionally over the warmer parts of most tropical oceans, but not in close proximity to the equator, and probably nowhere in the South Atlantic. There are a number of areas of marked concentration of these storms (Fig. 10.18). These are (a) the China Sea, the typhoons of which affect particularly the Philippines, southeastern China, and southern Japan; (b) the Arabian Sea and the Bay of Bengal, on either side of peninsular India; (c) the Caribbean Sea, the hurricanes of which are felt in the West Indies, Yucatan, and the southeastern United States; (d) the eastern North Pacific in the region west of Mexico; (e) the South Indian Ocean east of Madagascar; and (f) the tropical waters both northeast and northwest of Australia.

THUNDERSTORMS

General characteristics   A *thunderstorm* is an intense convectional shower accompanied by lightning and thunder. In its mature stage it is characterized by several

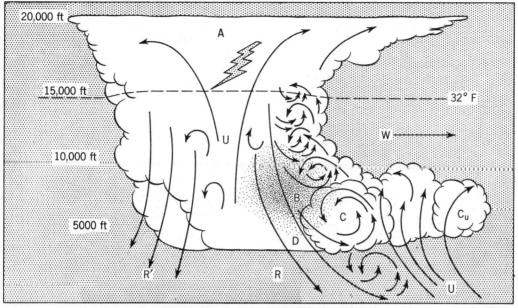

Key to diagram of cumulonimbus cloud

A – Anvil top   U – Up drafts
B – Dark area   R – Primary rain area
C – Roll cloud   R' – Secondary area
C_u – Advance cumulus clouds   W – Wind direction
D – Down drafts

FIG. 10.21   Vertical section through a thunderstorm and its cumulonimbus cloud.

chimneys of vigorously ascending warm air, each surrounded by compensating cooler downdrafts. This strong turbulence is evidenced in the seethings and convulsions that can be observed in the awesome cumulonimbus cloud, or thunderhead (Fig. 10.21).

Since rapid, vertical upthrusts of air commonly accompany high surface temperatures, it is not surprising to find thunderstorms most numerous in the warmer latitudes of the earth, in the warmer seasons in the middle latitudes, and in the warmer hours of the day. Heat and thunderstorms are closely related.

But heat is not the only requirement for thunderstorm development. The warm air must also be relatively rich in water vapor, for abundant heat of condensation released in

the rising air is the principal source of energy for the storm. Indeed, the intensity of the storm depends very largely upon this supply of latent energy. Without exception the phenomena commonly associated with thunderstorms—torrential local rain, hail, violent squall winds, lightning, and thunder—are directly related to vigorous convectional overturning in warm, humid air.

Most thunderstorms appear to occur in connection with some weather control which favors an upward movement of air. This may be a terrain obstacle or, more commonly, the general convergence that is present in most extensive atmospheric disturbances of the low-pressure variety. Because of the latter, much thunderstorm activity is organized in character, and shifts position with the progress of the general disturbance of which it is a part. In middle-latitude cyclones thunderstorms are commonly concentrated in the vicinity of fronts, especially vigorous cold fronts, where upward movement of air is intensified.

Precipitation As indicated earlier, rainfall in thunderstorms is likely to be more vigorous but of shorter duration than rainfall associated with cyclones. A cumulonimbus cloud is so small in area that it quickly drifts by and the rain ceases. One speaks of thundershowers rather than thunder rains. This downpouring nature of the precipitation is related to (*a*) the more rapid ascent of air in thunderstorms than in most cyclones (a rise of at least 2,400 ft per min must occur), and (*b*) the higher temperature and thus higher specific humidity of the air in the summer season when thunderstorms are prevalent. The vigorous and local nature of thunderstorm rainfall, plus the fact that in middle latitudes it is concentrated in the growing season, has important economic consequences, some beneficial, others not.

Hail Occasionally hail, the most destructive form of precipitation, is developed in very intense thunderstorms. Fortunately it occurs in only a few, and usually falls only in restricted areas or belts in any particular storm. When convection is most vigorous and air is ascending at a rate of 25 to 50 miles an hour or more, raindrops caught in the upward-surging currents are carried up into atmospheric regions of below-freezing temperatures, so that on mixing with snow they freeze as globules of cloudy ice. These ice pellets then may fall a long distance from the high freezing level through a great thickness of subfreezing cloud layers, striking and capturing supercooled water droplets and

snow crystals on the way and thus growing into hailstones. When the strong upward-moving currents are temporarily halted, such hailstones fall to earth, often doing serious damage to crops and such structures as greenhouses, and occasionally even killing livestock in the fields.

Although hail falls only in conjunction with thunderstorms, hail and thunderstorms are not similarly distributed. For example, hail is practically unknown in the tropics where thunderstorms are most numerous, and is rare in the warmer, subtropical parts of the United States, such as Florida and the Gulf Coast, where thunderstorms are at a maximum. Hail and hail damage in the United States are startlingly local in distribution but occur most frequently over parts of the Rocky Mountains and the Great Plains.

Lightning, thunder, and squall winds Three other common phenomena of thunderstorms need brief comment: lightning, thunder, the *squall wind*, or *thundersquall*. Lightning results from the disruption of raindrops, with consequent development of static electricity, in rapidly ascending air currents. Like hail, therefore, it is largely confined to the vigorous convectional storms which are most numerous in the warm season. As raindrops in a storm grow larger and larger, their limit of cohesion is eventually passed, and in the vigorous updrafts of air they begin to break up. Then droplets with contrasting electrical charges become concentrated in different parts of a cloud. The lightning flash, usually from one part of a cloud to another but sometimes from cloud to earth, serves to equalize these unlike electrical charges. The thunder is produced by violent expansion of the air caused by the tremendous heat of the lightning.

Probably not more than 1 per cent of

lightning flashes reach the earth's surface. Yet in the United States several hundred persons lose their lives each year as a result of lightning, and twice as many are injured; and fire losses due to lightning amount to millions of dollars annually. Some of the greatest losses result from the kindling of forest fires.

The thundersquall is the strong, outrushing mass of cool air just in front of a thunderstorm (Fig. 10.21). Its speed at times attains hurricane violence; thus it may do serious damage. The force of the squall is due in part to the cool air which has been brought down from aloft with the mass of falling rain and spreads out in front of the storm, underrunning the warm air.

Tornadoes   Very occasionally, severe thunderstorm activity, of the sort that occurs in association with well-developed cold fronts and squall lines, may be accompanied by scattered *tornadoes,* the most violent and destructive of all atmospheric disturbances. But spectacular and awesome as it is, the tornado is of minor consequence in world climates. Its distribution is limited to a few regions, its occurrence is infrequent, and the width of its destructive path usually does not exceed ½ mile.

Distribution of thunderstorms   Taking the average of their occurrence at all longitudes, thunderstorms are found to be most numerous near the equator and decrease in frequency poleward (Fig. 10.22). Beyond latitudes 60°–70° thunderstorms are few. This distribution reflects chiefly the general decline in air temperature from equator to poles and the associated decline in the humidity content of the atmosphere. But air temperature is not the only control of their distribution, for while thunderstorm frequency declines sharply between latitudes 0 and 20°, temperatures drop little if at all. Thus the

strong equatorial maximum is also a consequence of the convergent nature of the airflow and its deep humidification near the equator. The marked falling off in thunderstorm frequency away from the equator reflects decreasing humidity and increasing subsidence and horizontal divergence as the subtropical anticyclones are approached.

Greater frequency of thunderstorms over land areas than over oceans in similar latitudes is to be expected because of the higher summer temperatures of the former. Some equatorial land areas record over 100 days with thunderstorms during the year; a few places even experience 200 such days.

In the United States the fewest thunderstorms are experienced in the Pacific Coast states, which are dominated by stable anticyclonic air masses in summer (Fig. 10.23). There are two regions of maximum occurrence: (*a*) the subtropical Southeast, and (*b*) the Rocky Mountain area in New Mexico, Colorado, and Wyoming. The eastern Gulf Coast region in the United States is the most thundery area outside of the tropics, having 70 to 80 days per year with thunderstorms. In this region heat and humidity combine to produce an environment ideal for the development of convective overturning.

FIG. 10.22   Latitudinal distribution of the average number of days per year with thunderstorms, averaged for all longitudes. *(From Brooks.)*

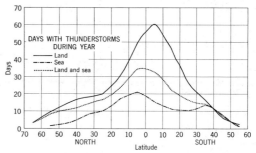

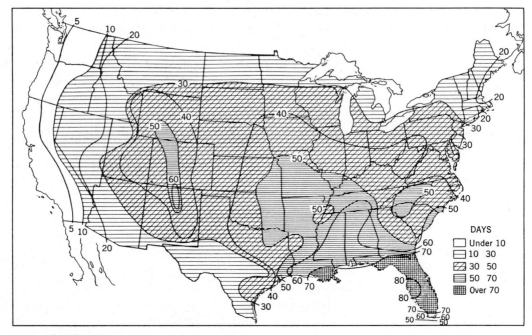

FIG. 10.23 Distribution of the average number of days per year with thunderstorms.

SELECTED REFERENCES

Blair, Thomas A., and Robert C. Fite: *Weather Elements,* 4th ed., Prentice-Hall, Inc., Englewood Cliffs, N. J., 1957.

Kendrew, W. G.: *Climatology,* 2d ed., Oxford University Press, London, 1957.

Kimble, George H. T.: *Our American Weather,* McGraw-Hill Book Company, Inc., New York, 1955.

Koeppe, Clarence E., and George C. DeLong: *Weather and Climate,* McGraw-Hill Book Company, Inc., New York, 1958.

Miller, Arthur Austin: *Climatology,* E. P. Dutton & Co., Inc., New York, 1943.

Petterssen, Sverre: *Introduction to Meteorology,* 2d ed., McGraw-Hill Book Company, Inc., New York, 1958.

Riehl, Herbert: *Tropical Meteorology,* McGraw-Hill Book Company, Inc., New York, 1954.

Taylor, George F.: *Elementary Meteorology,* Prentice-Hall, Inc., Englewood Cliffs, N. J., 1954.

Trewartha, Glenn T.: *An Introduction to Climate,* McGraw-Hill Book Company, Inc., New York, 1954.

Watts, I. E. M.: *Equatorial Weather,* University of London Press, Ltd., London, 1955.

CHAPTER 11

Classification of climates and their distribution; the tropical humid climates

In the preceding chapters temperature and precipitation, the two elements which in combination largely determine any climate, have been analyzed, and their distributions have been described. In addition, the effects of the great controls of climate on temperature and precipitation have been examined. It has been seen how the climatic controls determine regional variations in the amount, intensity, and seasonal distribution of both temperature and precipitation, resulting in changeful combinations of these two great climatic elements. In this manner are created the great variety of climates, which will now be described.[1]

Because of the exceedingly numerous combinations of temperature and precipitation that exist on the earth, it becomes necessary, in order to appreciate the general world pattern of climate, to reduce the great variety of regional and local climates to a relatively few large groups and types having important characteristics in common. This reduction is essentially accomplished through classification, a process common to all sciences.

[1] Since ocean currents are a climatic control of at least modest significance, even if not as important as the controls already studied, it is suggested that the student acquaint himself with the world patterns of the oceanic circulation before proceeding to a study of the climatic types and their distribution in this chapter and Chaps. 12 through 14. For this discussion see Chap. 15, pp. 277–291 ff.

CLASSIFICATION: CLIMATIC REGIONS, GROUPS, AND TYPES

A *climatic region* is any portion of the earth's surface over which the broad climatic characteristics are similar, though not necessarily identical. Similar climatic regions, that is, areas with similar climates, are found in widely separated parts of the earth (Plate 2). But they are commonly found in correspond-

FIG. 11.1 Locations of the five great climatic groups on a hypothetical continent of relatively low and uniform elevation.

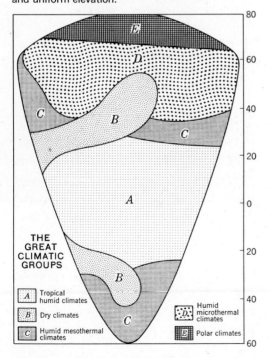

FIG. 11.2 Locations of the types of climate, which are subdivisions of the climatic groups, on a hypothetical continent of relatively low and uniform elevation.

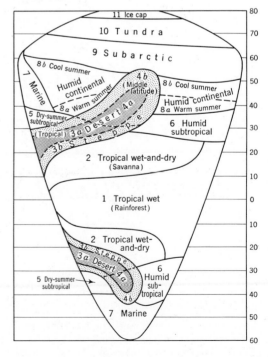

ing latitudinal and roughly corresponding continental locations, which suggests that there is order and system in the origin and distribution of the climatic elements. The correspondence indeed makes possible the gathering of the numerous climatic regions into a few principal *climatic groups* (Fig. 11.1) and *climatic types* (Fig. 11.2), each type comprising a number of separate regions.

Plate 2 shows that a recognizable world pattern of climatic distribution exists, for there the several climatic regions comprising a type are seen to fairly repeat each other in

terms of latitudinal and continental locations. Nor should the existence of the pattern be surprising: the greatest controls of climate are in the distribution of solar energy and the general circulation of the atmosphere, both with clearly distinguishable world patterns.

In Figs. 11.1 and 11.2 an attempt is made to show in diagrammatic form the climatic arrangement as it might appear on a hypothetical continent of relatively low and uniform elevation. The continent is designed to show typical positions and arrangements of the climatic types and groups divorced from

Classification of Climates* *know*

Groups

A. Tropical humid climates

around equator
constantly warm
form wides belt on
eastern side of continent

B. Dry climates

C. Humid mesothermal climates

(enough)

D. Humid microthermal climates

(small)
not enough heat

E. Polar climates

H. Highlands

Types

I. Low latitudes (the tropics)
   1. Tropical wet (*Af*, constantly wet)
              (*Am*, monsoon variety)
   2. Tropical wet-and-dry (*Aw*)

   3. Low-latitude dry climates
     a. Low-latitude desert (*BWh*, arid)
     b. Low-latitude steppe (*BSh*, semiarid)

II. Middle latitudes (intermediate zones)
   4. Middle-latitude dry climates
     a. Middle-latitude desert (*BWk*, arid)
     b. Middle-latitude steppe (*BSk*, semiarid)

   5. Dry-summer subtropical (*Cs*)
   6. Humid subtropical (*Ca*)
   7. Marine (*Cb, Cc*)

   8. Humid continental climates
     a. Humid continental, warm summer (*Da*)
     b. Humid continental, cool summer (*Db*)
   9. Subarctic (*Dc, Dd*)

III. High latitudes (polar caps) or high altitudes
   10. Tundra (*ET*)
   11. Icecap (*EF*)
     Not divided into distinct types

* Temperature and precipitation data for representative stations are presented in tables accompanying the text for each type of climate.

peculiarities associated with individual real continents by reason of their size, shape, and surface configurations.

In a study of the text materials on groups and types of climate to follow, continuing reference should be made to Figs. 11.1 and 11.2 as well as to Plate 2. In addition, Fig. 11.2 and Plate 2 should be compared, because the resemblances between them are important.

The plan of climatic classification employed in this book is a simplified and otherwise modified version of the well-known Köppen system, which uses letter symbols to designate climates. Five great climatic groups are recognized, and each of these is subdivided into a relatively few climatic types. In the book the groups and types are named, and the corresponding Köppen symbols follow each name in parenthesis. Since the two classifications are similar but not identical, the

symbols indicate only comparable climates, and should not be understood to imply complete agreement.

The five groups of climate (Fig. 11.1) are as follows: In the low latitudes near the equator is a winterless region with adequate rainfall. This group is called the *tropical humid climates* (*A*). Poleward from this group and extending far into the middle latitudes are the *dry climates* (*B*). The humid middle latitudes with their seasonal contrasts in temperature are divided into two climatic groups, one in which the winters are short and mild, the *humid mesothermal climates* (*C*), and the other in which they are severe and long, the *humid microthermal climates* (*D*). Finally, in the higher latitudes are the summerless *polar climates* (*E*).[2] The outline of climatic classification is presented in more detail in the preceding table. The tropical humid climates will be considered first.

THE TROPICAL HUMID CLIMATES: LOCATION, BOUNDARIES, AND TYPES

The tropical humid climates (*A*) form a somewhat interrupted belt 20 to 40° wide around the earth astride the equator (Fig. 11.1, Plate 2). This belt is distinguished from all other humid areas of the earth by the fact that it is constantly warm; in other words, it lacks a winter. On its poleward margins the group of tropical humid climates may be terminated either by diminishing rainfall or by decreasing temperatures. Usually it merges with dry climates in the western and central parts of continents (Fig. 11.1). On the more humid eastern sides it extends poleward until a season of cold develops. (The accepted boundary is where the average temperature of the coolest month falls below 64°.) Highlands, with their low temperatures,

are responsible for the principal interruptions in the belt of tropical humid climates over the continents.

Normally the tropical humid climates form a wider belt and thus extend farther poleward along the eastern side of a continent than toward the west side. This reflects the facts

[2] The Köppen definitions of the five great climatic groups are as follows:

    A   temperature of coolest month over 64.4° (18°C)
    B   potential evaporation exceeds precipitation
    C   temperature of coldest month between 64.4° (18°C) and 26.6° (−3°C)
    D   temperature of coldest month under 26.6° (−3°C); warmest month over 50° (10°C)
    E   temperature of warmest month under 50° (10°C)

The Köppen designations for types of climate will be noted and explained as the types are defined in the discussion.

(a) that the air is more stable in the eastern than the western part of an oceanic subtropical anticyclone, and (b) that the ocean water is cooler along the western tropical coasts.

Since temperatures are constantly high, the two principal types of climate within the tropical humid group are distinguished from each other on the basis of the annual distribution of precipitation. One type, *tropical wet*, has abundant rainfall throughout the year with no marked dry season. The second type, *tropical wet-and-dry*, usually has less total rainfall, and there are a distinctly wet and a distinctly dry season.

TROPICAL WET CLIMATE (TROPICAL RAINFOREST)

TYPE LOCATION

(a) Uniformly high temperatures and (b) heavy precipitation distributed throughout the year, so that there is no marked dry season, are the two most distinguishing characteristics of the tropical wet (Af) type of climate.[3] When typically located, it is found astride the equator and extending out 5 or 10° on either side, but the latitudinal spread may be increased to 15 or even 25° along the eastern margin of a continent (Fig. 11.2). Tropical wet climate is sometimes called the *tropical rainforest* climate. This climate is closely associated with the doldrums, or intertropical convergence zone (ITC), where weak rain-generating disturbances are numerous and the air is unstable (Fig. 11.3). Characteristically, tropical wet climate is bounded by the tropical wet-and-dry type on its poleward side. Along the wetter eastern margins of continents, however, it usually extends farther poleward to make contact with the humid subtropical climate, one of the humid mesothermal group of climates of middle latitudes (Fig. 11.2).

Geographical location The Amazon River Basin in northern South America and the Congo River Basin and Guinea coast in central and western Africa are the two largest contiguous areas with tropical wet climate

(Plate 2). A third extensive but not contiguous area includes much of the East Indies, the Philippine Islands, and the Malay Peninsula in tropical southeastern Asia. There are smaller areas of tropical wet climate in eastern Central America, the windward parts of some islands in the West Indies, western Colombia, the coastal lowlands and slopes of sections of eastern Brazil, and eastern Madagascar.

TEMPERATURE

Annual and seasonal temperatures Lying as areas with the tropical wet type of climate commonly do, athwart the equator, and consequently in the belt of maximum insolation, it is to be expected that temperatures will be uniformly high, and yearly averages do usually lie between 77 and 80° (following table). Moreover, since the sun's noon rays are never far from a vertical position, and since days and nights vary little in length from one part of the year to another, the annual-insolation curve remains not only

FIG. 11.3 Locations of tropical wet (Af), tropical wet-and-dry (Aw), and dry (B), types of climate on the zonal profile of sea-level pressure.

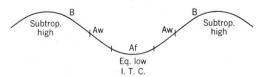

[3] In the Köppen system f = moist (*feucht*) throughout the year: no month with less than 2.4 in. of rain.

Climatic Data for Representative Stations with Tropical Wet Climate

	J	F	M	A	M	J	J	A	S	O	N	D	Yr	Range
Singapore, Malay Peninsula														
Temp.	78.3	79.0	80.2	80.8	81.5	81.1	81.0	80.6	80.4	80.1	79.3	78.6	80.1	3.2
Precip.	8.5	6.1	6.5	6.9	7.2	6.7	6.8	8.5	7.1	8.2	10.0	10.4	92.9	
Nouvelle-Anvers, the Congo														
Temp.	79.2	80.1	79.2	78.1	79.2	78.4	76.5	76.3	77.0	77.4	77.9	78.1	78.1	3.8
Precip.	4.1	3.5	4.1	5.6	6.2	6.1	6.3	6.3	6.3	6.6	2.6	9.3	67.0	

high but also relatively constant, with the result that there is little seasonal variation in temperature (Fig. 11.4).

Annual temperature range The annual temperature range, or difference between the average temperatures of the warmest and coolest months, is usually less than 5°, and it may be only 1 or 2° on islands and along coasts. It is not the high monthly-temperature averages but rather this constant succession of hot months—uniform, monotonous, with no relief from the heat—that characterizes the tropical wet climate. Thus, the average July temperatures of many nontropical American cities, such as Charleston, South Carolina, with 82°; Galveston, Texas, 83°; and Montgomery, Alabama, 82°, may equal, or even exceed by a few degrees, those of the hottest months at stations near the equator.

Daily temperatures The daily, or diurnal, range of temperature (difference between the warmest and coolest hours of the day) is usually 10 to 25°, several times greater than the annual range. For example, at Bolobo, the Congo, the average daily range is 16°, while the annual range is only 2°.

During the afternoons the thermometer ordinarily rises to temperatures varying from 85 to 93° and at night sinks to 70 or 75°. It is commonly said that night is the winter of the tropics.

During the day the heat, even though not extremely high, combines with slight air movement, intense light, and high relative humidity to produce an atmospheric condition with low cooling power. It is oppressive and sultry; the sensible temperature is very high.

Even the nights actually give little relief from the oppressive heat. Rapid nocturnal cooling is not to be expected where there are such excessive humidity and abundant cloudiness. The cooling is usually sufficient, however, to cause surface condensation in the near-saturated air, so that radiation fogs and heavy dew are common.

Daily march of temperature Figure 11.5 shows the daily march of temperature for the extreme months at a representative station within tropical wet climate. The graph illustrates a temperature regime in which sun is almost completely in control. There is a

Climatic Data for Calicut, India, a Representative Monsoon Rainforest Station (*Am*)

	J	F	M	A	M	J	J	A	S	O	N	D	Yr	Range
Temp.	77.8	79.8	81.6	83.6	83.1	78.5	76.7	77.4	78.3	79.1	79.5	78.3	79.5	6.9
Precip.	0.3	0.2	0.6	3.2	9.5	35.0	29.8	15.3	8.4	10.3	4.9	1.1	118.6	

marked diurnal regularity and periodicity about the changes, temperatures rising to about the same height each day and falling to about the same level each night, so that one 24-hr period almost duplicates every other. Irregular invasions of cool air, a feature common in the middle latitudes, are rare.

PRECIPITATION

Amount   Rainfall, as has been said, is both heavy and distributed throughout the year, there being no distinctly dry season (table, p. 214; Fig. 11.4). Indeed, taken as a whole, tropical wet climate is coincident with the belt of the world's heaviest precipitation (Plate 1). Ward estimates the average annual rainfall of the doldrum belt to be in the neighborhood of 100 in., with less over the continents and more over the oceans. In this area close to the equator conditions are ideal for rain formation. The air is warm, humid up to great heights, and unstable. Horizontal wind convergence with a consequent lifting of the air prevails. Rain-generating atmospheric disturbances are numerous. The result is an abundance of cumulus cloud and showery rainfall.

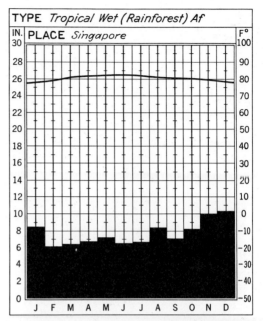

FIG. 11.4   Average monthly temperatures and precipitation amounts for a representative station with a tropical wet climate (*Af*). Monthly temperatures are much more uniform than monthly amounts of precipitation.

Seasonal distribution   Although there is no genuinely dry season in tropical wet climate where it is developed in its standard form, it should not be inferred that the rain-

FIG. 11.5   Daily maximum and minimum temperatures for the warmest and coolest months at a representative station with tropical wet climate (*Af*). Diurnal solar control is almost complete, as shown by the regular daily rise and fall of temperature.

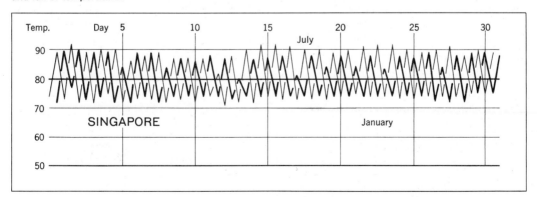

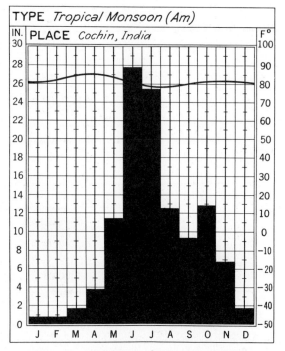

TYPE *Tropical Monsoon (Am)*

PLACE *Cochin, India*

FIG. 11.6 Average monthly temperatures and precipitation amounts for a representative tropical wet station where the monsoon control is strong (*Am*).

it is designated by the symbol *Am,* the *m* standing for monsoon.

Nature and origin of the rainfall Most of the precipitation originates in towering cumulus clouds of great vertical thickness, and is in the form of heavy showers of relatively short duration, frequently accompanied by lightning and thunder. More thunderstorms occur here than in any other latitudinal belt of the earth. There is relatively little rainfall of the steady continuous type falling from a uniformly gray overcast. Apparently, more rain comes during the warm afternoon and early evening hours when solar heating makes the humid air more unstable and buoyant, but night rains are by no means infrequent.

To what extent the tropical showers are the result of random thermal convection associated with daytime surface heating is controversial. Almost certainly, however, most of the rainfall is associated with extensive traveling atmospheric disturbances in which horizontal convergence of air streams creates an environment favoring vigorous convectional currents. As a consequence the shower activity is usually organized in belts or areas which coincide with the moving disturbances, and so shifts position from one day to another. Showers so developed may occur at night as well as day, although usually in a somewhat weakened condition. Because most of the shower activity takes place in conjunction with extensive disturbances, rainfall occurrence does not have the daily regularity so characteristic of temperature. Instead there are likely to be spells of prevalently showery days followed by others in which little or no rain falls. Thus, while the irregular, nonperiodic daily weather element is by no means as strong here as in the middle latitudes, it is certainly not absent as far as rainfall is concerned.

fall is *evenly* distributed throughout the year. Some months and seasons, while far from being dry, are still less wet than the rainiest (Fig. 11.4). In the rainier months precipitation falls on a large majority of the days, although there are usually a few days with none. Fewer rainy days and less rain on each day are characteristic of the less wet seasons. Precipitation varies much more throughout the year, and from one year to the next, than does temperature.

In some areas with tropical wet climate, rainfall is not so well distributed throughout the year, and a short moderately dry season even exists, usually at the time of low sun, or winter. Such a modified form of tropical wet climate is sometimes referred to as a monsoon subtype (Fig. 11.6). On Plate 2

RESOURCE POTENTIALITIES OF THE TROPICAL WET REALM

Although approximately 10 per cent of the earth's land surface has tropical wet climate, by no means does this part of the land contain a similar proportion of the earth's population. Also the earth's tropical wet areas have wide variations in population densities. The New World tropics are far emptier than those of the Old World.

Tropical wet is the most lavish and prolific of all climates. There is no dormant season for plant growth imposed either by a season of cold or a season of drought, so plants grow more continuously and rapidly than in any other climate. Since plants provide the ultimate food resource for human beings, this would seem to suggest a potential maximum food production within the rainforest areas. An offsetting factor, however, is the handicap which this climate is believed to impose upon the health, comfort, and general well-being of the people who live in it. Numerous tropical diseases, among them malaria, sleeping sickness, yellow fever, and tropical dysentery, have been veritable scourges to the inhabitants of the low latitudes. By some the constant heat and humidity are considered to be obstacles to the maintenance of mental and physical vigor. Nevertheless, there is now a growing hope that modern hygiene and sanitation in association with improved medical care, together with electrical refrigeration which permits better food preservation, may greatly reduce the hazards and discomforts associated with living in a tropical climate.

Aside from the problem of human living conditions, the low-grade residual soils of tropical wet climate offer a serious counterbalance to the bountiful climatic environment for plants by making difficult the growth of crops other than the deep-rooted bush and tree crops. The strong leaching effects of the abundant and warm rains continuing throughout the entire year leave the soil deficient in mineral plant foods and in organic material. A very few years of cropping is enough to exhaust the topsoil, so that the native agriculturist is forced to migrate or at least to shift his fields. On the other hand, these same soils which are deficient in mineral plant foods are coarsely granular in structure, so that they are friable and easy to till. This characteristic recommends them to the native agriculturist who operates with relatively ineffective tools.

No other climate produces such a dense growth of large trees, so that no other forest region of the earth provides such a storehouse of wood and lumber, although the exploitation of this resource is associated with many obstacles. To the agricultural settler who is obliged to clear the land, this forest is much more of a handicap than a resource, of course.

Given the advantages and the disadvantages of the tropical wet regions, the value of the plentiful unoccupied land there for future settlement is an actively debated question, although there is more optimism at present about the future of these areas than at any previous time. Of the earth's three most extensive types of land with low or modest population densities—the cold, the dry, and the humid tropics—the last appears to possess the greatest potentialities for future settlement.

TROPICAL WET-AND-DRY CLIMATE (SAVANNA)

As previously stated, tropical wet-and-dry climate (Aw)[4] differs in two principal respects

---

[4] In the Köppen system w = dry season in winter, or low-sun period: at least 1 month with less than 2.4 in. of rain.

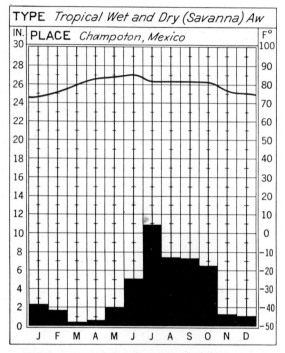

TYPE *Tropical Wet and Dry (Savanna) Aw*
PLACE *Champoton, Mexico*

FIG. 11.7 Average monthly temperatures and precipitation amounts for a representative station with a tropical wet-and-dry climate.

from tropical wet climate: (*a*) it usually has less total precipitation, and (*b*) rainfall is unevenly distributed throughout the year, there being a distinctly wet and a distinctly dry season. These climatic contrasts result in replacement of the dense forest cover typical of areas near the equator by open forest and tree-studded grassland in the wet-and-dry climate, which is sometimes called *savanna* climate.

TYPE LOCATION AND BOUNDARIES

On the hypothetical continent of Fig. 11.2, tropical wet-and-dry regions lie on the poleward and interior sides of the tropical wet climate, and between it and the dry climates. This arrangement is also shown in Fig. 11.3. Toward the rainier eastern side of a continent the wet-and-dry climate commonly makes contact on its poleward side with the humid

subtropical type of climate of the middle latitudes.

The typical latitudinal location of the tropical wet-and-dry climate is from about 5°–10° to 15°–20°, and it may extend still farther poleward on the eastern side of a continent. This places wet-and-dry in an intermediate position between the ITC and its unstable air masses on the equatorial side, and the subtropical anticyclones with their stable subsiding and diverging air masses on the poleward side (Fig. 11.3). During the course of the year, with the north-south shifting of the sun and the pressure and wind belts, latitudes 5 to 15° are encroached upon by the wet ITC and its rainbringing disturbances at the time of high sun, and by the drier parts of the trades and the subtropical anticyclones at the time of low sun. The result is rainy summers and dry winters.

Geographical location   It becomes evident from a comparison of Plate 2 and Fig. 11.2 that most of the extensive areas with tropical wet-and-dry climate are actually located on the individual continents in approximately the positions suggested in the analyses of type location just preceding. The llanos of the Orinoco River Valley in Colombia and Venezuela and the adjacent parts of the Guiana Highlands in northern South America, the campos of Brazil south of the equator in the same continent, the extensive Sudan north of the Congo River Basin and the veld south of it in Africa, the great wet-and-dry area in northern Australia, and that in tropical southern and southeastern Asia—all are situated approximately as represented on the hypothetical continent (Fig. 11.2). Most parts of these representative areas lie between latitudes 5°–10° and 15°–20° and have a tropical wet climate on their equatorward sides, a dry climate or a humid subtropical climate on their poleward frontiers.

Aw is more impt on Eastern side of equator

Climatic Data for Representative Stations with Tropical Wet-and-Dry Climate

	J	F	M	A	M	J	J	A	S	O	N	D	Yr	Range
Timbo, Guinea (10°40′N)														
Temp.	72	76	81	80	77	73	72	72	72	73	72	71	74	10
Precip.	0.0	0.0	1.0	2.4	6.4	9.0	12.4	14.7	10.2	6.7	1.3	0.0	64.1	
Cuiabá, Brazil (15°30′S)														
Temp.	81	81	81	80	78	75	76	78	82	82	82	81	80	7
Precip.	9.8	8.3	8.3	4.0	2.1	0.3	0.2	1.1	2.0	4.5	5.9	8.1	54.6	

TEMPERATURE AND PRECIPITATION

The temperature differences between tropical wet-and-dry climate and tropical wet climate are not great. Constantly high temperatures are still the rule in tropical wet-and-dry, for the noon sun is never far from a vertical position, and days and nights change little in length from one part of the year to another. In general, yearly temperature ranges are somewhat greater than in typical rainforest regions but still small, usually over 5° but seldom exceeding 15° (Fig. 11.7). These slightly larger ranges may result from the fact that the high-sun months are often slightly hotter and the low-sun months are slightly cooler than in regions nearer the equator (Figs. 11.7, 11.8).

Not infrequently the hottest period occurs just before the time of highest sun and the rainy season, which come together. Tropical wet-and-dry climate, like tropical wet, shows a remarkable diurnal regularity in its daily march of temperature (Fig. 11.8), reflecting the dominance of sun control.

Amount of rainfall   Since regional temperature variations are not great within the wet tropics, rainfall is a more critical element in setting apart the several climatic types of the low latitudes. Characteristically, 40 to

FIG. 11.8   Daily maximum and minimum temperatures for the warmest and coolest months at a station with tropical wet-and-dry climate (*Aw*). Note the strong dominance of diurnal solar control and the weakness of any nonperiodic control by atmospheric disturbances.

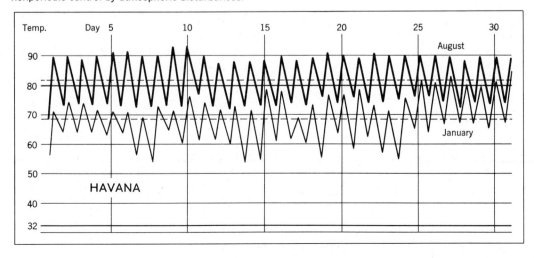

60 in. of rain falls a year in regions with wet-and-dry climate, less than in regions with tropical wet climate. But since the wet-and-dry climate usually occupies transitional belts between the constantly wet and the constantly dry climates, there naturally is considerable contrast between the amounts of rainfall on its equatorward and poleward margins. As a general rule there is a decrease poleward.

Seasonal rainfall It is not the total amount of precipitation which chiefly differentiates the two climates of the humid tropics; it is rather the fact that there is much more seasonal variation of precipitation in the wet-and-dry than in the wet climates (Fig. 11.7). This contrast between the two types is principally due to their latitudinal locations. As previously stated, the tropical wet type is constantly in or near the ITC where atmospheric disturbances are numerous and there is a large-scale ascent of warm, humid, unstable air masses; the wet-and-dry type, on the other hand, is on the margins of the ITC and therefore in an intermediate position between it and the dry settling air masses of the subtropical anticyclone and the poleward margins of the trades.

The seasonal distribution of rainfall in tropical wet-and-dry climates is a complex subject in itself, of course, which an example, the Sudan of Africa north of the equator, will be used to clarify.

As the sun's vertical rays move northward from the equator after the spring equinox, their thermal effects cause pressure and wind belts to shift in the same direction but a month or two behind in time. Thus the ITC with its unstable air masses and heavy rains gradually shifts northward over the Sudan, and convectional showers and thunderstorms begin to occur there in March and April. The rainfall continues to increase in amount until July or even August, when the ITC reaches its maximum northward migration. With the southward retreat of the ITC following the sun the rains decline in amount, until by October or November the dry, subsiding, stable air masses associated with the subtropical anticyclone and poleward margins of trades are prevailing over the Sudan, and drought grips the land. The lengths of the wet and dry seasons are variable, depending upon distance from the equator.

There is no abrupt boundary between the constantly wet and the wet-and-dry climates, but a very gradual transition from one to the other (Fig. 9.14). Thus on the equatorward margins of the wet-and-dry regions the rainy season persists for almost the entire year, while on the poleward margins it is short. Conversely, on the dry poleward margin the period of absolute drought may last several months, while on the rainy margin, where wet-and-dry climate makes contact with tropical wet climate, there may be no month absolutely without rain. For emphasis it bears repeating that the rainy season closely coincides with the period of high sun and the dominance of converging, unstable air masses, whereas the dry season is identified with the period of low sun when stable, diverging, and subsiding air masses prevail. In short, rainfall follows the sun.

Seasonal weather During the rainy season tropical wet-and-dry weather is identical with that of tropical wet regions. Cloud of the cumulus type is abundant, and spells of showery rainfall with frequent thunderstorms are numerous. In the low-sun, or dry, season, on the other hand, the weather is like that of the deserts. The humidity becomes very low—so low that the skin is parched and cracked. (Yet the dry season is welcomed after the humid, oppressive heat of the rainy period.) During the dry season the landscape is parched and brown, the trees lose their leaves, the rivers become low, the soil cracks, and all nature appears dormant. Smoke from grass fires and dust fills the air, so that visibility is usually low.

Rainfall reliability   Rainfall in the tropical wet-and-dry climate, besides being sparser and more seasonal than in tropical wet climate, is less reliable: there is wider fluctuation in the amount from year to year (Fig. 11.9). One year may bring enough rain to flood the fields, rot the crops, and increase the ravages of injurious insects and fungi; the following year there may be even more severe losses from drought.

RESOURCE POTENTIALITIES OF THE TROPICAL WET-AND-DRY REALM

Tropical wet-and-dry climate characterizes close to 15 per cent of the earth's land area. On a map showing the distribution of the earth's inhabitants, many of the wet-and-dry areas are conspicuous because of their dearth of people. This is especially true of the extensive wet-and-dry regions of the New World and of Australia. Peninsular India is the most striking exception, for there human life is abundant. Portions of the African Sudan and of the upland wet-and-dry areas of eastern Africa are intermediate in their population densities.

Although temperatures are constantly high in tropical wet-and-dry climate, the fact that there is a dormant season imposed by drought makes the productiveness of wet-and-dry climate considerably less than that of tropical wet climate. The smaller total amount of precipitation and its undependability emphasize this contrast.

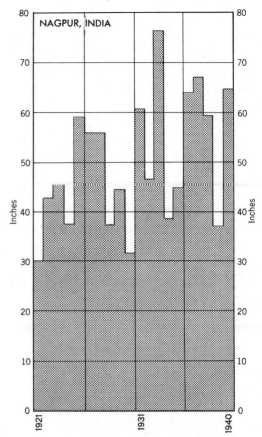

FIG. 11.9   Variations in amounts of annual rainfall over a 20-year period at Nagpur, India, a station with tropical wet-and-dry climate. Large annual variations in precipitation are characteristic of this type of climate.

Reflecting the reduced climatic energy, the vegetation cover is one of tall, coarse grasses with scattered trees, and of open forest with grass, instead of the dense evergreen forest that characterizes the tropical wet climate. Much of the woodland is of little value commercially, and the mature natural grasses are too tall, coarse, and unnutritious to support an important grazing industry. To the native agriculturist the tough-grass sod offers a more formidable obstacle than does the luxuriant rainforest.

Little is known about the mature soils of

the wet-and-dry climate, but generally they appear to be leached and infertile. There is some evidence that they are even inferior to those that develop under the tropical rain-forest. As in most regions of infertile or difficult soils, the fresh, young, unleached alluvial surfaces are the most attractive sites for cultivation.

UPLAND TROPICAL CLIMATE

In tropical latitudes on several continents, especially Africa and South America, there are extensive upland areas, possessed of many of the normal characteristics of tropical wet and tropical wet-and-dry climates but also differing, chiefly in their somewhat lower temperatures, which are the result of modest altitude. Some of these uplands, such as those of eastern Brazil and of eastern Africa, are among the best-developed tropical areas, for the lower temperatures make them more attractive to agricultural settlers. These uplands are included within the general wet-and-dry type of climate but on Plate 2 are set apart from the more standard lowland variety by a light stippling. (Climatic modifications imposed by altitude are discussed in Chap. 14.)

CHAPTER 12

The dry climates

CLASSIFICATION, BOUNDARIES, AND CHARACTERISTICS

Definition; desert and steppe types A dry climate (*B*) may be defined as one in which the annual water losses by evaporation from soils and vegetation potentially exceed the annual water gains by precipitation. In other words, there is a rainfall deficiency, and as a result there is no surplus of water to maintain a constant ground-water supply, so that permanent streams rarely *originate* within dry-climate areas.

Since the amount of water lost through evaporation increases with temperature and thus is greater in warm climates than in cold ones, the amount of annual rainfall distinguishing between dry and humid climates must also vary; that is, warm dry climates can have more annual rainfall than those which are cool.

Two types of dry climate are commonly recognized: (*a*) the *arid,* or *desert,* type and (*b*) the *semiarid,* or *steppe,* type. In general the steppe is a transitional belt surrounding the desert and separating it from the humid climates beyond (Fig. 11.2). The boundary between arid and semiarid climates is somewhat arbitrary, but in the Köppen system it is defined as one-half the amount of annual rainfall separating steppe from humid climates.

Type location   Of all the climatic groups dry climates are the most extensively developed over the continents, occupying over one-quarter of the earth's land surface. As Fig. 11.2 and Plate 2 show, they are to be found both in the tropics (including the subtropics) and in the middle latitudes.

In the tropics dry climates are concentrated between about latitudes 15°–20° and 30°, which are influenced by the subtropical anticyclones. Here the dry climates characteristically are shifted away from the eastern side of a continent toward its western and central parts, an asymmetry reflecting the fact that subsidence and atmospheric stability are greater in the eastern part of an oceanic subtropical anticyclone than along its western margins.

In the middle latitudes drought conditions are best developed in the deep interiors of the great land masses, areas which feel the effects of a cold anticyclone in winter and which are also farthest removed from the oceanic sources of moisture.

TEMPERATURE

Since dry climates exist in a wide range of latitudes, their average annual temperatures vary a great deal. Some dry climates are hot, others cold, still others intermediate in average annual temperature. On the other hand, dry climates at any latitude are generally characterized by seasonal temperatures that are more severe than the average for the latitude. In other words, summers in dry climates are likely to be notably warm or hot and winters notably cool or cold as compared with the summers and winters of humid climates in the same latitude. Large annual ranges of temperature are therefore representative. Such seasonal extremes and large

annual ranges are related to the leeward and interior locations of most dry climates, and to their prevailingly clear skies and dry atmosphere.

Even more striking than these annual ranges are the large daily ranges of temperature in dry climates, where the cloudless skies and relatively low humidity permit an abundance of solar energy to reach the earth by day and allow a rapid loss of earth energy at night. In deserts large diurnal ranges are also associated with the meager vegetation cover, which permits the dry, barren surface to become intensely heated by day.

Precipitation and humidity   Rainfall in the dry climates is always meager, and in addition so extremely variable from year to year that even the low average is not to be depended upon (Fig. 12.1). Significantly also, there are more years when rainfall is below the average than above, for it is the occasional humid year which tends to lift the average. It is a general rule, worthy of memorization, that dependability of precipitation usually decreases with decreasing amount; thus (*a*) meagerness and (*b*) unreliability of rainfall seem to go together.

With a few exceptions, relative humidity is low in the dry climates, 12 to 30 per cent being usual for midday hours, and conversely, potential evaporation is characteristically high. Thus there is little cloudiness, and the amount of sunshine is great: direct sunlight, as well as that reflected from the bare, light-colored earth, is blinding in intensity.

Absolute humidity, on the other hand, is by no means always low, for desert air in warm and hot climates usually contains a considerable quantity of water vapor, even when the air is far from saturated.

Winds   Dry regions are usually windy places, there being little friction between the moving air and the low and sparse vegetation

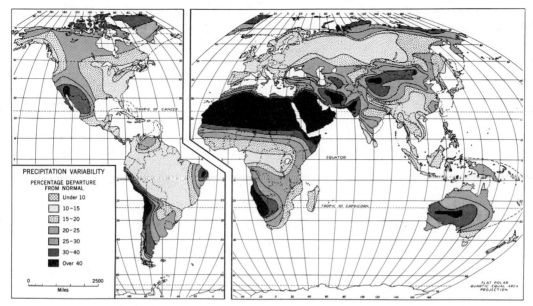

FIG. 12.1 Rainfall variability is normally at a maximum in dry and subhumid climates. *(From Biel, Van Royen, and others.)*

cover. In this respect dry regions are like the oceans. The daylight hours, when surface heating and convective overturning are at a maximum, are especially windy; nights are much calmer.

Because of the strong and persistent daytime winds, desert air is often murky with fine dust which fills the eyes, nose, and throat, causing serious discomfort. Much of this dust is carried by the winds beyond the desert margins to form the loess deposits of bordering regions. The heavier, wind-driven rock particles, traveling close to the surface,

are the principal tool of the wind in sculpturing the land forms of the deserts themselves.

Geographical classification The already-explained division of dry climates into desert and steppe types is supplemented in the classification of climates employed here by recognition of two great geographical divisions related to temperature contrasts. They are (*a*) the dry climates of the tropical and subtropical low latitudes, or the hot steppes and deserts, and (*b*) the dry climates of the middle latitudes, or the cold (in winter) steppes and deserts.

LOW-LATITUDE DRY CLIMATES

TYPE LOCATION

As indicated earlier, low-latitude dry climates (*BWh* and *BSh*)[1] owe their origin chiefly to the stabilizing effects of the sub-

[1] In the Köppen system, W = desert (*Wüste*), S = steppe, and h = hot (*heiss*): annual temperature over 64.4° (18°C).

sidence and horizontal wind divergence associated with the subtropical anticyclones (Fig. 11.3). It was also pointed out that since subsidence and divergence are concentrated in the eastern and central parts of an oceanic anticyclonic cell, drought conditions ordinarily do not extend over to the eastern margins of a continent (Fig. 11.2).

Along west coasts in these tropical and subtropical latitudes, by contrast, drought conditions reach down to the sea margins and even far beyond over the ocean. Here the drought-producing effects of strong subsidence in the eastern parts of an oceanic anticyclone are augmented by those of the cool ocean currents with upwelled water which characteristically parallel tropical west coasts. The cold water acts to chill and stabilize the surface air and to intensify the aridity, so that along these west coasts dry climates may be carried 5 to 10° farther equatorward than normal. Indeed it appears to be a general rule that while tropical humid climates extend unusually far poleward along the eastern sides of the continents (eastern Brazil, eastern Central America, and eastern Madagascar), tropical dry climates are carried equatorward beyond their normal latitudes along the western littorals (western Peru and western Angola in southwestern Africa).

PRECIPITATION

Annual amount and dependability The deserts of low latitudes are the most nearly rainless regions of the earth. Here the persistent anticyclonic control consistently holds at bay the rainbringing disturbances that attempt to encroach from north, south, and

east. In the steppes that usually surround the deserts, the same disturbances are present often enough to add appreciably to the total rainfall.

Probably most of the tropical desert has an annual rainfall below 10 in., and extensive areas receive less than 5 in. In parts of the Chilean desert no rain may fall for 5 to 10 years in succession. Over the steppe lands 10 to 25 in. of rain is more common. Actually, averages are of little value in providing a correct impression of the year-by-year amount or the seasonal distribution of desert and steppe rainfall, for it is not only small but also undependable in amount, and uncertain in its time of occurrence. As an illustration, no rain fell at Iquique in northern Chile during a period of four years; then in the fifth year one shower provided 0.6 in., which made the average annual rainfall for the five-year period 0.12 in.

In the dry tropics, as in the humid tropics, most of the rainfall is of the showery convective type which falls from cumulus clouds. It is chiefly in the poleward parts of the low-latitude dry climates, which lie closest to the cyclone tracks of middle latitudes, that widespread general rains falling from a gray overcast are likely.

Seasonal distribution In the deserts, where total annual rainfall is so meager, it is almost useless to speak of a seasonal distribu-

Climatic Data for Representative Stations in Low-latitude Deserts

	J	F	M	A	M	J	J	A	S	O	N	D	Yr	Range
Jacobabad, Pakistan														
Temp.	57	62	75	86	92	98	95	9.2	89	79	68	59	79	41
Precip.	0.3	0.3	0.3	0.2	0.1	0.2	1.0	1.1	0.3	0.0	0.1	0.1	4.0	
William Creek, Australia														
Temp.	83	83	76	67	59	54	52	56	62	70	77	81	68	31
Precip.	0.5	0.4	0.8	0.4	0.4	0.7	0.3	0.3	0.4	0.3	0.4	0.3	5.2	

Climatic Data for a Representative Low-latitude Steppe Station with High-sun Rainfall

	J	F	M	A	M	J	J	A	S	O	N	D	Yr	Range
						Kayes, Sudan								
Temp.	77	81	89	94	96	91	84	82	82	85	83	77	85	19
Precip.	0.0	0.0	0.0	0.0	0.6	3.9	8.3	8.3	5.6	1.9	0.3	0.2	29.1	

Climatic Data for a Representative Low-latitude Steppe Station with Low-sun Rainfall

	J	F	M	A	M	J	J	A	S	O	N	D	Yr	Range
						Benghazi, Libya								
Temp.	55	57	63	66	72	75	78	79	78	75	66	59	69	24
Precip.	3.7	1.8	0.7	0.1	0.1	0.0	0.0	0.0	0.1	0.3	2.1	3.1	12.0	

tion or to distinguish wetter and drier seasons. This is less true of the steppe climate, where annual rainfall is greater. As a rule, those steppes lying on the poleward margins of a tropical desert and therefore closest to the dry-summer subtropical climate[2] (in northernmost Africa, for example) receive their maximum rainfall in winter, or the time of low sun, when the cyclonic belt has shifted farthest equatorward (Plates 1, 2). By contrast, those steppes situated on the equatorward borders of the tropical desert and therefore adjacent to tropical wet-and-dry climate, such as parts of the Sudan, experience most of their rainfall in summer, or the time of high sun. This is the season when the ITC and its disturbances are displaced farthest poleward (table, p. 227: compare data for Benghazi and Kayes).

As might be expected cloudiness is meager and sunshine abundant in dry climates. In the Sonora desert of northwestern Mexico and adjacent parts of the United States, about 75 per cent of the possible sunshine is ex-

[2] Dry-summer subtropical, or Mediterranean, climate will be considered in detail in the next chapter.

perienced in winter and 90 per cent in the other seasons. The blinding glare of direct and reflected sunlight is a characteristic feature.

TEMPERATURE

Seasonal temperatures It has been pointed out earlier that dry climates as a group are characterized by large seasonal and diurnal extremes of temperature. In the low-latitude dry climates specifically, scorching, dessicating heat prevails during the period of high sun. Average hot-month temperatures are usually between 85 and 90°, and those of the winter season between 50 and 60° (Fig. 12.2). Thus an annual range of 25 to 30° or even more is to be expected. Such relatively large seasonal differences are not to be found in any other tropical climates. They reflect the greater seasonal extremes of solar energy here, as well as the clear skies, low humidity, and sparseness of vegetation.

Daily temperatures The temperature difference between day and night (diurnal range) may equal or even exceed that between winter and summer. Midday readings of 100

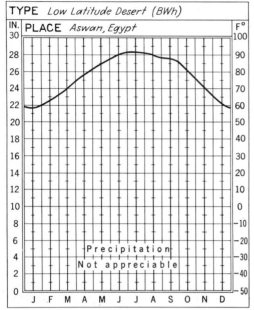

TYPE *Low Latitude Desert (BWh)*

PLACE *Aswan, Egypt*

FIG. 12.2 Average monthly temperatures for a low-latitude desert station with an interior location. Note the relatively large annual range for the tropics.

to 110° are common in summer, and over 130° has been recorded (Fig. 12.3). At Yuma, Arizona, the daily maximum exceeded 100° on 80 consecutive days in one summer, except for 1 day. On summer nights the temperature may drop to 75 or 80°, a welcome relief after the parching daytime heat, but still relatively warm.

During winter midday temperatures are pleasantly warm, averaging 65 to 75°, while nights are distinctly chilly, the minimum temperatures dropping to 45 to 55°. Occasionally, light frosts are experienced in the tropical deserts. Thus, diurnal ranges of 25 to 35° are characteristic.

Daily weather Weather in the tropical dry climates is dominated by a diurnal regularity, which bespeaks solar control (Fig. 12.3). For any locality one day is markedly like another, with temperature rising to about the same level during the period of afternoon

FIG. 12.3 Daily maximum and minimum temperatures for the warmest and coolest months at a station with low-latitude desert climate (*BWh*). The station, at Yuma, Arizona, is located in the subtropics rather than in the real tropics, so that while diurnal sun control is dominant, there is some evidence of nonperiodic cyclonic, or air-mass, control also.

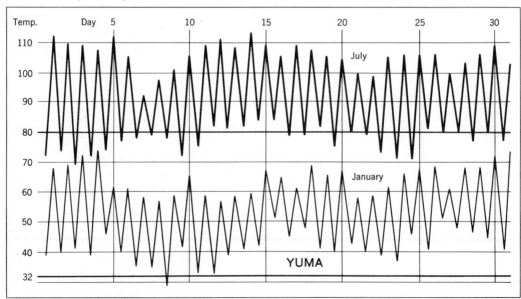

heat and falling to nearly the same minimum at night. Some nonperiodic variety in weather is added in the more marginal parts, where disturbances bring spells of showery or rainy weather on the low-latitude frontier in summer and the poleward frontier in winter. The poleward margins likewise experience some nondiurnal temperature variations derived from passing middle-latitude fronts accompanied by invasions of polar air.

COOL MARINE DRY CLIMATES

The previously mentioned extension of drought conditions to tropical west coasts produces an unusual subtype of desert along several tropical coasts paralleled by cool ocean currents—a desert with *cool marine dry climate (Bn)*.[3] The locations of these deserts are shown on Fig. 12.4. The normal features of low-latitude dry climates—hot summers, large annual and daily temperature ranges, low humidity, and meager cloudiness—are strikingly modified in these locations.

Temperature Along these cool-water desert coasts average summer-month temperatures are 10 to 20° below those of interior locations. For example, the hottest month at Callao on the Peruvian coast has an average temperature of only 71° (as does July at Madison, Wisconsin); Port Nolloth in southwestern Africa has 60° (as does July at Archangel, U.S.S.R.). The result is daily and annual temperature ranges which are only a third to a half as great as at interior locations. Observation of the table of climatic data for Lima, Peru (p. 330), and comparison of Figs. 12.2 and 12.3 with Figs. 12.5 and 12.6 will illustrate these contrasts.

Precipitation and fog Rainfall along these cool tropical desert coasts is exceedingly

[3] In the Köppen system *n* = frequent fog (*Nebel*).

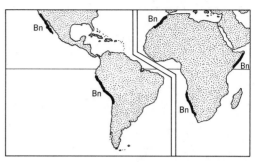

FIG. 12.4 Distribution of cool marine dry climates (*Bn*) in the tropics. Here fog is prevalent. Characteristically this subtype of low-latitude dry climates is located along coasts paralleled by cool ocean currents.

low, even lower than in much of the interior desert, because of the combined effects of two drought makers, (*a*) the stable eastern end of an oceanic subtropical anticyclone, and (*b*) the cool coastal water. For a distance of nearly 2,000 miles along the desert coasts of

FIG. 12.5 Average monthly temperatures for a marine desert station located on a tropical west coast paralleled by a cool ocean current. Temperatures are abnormally low and the annual range is very small. Compare with Fig. 12.2.

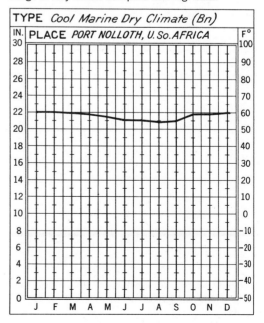

TYPE *Cool Marine Dry Climate (Bn)*
PLACE *PORT NOLLOTH, U. So. AFRICA*

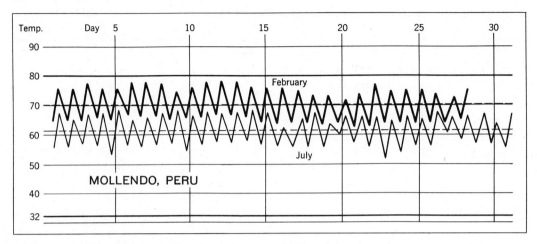

FIG. 12.6 Daily maximum and minimum temperatures for a low-latitude desert station located on a tropical west coast paralleled by a cool ocean current. Note the abnormally low average temperatures and the small daily ranges. Compare with Fig. 12.3.

Peru and northern Chile, annual rainfall is held to about 1 in.

But although precipitation is meager, fog and low stratus clouds are abundant, so that the persistent sunshine so common to most deserts is greatly reduced, especially in winter. At Swakopmund in southwestern Africa fog is recorded on 150 days of the year. Much of the surface fog is attributable to the chilling effects of the cool water upon air moving landward from the sea. The gray overcast aloft is associated with the strong temperature inversion produced by subsidence in the anticyclone. At times a drizzle falls from the stratus cloud.

Climatic Data for a Representative Desert Station on a Cool-water Coast

	J	F	M	A	M	J	J	A	S	O	N	D	Yr	Range
						Lima, Peru								
Temp.	71	73	73	70	66	62	61	61	61	62	66	70	66	12
Precip.	0.0	0.0	0.0	0.0	0.0	0.2	0.3	0.5	0.5	0.1	0.0	0.0	1.6	

MIDDLE-LATITUDE DRY CLIMATES

TYPE LOCATION

Deserts and steppes in the middle latitudes (*BWk* and *BSk*)[4] are usually found in the deep

[4] In the Köppen system *k* = cold (*kalt*): average annual temperature below 64.4° (18°C).

interiors of the great continents far from the oceans, which are the principal sources of the atmosphere's water vapor (Fig. 11.2; Plate 2). Significantly also, the driest regions usually have a basin configuration. Thus the aridity of some interior parts of the two great Northern

Hemisphere continents is intensified by their being largely surrounded by highland barriers that block the entrance of humid maritime air masses. Indeed, where high mountains closely parallel a coast, as in western North America, arid climates approach relatively close to the sea. The winter thermal anticyclone likewise acts to reduce the precipitation of the colder months.

Although *tropical* dry climates characteristically extend down to the ocean margins on the leeward (western) side of a continent, the leeward side of a continent in the middle-latitude westerlies (here the eastern side) may be far from dry, as in eastern North America and Eurasia, for example. This shifting of middle-latitude dry climates inland from the east coast is associated with (*a*) the presence along the eastern side of a large continent in the westerlies of air masses which are humid and not too stable, and (*b*) rain-generating cyclonic storms. Owing to an unusual combination of circumstances, dry climates do reach the east coast in Argentine Patagonia, but this is the exception. There the land mass is so narrow that all of it lies in the rain shadow of the Andes, where descending currents make for drought conditions.

TEMPERATURE

The interior location on large continents of most middle-latitude dry climates assures their having relatively severe seasonal temperatures and consequently large annual ranges. However, because they have such a wide latitudinal spread (15 or 20° in both North America and Asia), it is difficult to speak of *typical* temperature conditions, for the conditions are very different on their equatorward and poleward margins. Yet for any given latitude temperatures are severe.

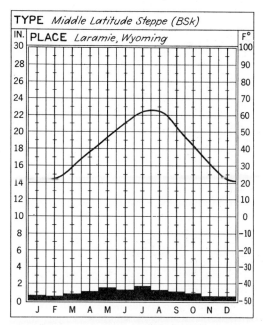

FIG. 12.7   Average monthly temperatures and precipitation amounts for a representative station having a middle-latitude steppe climate.

Summers are inclined to be warm or even hot, and winters are correspondingly cold (Figs. 12.7, 12.8; table, p. 232). Diurnal ranges are large for the same reasons noted previously for tropical steppes and deserts (Figs. 12.3, 12.8). Patagonia in Argentina is again somewhat the exception. There the narrow land mass and the cool waters offshore result in temperatures that are more marine than continental, so that summers are unusually cool and winters relatively mild.

PRECIPITATION

Probably no parts of middle-latitude deserts are so rainless as the most arid tropical deserts, and some precipitation, in all likelihood, falls every year. Unlike the dry climates of low latitudes, these of middle latitudes receive a part of their total precipitation in the form of snow, although the amount is small and

Climatic Data for Representative Stations in Middle-latitude Steppes

	J	F	M	A	M	J	J	A	S	O	N	D	Yr	Range
Williston, North Dakota														
Temp.	6	8	22	43	53	63	69	67	56	44	27	14	39.2	62.7
Precip.	0.5	0.4	0.9	1.1	2.1	3.2	1.7	1.7	1.0	0.7	0.6	0.5	14.4	
Quetta, Pakistan (5,500 ft)														
Temp.	40	41	51	60	67	74	78	75	67	56	47	42	58.1	38.2
Precip.	2.1	2.1	1.8	1.1	0.3	0.2	0.5	0.6	0.1	0.1	0.3	0.8	10.0	
Urga, Mongolia (3,800 ft)														
Temp.	−16	−4	13	34	48	58	63	59	48	30	8	−17	28	79
Precip.	0.0	0.1	0.0	0.0	0.3	1.7	2.6	2.1	0.5	0.1	0.1	0.1	7.6	

the snow cover is of variable duration, depending chiefly on latitude.

Again, it is not easy to generalize about the seasonal distribution of precipitation. Certainly much the larger parts of the middle-latitude dry climates, located as they are in the deep interior of a large land area, have the characteristic continental strong summer maximum and strong winter minimum (Fig. 12.7; table, p. 232, data for Williston). However, along western subtropical margins where the subtropical anticyclone strengthens in sum-

FIG. 12.8 Daily maximum and minimum temperatures for the warmest and coolest months at a station with middle-latitude steppe climate. Note the relatively stronger nonperiodic air-mass control, especially in January.

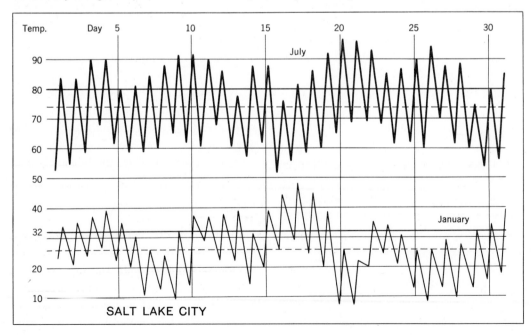

Climatic Data for Representative Stations in Middle-latitude Deserts

	J	F	M	A	M	J	J	A	S	O	N	D	Yr	Range
					Santa Cruz, Argentina									
Temp.	59	58	55	48	41	35	35	38	44	49	53	56	47.5	24
Precip.	0.6	0.4	0.3	0.6	0.6	0.5	0.7	0.4	0.2	0.4	0.5	0.9	6.1	
					Turfan, Sinkiang, China (−56 ft)									
Temp.	13	27	46	66	75	85	90	85	74	56	33	18	56	77
Precip.	No data													
					Fallon, Nevada (3,965 ft)									
Temp.	31	36	41	50	56	65	74	72	61	51	40	32	50.0	42.7
Precip.	0.6	0.5	0.5	0.4	0.6	0.3	0.1	0.2	0.3	0.4	0.3	0.6	4.8	

mer, a reversed situation, with a winter maximum, may prevail (table, p. 232, data for Quetta).

As in the dry tropics, precipitation amounts vary so greatly from year to year in middle-latitude dry climates that the average is not to be depended upon. This unreliability of precipitation is most serious in the semiarid steppe lands, which are marginal between agricultural and grazing economies. During a series of relatively humid years crop yields may be bountiful, but drought years with associated crop failures and lean incomes are bound to follow, so that agriculture is a precarious occupation (Fig. 12.9).

The weather element Although sun control, with its diurnal regularity of weather, remains strong (Fig. 12.8), it is by no means as dominant as in the dry tropics. Traveling cyclones and anticyclones are fairly numerous, and these disturbances induce nonperiodic episodes of alternating cold and warmth, rain and fair weather.

RESOURCE POTENTIALITIES OF THE DRY REALM

Dry climates, as previously stated, are characteristic of over one-quarter of the earth's land surface—more land than any other climatic group occupies. It is unfortunate that such an unproductive climate should be so extensively distributed because for the most part dry lands are coincident with great blank spaces on the world-population map, like parts of the wet tropics and nearly all of the cold polar and subarctic lands. Indeed, these three climates—the dry, the cold, and the constantly hot—offer the greatest obstacles to a large-scale redistribution of population on the earth.

Owing to the insufficiency and extreme year-to-year variability of the rainfall in dry climates, it appears that a large part of the earth's land surface is doomed to remain relatively unproductive. Recent successes attained in artificially producing rainfall by cloud-seeding methods and in converting sea water into fresh water have created a heightened optimism concerning expanded utilization of the dry lands. Yet no large-

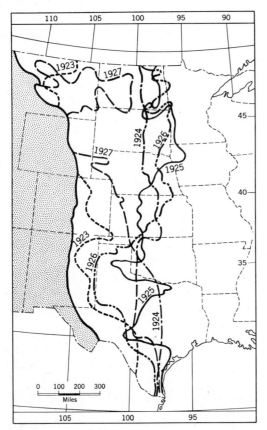

FIG. 12.9 Wide fluctuations during a period of 5 years in the location of the boundary separating dry from humid climates in the interior United States east of the Rocky Mountains. *(From Kendall.)*

The niggardly climate is responsible for a sparse vegetation cover which has relatively low resource value. Some deserts are almost barren wastes, practically devoid of plants having economic value. Other deserts have a thin mantle of widely spaced woody shrubs with some short desert bunch grass, but even the grazing value of this vegetation is very low. Over the desert area of the southwestern United States, for instance, more than 75 acres are required to supply natural forage for one steer. In the semiarid regions, short, shallow-rooted, widely spaced grasses prevail, and this steppe vegetation has a considerably higher grazing value than has the desert shrub; i.e., it is capable of supporting more livestock per unit area. This grass, the greatest natural asset of the steppes, forms the basis for a grazing industry, but grazing is an economy which is able to support only a small population.

Soils are of little consequence in deserts largely because the deficient rainfall makes it impossible to use them for agricultural purposes. Soils of the tropical steppes appear to be inferior to those of the steppes in middle latitudes, where the very modest amount of leaching and the humus (organic material) derived from the root mat of the grasses make for dark fertile soils of high resource value. Unfortunately this admirable soil resource of middle-latitude semiarid lands cannot be exploited to anything like its capacity because of the precipitation handicap. Thus, although the humid margins of some middle-latitude steppes have been brought under the plow, it appears that the meager and unreliable rainfall will go on tending to keep the larger part of the world's steppe lands out of cultivation and in natural grasses in the future. It is the old story of fruitful soils and prolific climates seldom being areally coincident.

scale increase in dry-land agriculture seems likely to result from these methods of creating new water sources within the near future.

It would appear, then, that the expansion of settlement in lands with dry climates will be associated with (*a*) an increased use of irrigation methods and (*b*) the further development and greater use of drought-resistant plants and their cultivation by dry-farming methods. But again, it is hard to be optimistic about the promise that either of these methods holds for opening up extensive areas of dry land for future agricultural settlement.

CHAPTER 13

Humid mesothermal climates

GENERAL CHARACTER AND TYPE LOCATIONS

In the tropics, where temperatures are constantly high, climates are distinguished on the basis of rainfall contrasts and seasons are designated as wet or dry. But in the middle latitudes temperature becomes coequal with, in places even superior to, rainfall as an aid in differentiating climates (excepting the middle-latitude dry climates, of course), and the dominant seasons are designated as winter and summer. Here the dormant season for plant growth is usually the season of low temperature, not of drought. Thus it is that in the humid middle latitudes there are two great groups of climate which are distinguished from each other on the basis of temperature: the milder humid mesothermal (C) which will be considered in this chapter, and the more severe humid microthermal (D).

Since winters in mesothermal climates must be relatively mild, the three types compris-

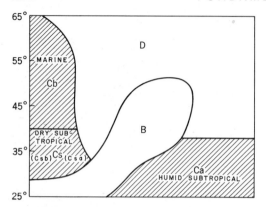

FIG. 13.1 Locations on a hypothetical continent of the three mesothermal (*C*) types of climate.

ing this group are found only where severe and long-continued winter cold is precluded. They are, as a consequence, restricted to two locations: (*a*) the equatorward margins of the middle-latitude continents where the latitude ensures winter mildness, and (*b*) marine locations farther poleward on the windward or western side of a continent (Figs. 11.1, 13.1). Two of the mesothermal climates, *dry-summer subtropical* and *humid subtropical,* occupy the first of the type locations mentioned above, while the third, *marine* climate, is typically found in the second (Fig. 11.2).

Throughout the discussion of middle-latitude climates to follow it should be borne in mind that in the middle latitudes the changeableness of the weather is a striking characteristic. It should be remembered that as the natural region of conflict for contrasting air masses expelled from the tropical and polar source regions, the middle latitudes are zones of horizontal air convergence, and that as a consequence, cyclonic storms and fronts, with their accompanying weather changes, are numerous.

DRY-SUMMER SUBTROPICAL CLIMATE (MEDITERRANEAN)

GENERAL FEATURES

For land areas as a whole it is common for summer to have more rainfall than winter, even where winter is far from being dry: it is a general rule that rainfall follows the sun. Consequently, where seasonal rainfall distribution is reversed, and winter is not only wet but summer is also dry, a most unusual climatic condition is present. Actually, a unique climatic condition is present, for dry-summer subtropical, or Mediterranean, climate (*Cs*)[1] has the distinction of being the earth's only type of humid climate in which the seasons of heat and drought coincide.

This climate—with its bright and sunny weather, blue skies, relatively few rainy days, and mild winters, and its usual association with abundant flowers and fruit—has quite deservedly acquired a glamorous reputation. The distinctive features of the type are marked, and not easily forgettable, and they are duplicated with notable similarity in the five regions where this climate occurs, viz., the borderlands of the Mediterranean Sea, southern California, central Chile, the southwestern tip of Africa, and parts of southern Australia.

TYPE LOCATION

Mediterranean climate characteristically is located on the tropical margins of the middle latitudes (30°–40°) along the western side of a continent (Fig. 11.2; Plate 2). Situated thus on the poleward slopes of the subtropical high, it is intermediate in location between

[1] In the Köppen system *s* = dry season in summer.

the dry subsiding air masses of the subtropical anticyclone and the rainbringing fronts and cyclones of the westerlies. With the north-south shifting of wind belts during the course of the year, these Mediterranean latitudes are joined to the dry tropics at one season and to the humid middle latitudes at the other season. Tropical constancy therefore characterizes them in summer, middle-latitude changeability in winter. Emphatically, this Mediterranean, or dry-summer subtropical, type is a transitional climate between the low-latitude steppe and desert, and the cool, humid, marine climate farther poleward.

In addition the Mediterranean climate, confined as it usually is to the western side of a continent roughly between latitudes 30 and 40°, in summer feels the especially strong subsidence characteristic of the eastern limb of an oceanic anticyclone.

In both central Chile and California, mountains terminate the type abruptly on the land side. The farthest poleward extent of southern Africa and southwestern Australia carries them barely to Mediterranean latitudes, so that on these continents the dry-summer subtropical climate occupies southern and southwestern extremities rather than distinctly west-coast location. Only in the region of the Mediterranean Sea Basin, which is an important route of winter cyclones, does this type of climate extend far inland; there it prevails inland for 2,000 miles or more, this most extensive development being responsible for the climate's regional name.

The interior and the eastern margin of a continent, where the summer anticyclone is relatively weak and where there is a tendency toward a monsoon wind system, are not conducive to the development of Mediterranean climate, especially its characteristic seasonal rainfall regime.

TEMPERATURE

Winter temperatures It is for its characteristically mild, bright winters with their pleasant living temperatures that Mediterranean climate is deservedly famed. People of the colder, higher latitudes seek it out for comfortable winter living. Absence of severe winter cold is to be expected here because of both the subtropical location and the proximity to the sea on the windward western side of the continent. Usually the winter months have average temperatures between 45 and 55°, with coastal locations somewhat milder than those inland (Figs. 13.2, 13.3). During midday hours the temperature commonly rises to 60° or even higher; at night it may drop to 40 or 45° and at times even

Climatic Data for Representative Dry-summer Subtropical Stations

	J	*F*	*M*	*A*	*M*	*J*	*J*	*A*	*S*	*O*	*N*	*D*	*Yr*	*Range*
					Red Bluff, California (interior)									
Temp.	45	50	54	59	67	75	82	80	73	64	54	46	62.3	37
Precip.	4.6	3.9	3.2	1.7	1.1	0.5	0.0	0.1	0.8	1.3	2.9	4.3	24.4	
					Santa Monica, California (coast)									
Temp.	53	53	55	58	60	63	66	66	65	62	58	55	59.5	13
Precip.	3.5	3.0	2.9	0.5	0.5	0.0	0.0	0.0	0.1	0.6	1.4	2.3	14.8	
					Perth, Australia (coast)									
Temp.	74	74	71	67	61	57	55	56	58	61	66	71	64	19
Precip.	0.3	0.5	0.7	1.6	4.9	6.9	6.5	5.7	3.3	2.1	0.8	0.6	33.9	

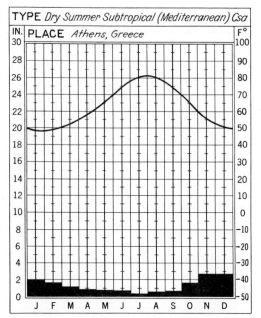

FIG. 13.2 Average monthly temperatures and precipitation amounts at an interior station north of the equator having a Mediterranean climate with a hot summer (*Csa*).

ample, during a period of 41 years at Los Angeles, California, near the Pacific Coast, there were 28 in which no killing frost occurred and the growing season was 12 months long, whereas at Sacramento, away from the coast, the temperature usually drops below 32° on several winter nights each year. Such frosts as do occur in the Mediterranean climate are generally the result of an invasion of cool *cP* air followed by further surface night cooling. Especially in Mediterranean climates, the freezing temperatures are confined to a shallow layer of cold surface air which tends to collect in low places. Thus preparations for frost are not extensive but sensitive crops are characteristically planted on slopes. Also, oil heaters occasionally are lighted in citrus groves in order to prevent frost damage.

FIG. 13.3 Average monthly temperatures and precipitation amounts at a coastal station south of the equator having a Mediterranean climate with a cool summer (*Csb*).

reach freezing (Fig. 13.4). Alternating spells of cooler and of warmer weather result from the advection of air from higher and from lower latitudes which is brought by the moderately frequent cyclonic storms of winter.

Frost It is not because of its frequency and severity that frost (which was discussed generally in Chap. 7) is so much dreaded in these regions of sensitive fruit and vegetable crops, but rather because of its infrequency. It is this infrequency that tempts the farmers to take a chance on the frost hazard, with the result that on occasion large losses are sustained. The growing season is ordinarily not quite the whole year, for frosts do occasionally occur during the 3 winter months; but they usually occur on only a few nights, and rarely are they severe freezes (Fig. 13.4). Never does the thermometer remain below freezing during the daytime hours. For ex-

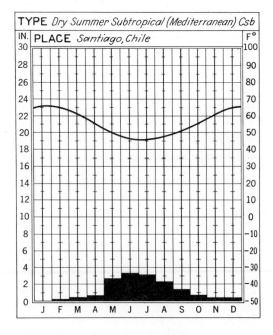

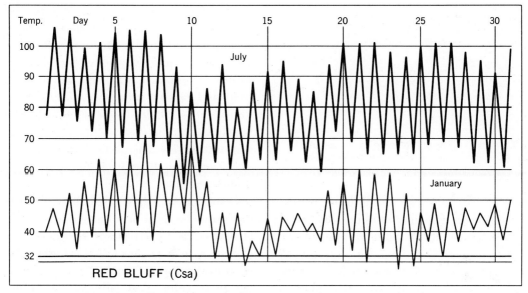

FIG. 13.4 Temperature conditions at an interior dry-summer subtropical station (*Csa*). Note the hot summer and the large diurnal range of temperature. Solar control is dominant in summer, but irregular, nonperiodic air-mass control is conspicuous in winter.

Summer temperatures On the basis of varying intensity of the summer heat as determined by proximity to the coast and cool water, two subdivisions of Mediterranean climate are recognized, the hot-summer subtype (*Csa*) and the cool-summer subtype (*Csb*).[2] Along coasts, particularly those bordered by cool ocean currents, average summer-month temperatures are low for the latitude, usually between 65 and 70° (Fig. 13.3). Elsewhere summer months are warm to hot, commonly 75 to 80° (Fig. 13.2). In the cool marine location daytime temperatures may reach only into the 70s and the diurnal range is small. Night fog and low stratus clouds are frequent. By contrast midday summer temperatures in the hotter interiors commonly reach 85 to 90°, sometimes even

[2] On Plate 2 the Köppen designations *Csa* and *Csb* are used; *a* = temperature of warmest month above 71.6° (22°C), and *b* = temperature of warmest month below 71.6°.

100° (Fig. 13.4). The dry summer heat of interior stations in California, for instance, greatly resembles that of a tropical steppe or desert.

PRECIPITATION

Amount As a general rule Mediterranean climate errs on the side of having too little rather than too much rainfall. Much of the area where this climate prevails just escapes being semiarid, and the normal 15 to 25 in. of annual precipitation in this climate justifies its being designated as subhumid rather than genuinely humid. It is usually bordered by steppe climate along its equatorward margin, so that it is driest along this frontier and rainfall amounts increase poleward. Thus San Diego in southernmost California receives only 10 in. of rain; Los Angeles, less than 100 miles farther north, 15 in.; and San Francisco, about 250 miles

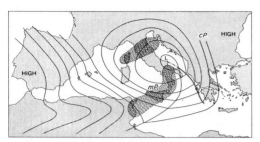

FIG. 13.5 The precipitation of dry-summer subtropical climate, concentrated in the cooler months, originates chiefly in cyclonic storms.

still farther north, 20 in. With increasing distance from the influence of the subtropical anticyclone, rainfall mounts. The general deficit in water and the variation in rainfall amounts from year to year are reflected in the large-scale use of irrigation water. Most of the modest rainfall on lowlands originates in cyclonic storms or along fronts, disturbances which are characteristic features of the middle-latitude westerly winds (Fig. 13.5).

Seasonal distribution To an unusual degree the year's rainfall is concentrated in the cooler half of the year (Figs. 13.2, 13.3). Winter characteristically is the rainiest of the 4 seasons, while summer is desertlike in character. Thus at Los Angeles over three-quarters of the year's rain comes during the 4 months from December to March and only 2 per cent from June to September. The rainfall regime, therefore, is that of the deserts in summer and that of the cyclonic westerlies in winter when rain is relatively abundant.

This seasonal alternation of drought and rainfall is, as previously indicated, a consequence of the north-south migration of the planetary winds and rainfall belts following the course of the sun. A poleward shifting of the sun in summer brings these subtropical latitudes along west coasts under the influence of the stable eastern margin of a sub-

tropical anticyclone. Subsiding and diverging air, a near absence of atmospheric disturbance, and cool ocean water along the coast all conjoin to produce aridity (Fig. 13.6). In winter, by contrast, when the sun and the wind and rainfall belts have reached their southernmost limits, these same latitudes largely escape the effects of the anticyclone, and instead are encroached upon by the westerlies with their cyclonic storms and frontal systems (Fig. 13.5).

Seasonal weather Although winter is the rainy season in dry-summer subtropical climate, it is by no means so dismal and gloomy as it is farther poleward along the coast in the marine climate. More often than not these subtropical latitudes lie on the

FIG. 13.6 The drought of summer in dry-summer subtropical climate is the result of stable air which originates in the eastern end of a subtropical oceanic anticyclone.

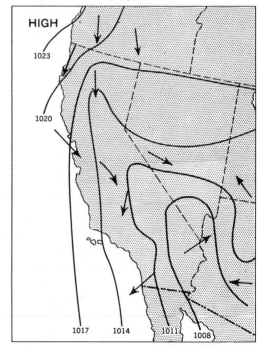

equatorward margins of most of the passing cyclonic storms, so that sunshine is abundant even in winter, and long-continued periods of cloud and rain are not characteristic. Nevertheless, since cyclones are most frequent in winter, it is to be expected that nonperiodic weather changes in both precipitation and temperature will be at a maximum during that season. The periodic diurnal rise and fall of temperature following the daily course of the sun is modified by the irregular importation—by the cyclonically induced winds from south and north—of alternating spells of warmer and cooler weather (Fig. 13.4). Short periods of cloudy, rainy weather separate others that are bright and sunny. Even in winter, however, it is common for these subtropical latitudes to experience 50 to 70 per cent of the possible sunshine.

Summer weather is less fickle and changeable than that of winter because cyclonic control is largely lacking. With the subtropical anticyclone dominating and sun control imposing a diurnal regularity upon the weather, one day is much like another and clear cloudless skies and bright sunny weather are the rule (Fig. 13.4). In interior California, for instance, midsummer months have over 90 per cent of the possible sunshine.

Snowfall   In all Mediterranean regions snow is so rare on the lowlands that it is something of an event when it does fall. Over the lowlands of central and southern California, for example, annual snowfall averages less than 1 in., and it is absent along the coast from San Luis Obispo southward. On adjacent highlands in Mediterranean regions, however, a moderate to heavy snow cover may be present, and meltwater from it provides an invaluable source of irrigation for the nearby drier lowlands.

RESOURCE POTENTIALITIES OF THE MEDITERRANEAN REALM

This, the most restricted of all the principal climatic types, embracing less than 2 per cent of the earth's land surface, is nevertheless one of the most unusual and alluring. Its abundance of sunshine, fruit, and flowers; its mild and relatively bright, sunny winter weather offering resort and outdoor-sport attractions; and its blue skies and even bluer waters create for the Mediterranean climate a reputation and renown far out of proportion to its small area. The Mediterranean realm is attractive as a winter playground for peoples from more severe climates especially, for here snow, ice, and frigid temperatures are left behind, and much out-of-doors living can be enjoyed throughout even the coolest months. The proximity of the sea is a further, year-round attraction. Certainly, in providing amenities conducive to pleasant living, climate looms large among the realm's resources.

In the dry-summer subtropical climate is found a unique combination of elements, some of which make for high agricultural productive capacity, and some of which have the opposite effect. Particularly the temperature elements—long, warm-to-hot summers with abundant sunshine; mild, bright winters; and an almost-year-round frost-free season—underlie the high agricultural potentialities of this climate. The Mediterranean realm and the humid subtropical realm, which will be studied next, approach the bountiful temperature regime of the tropics more nearly than any other part of the middle latitudes. This close approach to tropical temperature conditions, combined with their lying within the middle latitudes and profiting by proximity to the markets of these latitudes, gives to these two realms a considerable part of their distinctive character. In them is permitted the development of certain heat-loving or frost-sensitive crops, some of a luxury type—citrus, figs, viniferous grapes, rice, sugar cane, cotton—which can be grown in few other parts of the middle latitudes. The subtropical climates likewise allow the production of out-of-season vegetables and flowers for the markets of regions farther poleward, where a season of severe cold imposes a long dormant period. The possibility, within the Mediterranean realm specifically, of utilizing the middle-latitude winter as an active growing season offers unusual agricultural opportunities.

On the other hand, (*a*) the relatively meager total precipitation and (*b*) the long summer drought place definite climatic limitations upon production within the Mediterranean realm. This total water deficiency and its heightening in the warm months make summer, in spite of its abundant heat, a naturally dormant season. The relatively meager total precipitation and the arid summers also tend to place limitations upon the kinds of crops grown, causing emphasis on drought-resistant perennials, such as the olive and the vine, and on those annuals which mature quickly, such as barley and wheat. The large-scale development of irrigation within the Mediterranean realm is evi-

dence of the people's attempt to overcome the handicap of the dormant summer and provide a year-round growth for crops, and to take away the limitations on kinds of crops.

It is fortunate, since there is a season of drought, that it occurs in summer, i.e., that the usual 15 to 25 in. of rain is concentrated in the cooler months of the year when evaporation is at a minimum. If the same modest amount fell during the hot summer, when evaporation is excessive, much less of it would be effective for plant growth and the climate would be semiarid.

The modest precipitation and the summer drought produce a vegetation cover characterized by woody shrubs and widely spaced, stunted trees; in some Mediterranean regions scattered patches of desert bunch grass are also present. This plant cover is of some value for grazing, particularly of sheep and goats. But only on the higher hill lands and the mountain slopes are the forests of genuine commercial value, the stunted trees and the bushes of the valleys and the lower slopes being useful chiefly as checks to erosion.

Because of the widespread occurrence of hill land in this realm, mature residual soils are not extensively developed. On the slopes soils are inclined to be thin and stony, and to a considerable extent they remain uncultivated. It is the young alluvial soils of the valleys which are the attractive sites for cultivation.

HUMID SUBTROPICAL CLIMATE

Humid subtropical climate (*Ca*),[3] the other subtropical climate in the mesothermal

[3] In the Köppen system *a* = temperature of the warmest month over 71.6° (22°C).

group, differs from dry-summer subtropical climate in three principal ways: (*a*) it is characteristically located on the eastern rather than on the western side of a continent, (*b*) it has more total precipitation, and (*c*) its precipitation is concentrated in the warmer months, although in most areas winter is by no means dry.

TYPE LOCATION

As previously stated, the two subtropical climates are similar in latitudinal location, both lying on the tropical margins of the middle latitudes roughly between 30 and 40°, a fact which in itself would make for climatic likeness (Fig. 13.1; Plate 2). It is the dissimilar location of the humid subtropical climate on the eastern side of a land mass (Fig. 11.2) which fosters climatic difference. Thus the subtropical east-side location favors more rainfall than occurs on the subtropical west coast, for the east side of a continent in these latitudes feels the effects of the weaker western end of a subtropical oceanic anticyclone, where the air varies from being mildly stable to actually unstable. In addition, along the subtropical eastern side of a large continent, where the anticyclone is relatively weak, there is a tendency for humid, onshore monsoon winds to prevail in summer. The associated advection of tropical heat and humidity in turn favors summer precipitation.

These subtropical east coasts are paralleled by warm ocean currents originating in tropical latitudes, whose general effect is to stimulate the rain-making processes. This contrasts with the cool currents and their stabilizing effects along west coasts.

Although both subtropical types of climate lie on the tropical margins of the middle latitudes, they are flanked by quite unlike climates to north and south. Thus, while the dry-summer subtropical characteristically passes over into dry climate on its equatorward side, humid subtropical is bounded by tropical humid climates on that frontier. Sim-ilarly, dry-summer subtropical usually merges into mild, rainy marine climate on its poleward side, while, in Asia and North America at least, humid subtropical makes contact with severe continental climate on the north.

TEMPERATURE

Summer temperatures   In many of its temperature characteristics humid subtropical climate resembles its west-side counterpart. Both are mild climates, lacking long and severe winter cold, and characterized by a long growing season without killing frost. Still there are significant contrasts.

Completely lacking in the humid subtropics are the cool-summer coastal climates which are so characteristic of the subtropical west sides where cool ocean currents prevail. Along the subtropical east sides, coast as well as interior, the summer heat is like that of the humid tropics, with the average temperature of the warmest month reaching 75 to 80° (Fig. 13.7). This rather resembles the situation at inland stations in Mediterranean climates. But there is a difference, for in the humid subtropics the air is so moist that the heat is sultry and oppressive, while dry desertlike heat is more the rule in warm Mediterranean climates. Because of the humid atmosphere with more cloud, night cooling is usually less marked in the humid subtropics, so that the diurnal range of temperature is somewhat less than at interior locations in its west-side counterpart (compare Figs. 13.4 and 13.8).

Winter temperatures   In these subtropical latitudes winters must be mild, but there are important regional variations (Fig. 13.7). Thus in subtropical eastern Asia the largeness of the continent causes average January temperatures of 40° and even lower, while in Argentina and Australia the coldest month

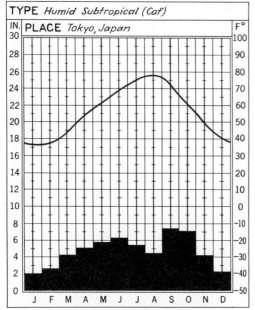

TYPE *Humid Subtropical (Caf)*

PLACE *Tokyo, Japan*

FIG. 13.7   Compare with Fig. 13.2. Seasonal rainfall distribution contrasts strikingly in the two subtropical types.

may be 10° warmer. The annual range of temperature is only moderate, but again it varies from region to region: only 23° at Buenos Aires, Argentina, 32° at Montgomery, Alabama, and over 40° at Shanghai, China. The larger the land mass, the colder the winters and the larger the annual ranges.

Midday temperatures in winter are likely to be pleasantly warm (50 to 60°) and on many more than half the winter nights the thermometer remains above freezing (Fig. 13.8). But the passage of cyclonic storms with their accompanying southerly and northerly winds results in irregular spells of warmer and colder weather, the latter often very uncomfortable because of the inefficient heating systems characteristic of many homes.

Frost   It is to be expected that the growing season, or the period between killing frosts, will be long, usually from 7 or 8

FIG. 13.8   Daily maximum and minimum temperatures for the warmest and coolest months at a humid subtropical station. Note the strong periodic (solar) control in summer. By contrast, winter shows stronger nonperiodic (air-mass) control.

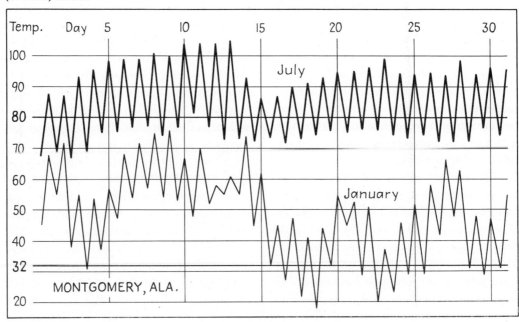

Climatic Data for Representative Humid Subtropical Stations

	J	F	M	A	M	J	J	A	S	O	N	D	Yr	Range
Charleston, South Carolina														
Temp.	50	52	58	65	73	79	82	81	77	68	58	51	66.1	32
Precip.	3.0	3.1	3.3	2.4	3.3	5.1	6.2	6.5	5.2	3.7	2.5	3.2	47.5	
Shanghai, China														
Temp.	38	39	46	56	66	73	80	80	73	63	52	42	49	42
Precip.	2.8	2.0	3.9	4.4	3.3	6.6	7.4	4.7	3.9	3.7	1.7	1.3	45.7	
Rosario, Argentina														
Temp.	77	76	70	62	56	49	51	52	57	62	69	75	63	26
Precip.	3.7	3.2	5.3	3.1	1.8	1.5	1.0	1.5	1.6	3.5	3.4	5.3	34.9	

months up to the entire year. In the Asiatic and North American humid subtropics, which are bordered on the north by harsh continental climates, winters are more severe and killing frosts much more frequent than in their Southern Hemisphere counterparts where broad continents are lacking to poleward. In the southeastern United States protective east-west highland barriers are lacking, so that strong thrusts of cold northerly air sweep unhindered from the Arctic to the Gulf of Mexico, resulting in occasional spells of severe cold. Temperatures as low as 10° have been recorded along the ocean margins of all of the northern Gulf states (Fig. 13.9).

PRECIPITATION

Amount The total annual rainfall is more abundant (30 to 60 in.) in the humid subtropics than in the dry-summer subtropics. This contrast is to be expected, given the fact that the subtropical east side is affected by the weaker western part of a subtropical anticyclone and a warm ocean current parallels the coast, while cold water and the stable east side of a high-pressure cell dominate the subtropical west side.

To be sure, there are variations in rainfall amounts within the humid subtropics. As a rule rainfall decreases inland, so that the driest parts are usually along the western margins where humid subtropical climate makes contact with steppe climate (Fig. 11.2).

Nature and origin Much of the summer precipitation is of the local showery type associated with convective overturning and falling from cumulus clouds. Strong heating of the invading maritime air over the warm land surface operates to make the air unstable and

FIG. 13.9 Weather controls giving rise to a spell of severe subfreezing night temperatures in the American humid subtropics. A cold anticyclone advancing southward from arctic Canada as a mass of cold *cP* air produced a minimum temperature of 20° at New Orleans and 8° at Memphis. The isotherm of 20° approximately coincides with the south Atlantic and Gulf Coasts.

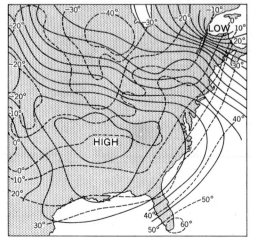

buoyant, so that it is ripe for precipitation. Thunderstorms are numerous, the south Atlantic and Gulf margins of the United States having an unusually large number. However, most of the showery rain appears to occur in conjunction with extensive, though weak, atmospheric disturbances. As a result the showers and thunderstorms are organized in character, occurring in belts or areas, and the shower areas move with the disturbance that generates them. Random convective showers are less common, and in spite of the prevailing heat all days are not showery.

Winter precipitation, by contrast, is more general and widespread in character, and convective showers are infrequent. In this season the land surface, being colder than any maritime tropical air moving landward, chills this air at its base and makes it stable and nonbuoyant. It is not inclined to rise un-

less forced upward by terrain barriers or by colder, denser air along a front. Most of the winter precipitation occurs in association with well-developed cyclonic storms and falls from a dull, gray, uniform cloud deck. Snow occurs now and then when a vigorous winter cyclone takes a course which carries it well equatorward, but it rarely stays on the ground for more than a few days.

Seasonal distribution Over most of the humid subtropics precipitation occurs throughout the year and there is no season of genuine drought, in contrast to the situation in the dry-summer subtropics along the west side of a continent (Fig. 13.7). As a rule more rain falls in the warmer parts of the year when the air contains the most moisture and the warm land increases the instability of the surface air. Yet winter is far from being a dry season in most areas. It is chiefly in parts of the humid subtropics of Asia, where the dry winter monsoon is best developed, that winter may be a genuinely dry season.

Seasonal weather Irregular, non-periodic weather changes are usually less marked in the humid subtropics than they are farther poleward, where the conflict between air masses is more marked and cyclonic storms more numerous. In summer when the storm belt is farthest poleward, irregular weather changes are at a minimum (Fig. 13.8). The sun largely controls the weather and so a diurnal regularity of temperature is a characteristic feature; humid, sultry days are the rule. Frequent spells of showery weather accompanying weak disturbances alternate with short periods of several days in which no rain falls (Fig. 13.10). To an unusual degree the weather resembles that of the wet tropics.

Late summer and fall are the dreaded hurricane season, and, although these storms are

FIG. 13.10 A common weather type of the summer season in the humid subtropics of Asia. Weak cyclonic storms are responsible for a considerable part of the summer precipitation. The area of precipitation has a stippled shading. *(From Japanese weather map.)*

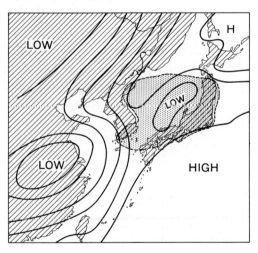

not numerous, their severity more than makes up for their infrequency. Sunny autumn days furnish delightful weather, although the equatorward-advancing cyclonic belt produces a gradually increasing number of gray, cloudy days and begins to import unseasonable temperatures as winter approaches.

In winter the belt of cyclonic storms is farthest equatorward, so that irregular weather changes are more frequent and extreme. The arrival of tropical air masses may push the day temperatures to well above 60 or even 70°, only to be followed by northerly winds of polar origin which may reduce the temperature as much as 30° within 24 hr, resulting occasionally in severe freezes. Bright, sunny winter days are distinctly pleasant and exhilarating out of doors. Spring again sees the retreat of the cyclonic belt and the gradual reestablishment of regular, diurnal sun control (Fig. 13.8).

RESOURCE POTENTIALITIES OF THE HUMID SUBTROPICS

Without doubt the humid subtropical is the most productive climate of the middle latitudes. Temperature and rainfall here combine to produce the closest approach to humid tropical conditions outside the low latitudes. The bountiful temperature regime of the Mediterranean realm, which was discussed earlier in this chapter, is, as indicated then, closely duplicated in this other subtropical climate. But the more abundant precipitation of the humid subtropics, in conjunction with the lack of a genuinely dry season, makes this realm potentially more productive climatically than its subhumid counterpart. To be sure, its sultry tropical summers are far from being ideal for human comfort, but they are nonetheless excellent for a luxuriant plant growth.

The abundant climatic energy, expressed in rainfall as well as temperature, induces an equally abundant vegetation, usually of forests, although in regions of more modest precipitation grasses may replace trees. Grasses are particularly prevalent in the westernmost parts of the American humid subtropics, in the Argentine Pampa, and in parts of Uruguay. The character of the forests varies so greatly among the humid subtropical regions that generalizations are difficult to make. Trees grow more rapidly in the humid subtropics than they do in other climates of the middle latitudes, so that natural or artificial reforestation is a quicker process than it is farther poleward.

The mature forest soils of the humid subtropics are characteristically of low fertility, which tends to offset seriously the effects of the realm's climate; and it seems like a geographic imperfection of first magnitude that the most productive climate of the middle latitudes should be associated with such infertile mature soils. The soil inferiority is not surprising, however, considering the high leaching power of the climate and the low humus-producing character of the forest vegetation. The red and yellow soils of the humid subtropics generally resemble those of the wet tropics, although the humid subtropical soils are not so completely leached. Under cultivation they deteriorate rapidly.

Where grasses replace forests, as they do in the subhumid portions of the subtropics, the soils are darker in color and much more productive. The lower rainfall results in less leaching, and the grasses provide a greater abundance of organic matter.

MARINE CLIMATE

TYPE LOCATION

Unlike the other two mesothermal climates, the marine, or maritime, type $(Cb)^4$ owes its mildness not to subtropical location but to its position on the windward, or western, side of a continent in the westerly winds (Fig. 13.1). It has a position which is poleward of the two subtropical types, extending from about 40 to 60° or even beyond and thus actually reaching relatively high latitudes. But even these latitudes can be temperate where winds from the sea rather consistently carry onshore the generally mild oceanic conditions and add to them the effects of the warm ocean currents which characteristically parallel the western margins of middle-latitude continents. An extensive development of this marine type on the eastern, or leeward, side of a large continent in middle latitudes is, of course, impossible. Even Japan, an island group, is

[4] In the Köppen system b = temperature of warmest month below 71.6° (22°C).

continental rather than marine in its temperature characteristics.

Where mountains closely parallel west coasts, as in western North America, Scandinavia, and South America, the marine climate does not extend far inland. But where extensive lowlands prevail, as in western Europe, the oceanic effects penetrate much deeper (Plate 2).

On its equatorward margins marine climate normally makes contact with the dry-summer subtropical type. On its poleward side it passes over into the subarctic or the tundra type (Fig. 11.2, Plate 2).

TEMPERATURE

Since during much the larger part of the year marine climate has its temperatures brought to it from the ocean by the westerly winds, it is not surprising to find that large seasonal extremes of temperature are absent (Fig. 13.11). Summers are likely to be rela-

Climatic Data for Representative Marine Stations

	J	F	M	A	M	J	J	A	S	O	N	D	Yr	Range
Valentia, Ireland														
Temp.	44	44	45	48	52	57	59	59	57	52	48	45	50.8	15
Precip.	5.5	5.2	4.5	3.7	3.2	3.2	3.8	4.8	4.1	5.6	5.5	6.6	55.7	
Seattle, Washington														
Temp.	40	42	45	50	55	60	64	64	59	52	46	42	51.4	24
Precip.	4.9	3.8	3.1	2.4	1.8	1.3	0.6	0.7	1.7	2.8	4.8	5.5	33.4	
Paris, France														
Temp.	37	39	43	51	56	62	66	64	59	51	43	37	50.5	29
Precip.	1.5	1.2	1.6	1.7	2.1	2.3	2.2	2.2	2.0	2.3	1.8	1.7	22.6	
Hokitika, New Zealand														
Temp.	60	61	59	55	50	47	45	46	50	53	55	58	53	16
Precip.	9.8	7.3	9.7	9.2	9.8	9.7	9.0	9.4	9.2	11.8	10.6	10.6	116.1	

tively cool and winters mild, considering the latitude, and the annual range is small.

Summer temperatures   In having a cool summer the marine climate resembles the oceanic littorals of the Mediterranean realm, but is quite in contrast to most parts of the two subtropical climates with their greater summer heat. Average summer-month temperatures of about 60 to 65° are 5 or 10° lower than are those of the continental interior in similar latitudes. Only occasionally are midday temperatures uncomfortably warm (Fig. 13.12).

Winter temperatures   Winter isotherms show a strong tendency to parallel the coast line, with temperatures decreasing inland from the sea—evidence that the land-water control is stronger than latitude especially in winter. Thus, compared with stations at the same latitudes but in the interior of the continent, the winter mildness is much more striking than the summer coolness (Fig. 13.12). For example, while Seattle is only 5° cooler than Montreal in July, it is 27° warmer in January.

Frost   Freezing temperatures are more frequent and more severe than in the dry-summer

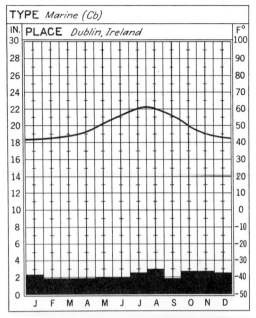

FIG. 13.11   Temperature and rainfall characteristics of a lowland marine station in western Europe. Note the small range of temperature and the modest amount of precipitation well distributed throughout the year.

subtropical climate farther south (Fig 13.12). Still, the growing season is long considering the latitude, 6 to 8 months being character-

FIG. 13.12   Daily maximum and minimum temperatures for the warmest and coldest months at a marine station on the Pacific Coast of Canada. Note the small diurnal range, especially in winter when skies are prevailingly cloudy.

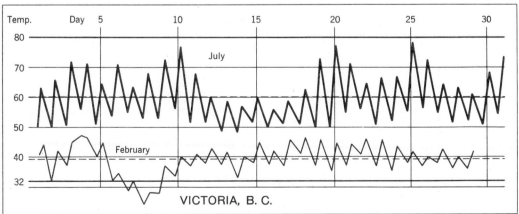

istic of the American North Pacific Coast region. At Paris, France, frost normally occurs only on about half the nights during the 3 winter months. However, winter usually is severe enough to produce a dormant season for plant life. During occasional cold spells the temperatures may remain constantly below freezing for several days in succession. Such cold spells occur when there is a westward and southward thrust of polar continental air from the interior of the continent (Fig. 13.13).

While irregular temperature variations are by no means as striking in these marine climates as they are in the continental interiors, still the passage of cyclones and anticyclones, with the resulting changes in wind direction, is bound to cause some degree of weather variability (Fig. 13.12).

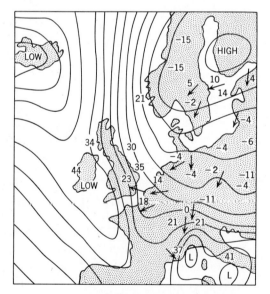

FIG. 13.13   Weather controls favoring unseasonably low winter temperatures in western Europe. A cold anticyclone to the north and east is delivering cold *cP* air to the regions west and south of its center. *(From Kendrew.)*

PRECIPITATION

Annual amount   Marine climates are humid, and there is usually adequate precipitation in all seasons (Fig. 13.11). However, depending upon the amount of relief, the total varies greatly from region to region. Where lowlands prevail, as they do in western Europe, rainfall is only moderate, usually 25 to 35 in. per year, but the humid marine climate extends well inland; where highlands are present, as in Chile and western North America, there may be heavy precipitation on the windward slopes, but eastward from the mountains dry climates prevail.

Snow   Snow is more common than in the subtropical climates of the humid mesothermal group, but on lowlands it ordinarily lies on the ground for only 10 to 15 days during the year. On highlands, however, snowfall is heavy, and a deep snow cover persists for several months. Such mountain snowfields have in the past created numerous valley glaciers, the erosion effects of which have been responsible for the characteristically irregular fiorded coasts of Norway, southern Chile, and British Columbia.

Annual distribution   Sufficient precipitation at all seasons and no marked period of drought are typical of the marine climate (Fig. 13.11). Normally there is no dormant season imposed upon vegetation because of rainfall deficiency. Both in the most definitely marine locations and in those parts lying closest to the dry-summer type, winters commonly are rainier than summers, although a summer month is really dry only in a few places.

Origin   Over lowlands, where orographic effects are absent, the precipitation is chiefly frontal, or cyclonic, in origin. Much of it falls as long-continued steady but light rain from a gray, leaden overcast (Fig. 13.14).

Because of the general lack of high temperatures, thunderstorms are few, but showery rain
is nevertheless fairly common in the fresh
westerly maritime air following the passage of
a cyclonic center.

As previously stated, the total precipitation
on lowlands is only modest or moderate in
amount; but the number of days on which rain
falls is unusually high. This can only mean
that the precipitation is usually light or moderate in its rate of fall. Thus, while Paris
receives only about 23 in. of precipitation a
year, this amount is spread over 188 rainy
days.

As might be expected, the amount of cloud
is great, the marine climate being one of the
earth's most cloudy types. Dark, gloomy,
overcast weather is very common. Over extensive areas in western Europe cloudiness is
greater than 70 per cent, the sun sometimes
remaining hidden for several weeks in succession, especially in winter and fall.

The weather element   Since numerous
cyclonic storms, each with its accompanying
converging system of winds and its cloud
deck, cross these marine west-coast areas,
nonperiodic weather changes are a dominant
feature of the climate (Fig. 13.12). *Fall* and
winter, in spite of mild temperatures, are
stormy seasons, so that periods of gloomy,
dripping cyclonic weather are frequent (Fig.
13.13). Spells of bright, sunny anticyclonic
weather associated with *cP* air masses are the
exception, but when they do occur this climate is likely to experience its most severe
freezes.

As *spring* advances, cyclones become fewer
and sunshine more abundant. The air is still
cool, but the sun is strong; thus in western
Europe, for example, late spring is acclaimed
the most delightful season. *Summer* temperatures make for a sense of physical well-being,

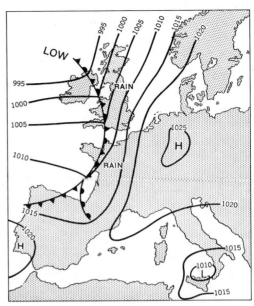

FIG. 13.14   A strongly occluded storm in
western Europe, producing light but steady and
widespread rainfall, a low cloud ceiling, and low
visibility. Most of the cyclones which affect west
coasts in middle latitudes are in an advanced stage
of occlusion. Such storms, while they produce
much cloud, yield only a modest amount of
precipitation over lowlands.

and where sunny days are numerous, as in
the American Pacific Northwest, a more
pleasant summer climate would be hard to
find. When cloudy, rainy days do occur in
summer, they may be unpleasantly chilly.

RESOURCE POTENTIALITIES OF THE MARINE REALM

Two of the most significant climatic elements affecting the potential productivity of
the marine realm are (*a*) its unusually long
frost-free season, considering its latitude, and
(*b*) its relatively mild winters. To be sure, there
is a marked dormant season imposed by killing frosts, so that the growth of sensitive and
of out-of-season crops characteristic of both

the dry-summer subtropics and the humid subtropics is excluded from this realm. Nevertheless, the frost-free period of 6 to 8 months and the relatively mild winters permit many cereal crops to be sown in fall, and animals can graze out of doors nearly 12 months, if not the entire year. Large-scale storage of animal feeds for winter use is therefore much less necessary than in the more severe continental climates.

Somewhat offsetting the advantages of the mild winters and the long frost-free season in marine climate is the deficiency of summer heat. Just as the winters are marine, so also are the summers. Thus, while warm-month temperatures of 60 to 65° are ideal for human comfort, and may represent the optimum conditions for physical activity as well, they are not ideal for many crops; for instance, they may be too low for the best growth of some grain crops, especially maize. On the other hand, grass finds almost ideal conditions here, so that pastures are usually excellent and hay and forage crops thrive.

The adequate amount of rainfall and the fact that there is no season of marked drought are climatic assets of the first magnitude for crop growth generally. Another asset is the dependability of the precipitation year in and year out which is reflected in high uniformity of crop yields.

In these mild, humid, west-coast regions the original vegetation cover was chiefly forest, and because of the hilly and mountainous nature of large parts of the realm, trees still cover extensive areas. In the North American marine region, for instance, is the earth's finest coniferous (needle-leaf) forest, the world's principal source of high-grade softwood lumber. In Europe the original forest was composed largely of broadleaf deciduous trees, with oaks predominating. Conifers occupied chiefly the highland and sandy areas. Here, however, centuries of occupance by civilized peoples have resulted in a removal of the forest cover from the plains, and even that of the highlands has been greatly modified. Forests of the Southern Hemisphere marine regions are moderately dense and luxuriant, but they are composed of species most of which produce inferior lumber.

The podzolic forest soils which are rather characteristic of lowlands with this type of climate are the best of the world's forest soils. They are by no means the equal of the dark-colored grassland soils, for they have been moderately leached and the supply of organic matter from the forest cover is not abundant. On the other hand, they are distinctly better than the red and yellow soils of the wet tropics and subtropics. Under constant cultivation they deteriorate, to be sure, but less rapidly than the other light-colored soils, and with less care and attention they can be kept in good condition and fitted for a variety of crops.

CHAPTER 14

Humid microthermal, polar, and highland climates

THE HUMID MICROTHERMAL CLIMATES

TYPE LOCATION

The humid microthermal climates (*D*) stand in contrast to the humid mesothermals by reason of having (*a*) a colder winter, (*b*) a longer-lasting snow cover, (*c*) a shorter frost-free season, and (*d*) a greater annual range of temperature. In other words, the microthermals are more severe than the temperate mesothermals. This greater severity results primarily from locational differences in both

253

latitude and position on the continents, that is, from the facts that the humid microthermal climates lie poleward from the subtropical types and occupy more interior and leeward locations on the great land masses than the marine climate (Fig. 11.1; Plate 2).

These specific locational differences suggest the basic locational facts about the microthermal climates, that they are land-controlled and can develop only in large continents in the higher middle latitudes, and thus are confined exclusively to the Northern Hemisphere, only Eurasia and North America being able to produce them. Of the Southern Hemisphere continents, South America alone extends poleward far enough to permit the development of severe climates; but the narrowness of that land mass south of latitudes 35°–40° prevents genuinely extreme seasonal conditions in spite of the latitude.

Microthermal climates are excluded from the western, or windward, side of the two Northern Hemisphere continents because of the dominance there of maritime air masses. They occupy, instead, the interiors of these continents and extend down to tidewater on their leeward or eastern sides where, in spite of proximity to the sea, modified continental conditions prevail.

Unlike the mesothermal climates, those of the microthermal group have temperature regimes which differ substantially from one another largely in the degree of summer heat and winter cold. Here, moreover, there are no strongly contrasting seasonal rainfall regimes. Therefore, the general aspects of microthermal climates as a group will be discussed before the individual types of climate are analyzed.

TEMPERATURE

Because they extend through a wide range of latitude, there are marked temperature

contrasts within the regions classed as humid microthermal. However, these climates are sure to have relatively severe seasons for any particular latitude, so that annual ranges are large. The winter cold is more characteristic and distinctive than the summer heat, but summers are warm for the latitude. Furthermore, the seasons are not only extreme but also variable in temperature from one year to another. In marine climate one year's winter is likely to be much like another's, but wide departures from the normal seasonal temperature are characteristic of severe continental climates.

Effects of a snow cover on temperature   In the microthermal, polar, and highland climates—and, indeed, only in these climates—the snow cover is of sufficiently long duration to have a marked effect upon winter temperature. In these climates once a region is overlain by such a lasting white snow mantle, the ground itself underneath the snow cover has little influence upon air temperature: sunlight falling upon the snow is largely reflected back to space continually, so that little of the solar energy is effective in heating the ground and then the atmosphere. Moreover, while loss of energy by earth radiation goes on very rapidly from the top of a snow surface, the low conductivity of snow tends, as long as the snow lasts, to retard the flow of heat upward from the ground to replace that which is lost. Clearly, then, the total effect of a lasting snow cover is markedly to reduce winter temperatures. On the other hand, the snow cover operates to keep the soil underneath the snow warm and prevents deep freezing.

PRECIPITATION

Annual precipitation in most lowland regions of microthermal climate errs on the side of being too meager rather than too great. Well over half the area of such regions has under 20 in., and the area with more than 40 or 45 in. is very limited. Considering both the latitudinal and geographical locations of microthermal climate, this modest amount of precipitation is to be expected. Characteristically the amount declines (*a*) from the sea margins toward the interior, and (*b*) northward with the decline in temperature and specific humidity.

Although winter is not without precipitation, summer is normally a season of a strong precipitation maximum in microthermal climates, and this concentration of much of the year's precipitation in the warmer months is as distinct a hallmark of continental climates as their severe winters and large annual ranges of temperature.

This seasonal distribution is related to the following conditions: (*a*) Low temperatures make the specific humidity, or reservoir of water vapor in the atmosphere, markedly lower over the continent during the winter than it is in summer when temperatures are much higher. (*b*) During winter the settling air in the continental seasonal anticyclone is also conducive to low specific humidity, and makes for increased stability of the atmosphere as well. (*c*) The continental anticyclones, which develop over the colder, more northerly parts of the land masses in winter, are areas of diverging air currents, and thus antagonistic to the development of fronts and cyclones. This applies particularly to the more severe microthermal climates, such as the subarctic, where the winter anticyclone is best developed. In summer, although cyclones may be fewer and weaker, they can, nevertheless, penetrate deeper into the continents. (*d*) Convection is at a minimum during the winter months, for at that season the cold snow sur-

face tends to increase the stability of air masses. In summer, on the other hand, the warm land surface has a tendency to make unstable the air masses moving over it. (*e*) Consequent upon the seasonal extremes of temperatures and hence of pressure, a tendency toward a monsoon system of winds is developed, which leads to an outflow of dry, cold *cP* air in winter, and to an inflow of tropical maritime air with high rainfall potentialities in summer.

The occurrence of these conditions making for drier winters and wetter summers is a fortunate thing, for in severe climates with a short frost-free season it is of the highest importance for crop agriculture that rainfall be concentrated in the warm growing season. This is especially true where the total amount of precipitation is relatively modest, as it is over extensive areas within this group of climates. In the tropics, where it is constantly hot, it matters not at all when the rain falls, and even in the subtropics winter rainfall is effective for plant growth. But in the microthermal climates, where the severe winter creates a completely dormant season for plants, it is essential that periods of sufficient heat and sufficient rainfall to foster growth coincide.

TYPES

Two principal types of climate are included within the microthermal group: (*a*) the *humid continental* climate, including both warm-summer and cool-summer subtypes, and (*b*) the *subarctic* climate. The first type, an important agricultural climate, characteristically lies on the equatorward margins of the subarctic type, which itself occupies such high latitudes that agriculture ceases to be of great importance.

HUMID CONTINENTAL CLIMATE

Humid continental climate, as might be expected, has interior and lee location in both North America and Eurasia, with a latitudinal spread of 10 to 20° extending from about 40° on the south to 50°–60° on the north (Fig. 11.2; Plate 2). But there are differences in location on the two continents. In Eurasia, where lack of mountain barriers on the west side allows the oceanic air to enter freely, this climate is positioned both to the west and to the east of the dry interior, while in North America it lies only to the east of the dry climates. In both eastern Asia and eastern North America humid continental climate is bordered by subarctic climate on the north and humid subtropical on the south. But in Europe and western Asia it meets Mediterranean and dry climates on its southern margins.

It may seem somewhat surprising that this land-controlled climate should extend eastward to the ocean margins in both Asia and North America, but not if it is remembered that the prevailing west-to-east atmospheric circulation in these latitudes makes deep and persistent entrance of maritime air on the lee, or east, side unlikely.

TEMPERATURE

Seasonal temperature   Summers that vary from warm in the south to cool on the northern frontier, and winter always cold but actually varying more in degrees of temperature, are characteristic of humid continental climate. Depending largely on latitudinal location, the average July temperature may vary from 75° or even more (in the south) to 65° (in the north). The January average shows a much greater variation: from zero or below

in the north to 25° or above in the southern parts. As a consequence, the annual range of temperature is everywhere large, and it increases both to the north and with distance from the sea. At Peoria, Illinois (41°N), for example, the January and July averages are 24 and 75°, so that there is an annual range of about 50°. But at Winnipeg, Canada, at about 50°N, the comparable figures are −4° and 66° and the range is 70°. Similarly, New York City on the Atlantic Coast has a range of 42°, while Omaha, Nebraska, at a comparable latitude but inland, records 55°.

In correspondence to the varying temperature regime, the growing season changes in length from south to north, approaching 200 days on the southern margins and declining to about 100 days on the subarctic side.

Seasonal gradients   Summer and winter present remarkable contrasts in the rate of change in temperature in a north-south direction (Fig. 14.1). In the cold season the isotherms are much more closely spaced than in summer, so that in the central and eastern United States, for instance, the temperature gradient is two to three times as steep in January as in July. Thus sudden and marked temperature changes associated with shifts in wind direction are much more likely in winter than in summer.

PRECIPITATION

Amount and seasonal distribution Modest amounts of annual precipitation, with a seasonal concentration in summer, are the rule in the humid continental climate as in the humid microthermal group as a whole (pp. 261, 263). With increasing distance from the sea, the total amount of precipitation declines as the inner frontier where humid continental makes contact with dry climate is approached, as well as a greater annual range of precipitation, with winter becoming more of a dry season. An example of this range is Omaha, Nebraska, which receives 29 in. of rain a year: in July it receives 4.7 in., in January only 0.7.

Another feature of the less humid interior, especially in the United States and central Europe, is a shift of the precipitation maximum to early summer, so that June is wetter than July.

Winter precipitation Cool-season precipitation is largely frontal or cyclonic in origin. In North America, mT Gulf air masses move poleward up the Mississippi River Valley with no relief obstacles to interfere, being chilled and thus stabilized by the cold land surface. Occasionally the tropical air may flow poleward at the surface as far north as Iowa and the southern shores of the Great Lakes. More commonly, however, it comes into conflict with colder, heavier air masses before reaching so far inland and is forced to ascend over them, and widespread frontal precipitation results. The North American continental climate, therefore, has a moderate amount of winter precipitation. The amount increases eastward as the ocean is approached, until along the Atlantic seaboard winter is equally as wet as summer. In northeastern Asia where the outward-flowing winter monsoon is stronger, mT air is unable to advance so far poleward, so that winter precipitation in northern China and Manchuria is very meager; for example, Peking, which receives 25 in. a year, has 9.4 in. in July, and only 0.1 in. in January.

A portion of the winter precipitation is in the form of snow, and a permanent snow cover, varying from a few weeks to several months in duration, is typical (Fig. 14.10). In those parts of the northeastern United States and southeastern Canada where winter

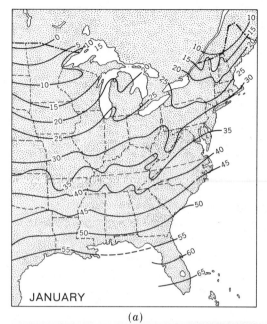

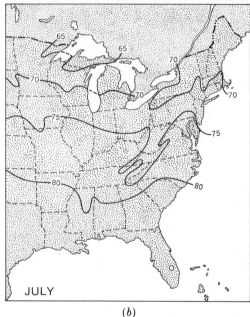

FIG. 14.1 Surface-temperature gradients in microthermal climates are much steeper in winter (*a*) than in summer (*b*).

cyclones are particularly numerous and well developed—the Great Lakes region, the St. Lawrence River Valley, northern New England, and the Canadian Maritime Provinces—snow becomes very deep. Thus northern New England and northern New York have more than 7 ft of snowfall during an average winter, and the snow cover remains on the ground for more than 4 months.

Summer precipitation   While steady, long-continued cyclonic rain falling from a gray overcast is not absent in summer, more common by far is showery rainfall, much of it associated with lightning and thunder. This is because the warmer, more humid summer air has been made buoyant and unstable by heating from below while passing over a warm land surface. For example, 75 to 90 per cent of the summer rainfall at Madison, Wisconsin, occurs in association with thunderstorms. Yet even most of the convective showers and thunderstorms of summer occur in conjunction with some form of extensive atmospheric disturbance such as a front or a weak cyclonic storm.

The nonperiodic weather element   In no other type of climate are rapid and marked nonperiodic weather changes so characteristic as in the humid continental, for it is here that the conflict between polar air masses and tropical air masses reaches a maximum development.

This nonperiodic control of weather is strongest in the cold season, when the sun, accompanied by the jet stream and the storm belt, has retreated farthest south. At this season, with weather conditions dominated by moving cyclones and anticyclones associated with the invading, rapidly shifting air masses and the fronts along their boundaries, the daily rise and fall of temperature with the sun is often obscured by larger nonperiodic oscillations (Figs. 14.7, 14.9). The central and eastern United States, which are freely open to the movements of air masses both from north and south, are regions of unusual

storminess; storm control is less marked in eastern Asia.

In summer throughout the humid continental regions, air masses show weaker temperature contrasts and move less rapidly, so that fronts are fewer and weaker, and the weather is somewhat more diurnally regular and sun-controlled (Fig. 14.7).

Special seasonal weather types   The normal cycle of middle-latitude weather changes with the passage of a well-developed cyclone, as well as the normal effects of the associated anticyclone, was described in Chap. 10. But at the same time it was pointed out that there is almost an infinite variety of weather variations related to these storms in these latitudes, depending upon the season, the size and intensity of the atmospheric disturbance, the nature of the air masses involved in the storm, the track followed by the storm, and the contrasting patterns of high-level atmospheric circulation.

As a consequence of this great variety of weather combinations no universally satisfactory classification of types of weather has ever been developed. Yet even the layman is aware that there are some weather types which are sufficiently distinctive to have been given names. Warm wave, cold wave, Indian summer, blizzard, and January thaw are such, and much more numerous are the unnamed ones. Furthermore, it is certain that no real comprehension of humid continental climate is possible without an appreciation of the variety of weather types which in combination produce the seasonal climates. But this requires more than a layman's effort; indeed, this requires a study of the daily weather map in conjunction with a firsthand observation of weather conditions.

A very few of the numerous weather types characteristic of humid continental climate are shown in Figs. 14.2 to 14.5. These

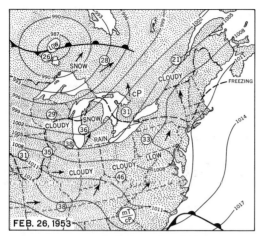

FIG. 14.2   A common winter weather type. Here a cyclone traveling on a northern track is producing cloudy, mild weather and light precipitation over extensive areas of the north central United States. Temperatures shown are for 1:30 A.M.

sketches of synoptic weather charts of parts of North America are worthy of careful study.

Winter, the season of strongest temperature gradients and of greatest air-mass contrasts, is the period of greatest weather variety.

A well-developed anticyclone arriving from arctic Canada as a mass of fresh *cP* air may produce bitterly cold weather, even subzero temperatures (Fig. 10.2). This sharp drop in temperature brought by the northwest wind is the well-known cold wave. Blizzardlike conditions with violent winds may even usher in the anticyclone if it is characterized by unusually steep pressure gradients. But if an invading cold anticyclone is composed of modified *mP* air from west of the Rocky Mountains, skies will be clear and temperatures only moderately low; and this control produces some of the finest winter weather.

A deep cyclonic storm, especially if it originates in the Texas area and takes a route northeastward across the country, is more than likely to bring extensive and heavy snowfalls to the humid continental climates of the Mississippi River Valley and the East

(Fig. 14.3). If the vigorous cyclone travels a more northerly route, the weather will be milder and the rain area more extensive. A weak low following a route to the north of the Great Lakes may bring generally gray, overcast weather but only very modest amounts of rain or snow (Fig. 14.2). But these are only a few of the far more numerous weather types which in combination produce the winters of humid continental climates.

In *summer,* temperature gradients are weaker, air-mass contrasts less striking, and the weather element, as controlled by passing atmospheric perturbations, is altogether less well developed. But while sun control and diurnal regularity are stronger than at other seasons, this period of high sun is by no means lacking in nonperiodic weather irregularities. A somewhat stagnant anticyclone to the south and east may envelop the humid continental area of the United States in a prolonged heat wave with a succession of days when the daily temperature maxima rise to between 90 and 100° (Fig. 14.4). Such a heat wave may be suddenly brought to an

FIG. 14.3   A well-developed winter storm originating in the Texas area and moving northeastward across the United States. Such storms are likely to bring heavy precipitation, much of it in the form of snow.

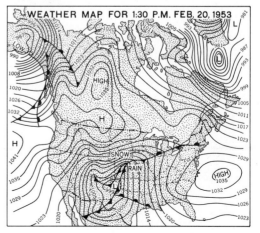

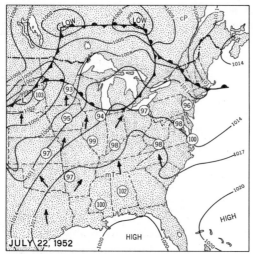

FIG. 14.4   A July heat wave—a summer weather type—over the central and eastern United States. Temperatures shown are the maxima for the 12 hr preceding. Tropical southerly air from a warm subtropical anticyclone controls the weather.

end by the passage of a V-shaped cyclonic storm with a well-developed cold front and associated cold-front thunderstorms. Then, following the passage of the cold front with its strong convectional activity, there may be

FIG. 14.5   A spring weather type. Here a cold anticyclone advancing southward as a mass of cold *cP* air with northwest winds carries low temperatures well into the subtropics and results in a severe spring freeze in the north central states.

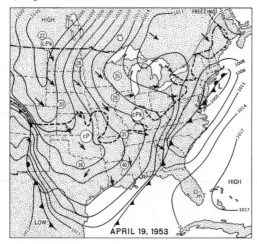

several days of delightfully cool weather, as an anticyclone with air of polar origin dominates the weather.

Spring and fall, the transition seasons, witness a more even struggle between storm and sun control. First the one and then the other is in the ascendancy, so that there is something of an oscillation between summer and winter conditions. Mild, warm days in April and early May, with a regular diurnal rise and fall of the thermometer resembling summer, may be followed by a reestablishment of winter conditions, as a passing cyclone lays down a snow cover and the following invasion of *cP* air drops the temperatures to an unseasonable frost (Fig. 14.5). Continental climates are particularly famous for the fickleness of their spring weather.

Autumn brings some of the loveliest days of the entire year but likewise some of the rawest, gloomiest weather. Bright, clear weather, with warm midday temperatures and crisp, frosty nights, comes with anticyclonic control. A reestablishment of hot-wave gradients with south winds in October and November, after severe frost and perhaps even snow have been experienced, may cause a temporary return of summer conditions, resulting in those much-cherished spells of warm weather with hazy, smoky atmosphere known as Indian summer. But well-developed cyclonic storms of this season may bring raw, gray days with chilly rain, and occasionally they produce a temporary snowy winter landscape as early as October.

WARM-SUMMER AND COOL-SUMMER SUBDIVISIONS OF HUMID CONTINENTAL CLIMATE

Two principal subdivisions of humid continental climate are here recognized: (*a*) the less severe *warm-summer* subtype (*Da*), and (*b*) the more extreme *cool-summer* subtype (*Db*).[1] The latter is characteristically located farther poleward, that is, on the northern side of the warm-summer subtype (Fig. 11.2).

As Plate 2 shows, the warm-summer subtype is to be found in three far-separated locations, the central eastern United States, central Europe, and eastern Asia. The cool-summer subtype is likewise represented in North America, Europe, and Asia.

Temperature and precipitation In the warm-summer subtype summer months are only 5 to 10° warmer than in the cool-summer subdivision, but this is sufficient to make for marked differences in their agricultural potentialities (following table). Moreover, the frost-free season of 5 to 6 months in the warm-summer climate is shortened to 3 to 5 months in the other (Figs. 14.6 and 14.8).

Summers in warm-summer areas are likely to have so many uncomfortably hot and humid days that human comfort is better

[1] In the Köppen system *a* = temperature of warmest month above 71.6° (22°C), and *b* = temperature of warmest month below 71.6°.

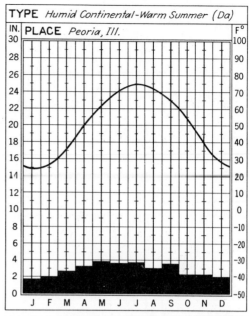

TYPE *Humid Continental-Warm Summer (Da)*
PLACE *Peoria, Ill.*

FIG. 14.6 Data of a station representing the warm-summer subtype of humid continental climate. A large annual range of temperature and concentration of precipitation in the warm season are characteristic.

served by the cooler summers farther north, even though they may offer more handicaps to agriculture. Winter temperatures, however, are usually 15 to 20° colder in the cool-

Climatic Data for Representative Stations in the Humid Continental Warm-summer Subtype (*Da*)

	J	F	M	A	M	J	J	A	S	O	N	D	Yr	Range
Peoria, Illinois														
Temp.	24	28	40	51	62	71	75	73	65	53	39	28	51	51
Precip.	1.8	2.0	2.7	3.3	3.9	3.8	3.8	3.2	3.8	2.4	2.4	2.0	35.1	
New York City														
Temp.	31	31	39	49	60	69	74	72	67	56	44	34	52	43
Precip.	3.3	3.3	3.4	3.3	3.4	3.4	4.1	4.3	3.4	3.4	3.4	3.3	42.0	
Bucharest, Rumania														
Temp.	26	29	40	52	61	68	73	71	64	54	41	30	51	47
Precip.	1.2	1.1	1.7	2.0	2.5	3.3	2.8	1.9	1.5	1.5	1.9	1.7	23.1	
Peking, China														
Temp.	24	29	41	57	68	76	79	77	68	55	39	27	53	55
Precip.	0.1	0.2	0.2	0.6	1.4	3.0	9.4	6.3	2.6	0.6	0.3	0.1	24.8	

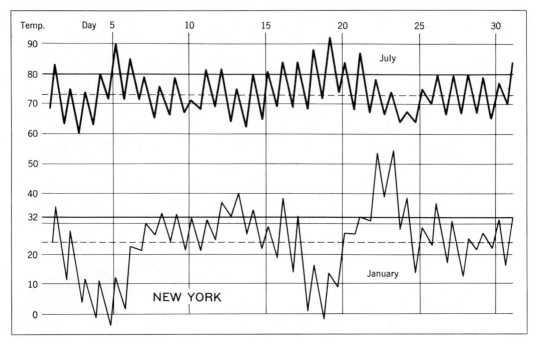

FIG. 14.7 Daily maximum and minimum temperatures for the warmest and coldest months for a station with humid continental warm-summer climate. Nonperiodic air-mass control is conspicuous, especially in winter.

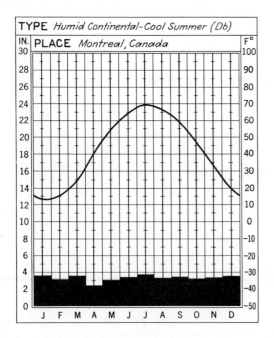

summer areas, and subzero temperatures and long spells of cold weather are more common there (Figs. 14.6–14.9).

The two subtypes are not conspicuously different in amount and seasonal distribution of precipitation. However, in those parts farther north a larger part of the winter precipitation is in the form of snow, and as a consequence the snow cover is more durable and long-continued there (Fig. 14.10).

FIG. 14.8 The cool-summer subtype of humid continental climate. Note the large annual range of temperature. At this station there is an absence of any seasonal concentration of precipitation, a feature characteristic of the northeastern United States and adjacent parts of Canada where winter cyclones are numerous.

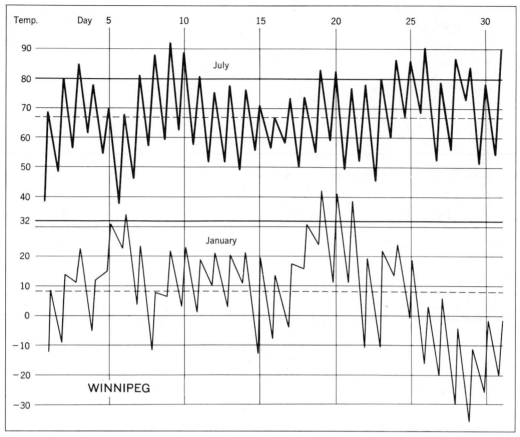

FIG. 14.9 The cool-summer subtype of humid continental climate. Note the very large and irregular temperature changes, evidence of strong air-mass control associated with cyclones and anticyclones.

Climatic Data for Representative Stations in the Humid Continental Cool-summer Subtype (*Db*)

	J	F	M	A	M	J	J	A	S	O	N	D	Yr	Range
				Madison, Wisconsin (marginal in location)										
Temp.	17	20	31	46	58	67	72	70	62	50	35	23	46	55
Precip.	1.2	1.3	1.9	2.6	3.7	3.4	3.5	3.3	4.1	2.3	2.0	1.4	30.7	
					Montreal, Canada									
Temp.	13	15	25	41	55	65	69	67	59	47	33	19	42	56
Precip.	3.7	3.2	3.7	2.4	3.1	3.5	3.8	3.4	3.5	3.3	3.4	3.7	40.7	
				Moscow, Union of Soviet Socialist Republics										
Temp.	12	15	23	38	53	62	66	63	52	40	28	17	39	54
Precip.	1.1	1.0	1.2	1.5	1.9	2.0	2.8	2.9	2.2	1.4	1.6	1.5	21.1	
					Harbin, Manchuria									
Temp.	−2	5	24	42	56	66	72	69	58	40	21	3	38	74
Precip.	0.1	0.2	0.4	0.9	1.7	3.8	4.5	4.1	1.8	1.3	0.3	0.2	19.3	

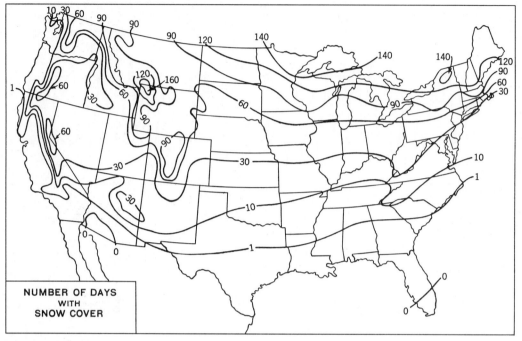

NUMBER OF DAYS
WITH
SNOW COVER

FIG. 14.10

RESOURCE POTENTIALITIES OF THE HUMID CONTINENTAL REALM

Climatically the humid continental realm is less bountiful than the humid subtropics, chiefly because of the shorter growing season and the cooler summer. This deficiency of heat tends to exclude many of the more sensitive crops and those requiring a long period between frosts. Greater dependence upon quick-maturing annuals is the result. Again in comparison with the subtropics, there is a shorter period during which animals can forage for their food and a much longer one during which they must be protected against the cold and fed from feeds stored in barns, silos, and granaries.

A further climatic handicap grows out of the fact that over extensive areas rainfall is only modest in amount, and is inclined to be undependable. The relatively wide fluctuations in crop yields from year to year reflect these disadvantages. But the seasonal concentration of the precipitation in the period of greatest heat somewhat compensates for them.

The original vegetation cover was largely forest in the more humid sections and prairie grass in the less humid parts. In their virgin state the prairies provided some of the earth's finest natural grazing land. Almost all of the prairie land has long since been brought under cultivation, however, for it is some of the world's best agricultural land. The forests of the more humid sections of the realm were various in nature. Thus a representative north-south cross section of the forests would show conifers predominating toward the northern margins of the realm, with mixed forests and purer stands of deciduous broadleaf trees prevailing farther south. Without doubt the virgin forests of the humid continental realm were among the finest and most extensive of the earth. For decades they were the world's principal source of lumber, and they are still important producers. But, because they were composed of such superior lumber trees and readily accessible, they have suffered rapid cutting. Much of the forest was removed by settlers in search of farm land; in less desirable agricultural regions the great lumber companies logged off the forest and left behind a desolate cutover country.

Soils in the humid continental climates show wide variations in quality. Under the broadleaf forest podzolic soils have developed which, although of only average quality, are still the best of the forest soils. Farther north in the coniferous region, poor, gray soils, the true podzols, prevail. In the less humid sections of the realm, where prairie grasses predominated, are to be found some of the earth's finest soils. There the lower rainfall results in less leaching, and the grasses provide an abundance of organic matter, so that the soils are high in soluble minerals and dark in color. Such excellent soils help to compensate in part for the less abundant and also less reliable rainfall of these sections.

Considerable areas in both the North American and European sections of the realm have been subjected to recent glaciation by continental ice sheets. In the parts of such areas where the relief is relatively great or the bedrock resistant, as, for example, in New England, northern New York State, and parts of Norway, Sweden, and Finland, ice erosion has been dominant, so that soils are thin and stony and lakes are numerous. In other parts where ice deposition prevailed, the drainage lines have been disrupted, so that both lakes and swamps are numerous, and a rolling and somewhat patternless terrain arrangement of rounded hills and associated depressions is characteristic. Here, although the soils may be deep, they vary greatly in composition and quality.

SUBARCTIC CLIMATE

TYPE LOCATION

Subarctic climate (*Dc, Dd*),[2] the most severe of the humid microthermal climates, is characteristically located in the broad northern parts of Eurasia and North America between about latitudes 55 and 70°N. On its northern margins, approximately at the poleward limit of forest growth, it makes contact with polar climate. On its equatorward side it is bordered by either humid continental or dry climate (Fig. 11.2, Plate 2).

[2] In the Köppen system *c* = cool summers, with only 1 to 3 months above 50° (10°C); *d* = cold winters, with the temperature of the coldest month below −36.4° (−38°C).

TEMPERATURE

Long and bitterly cold winters, very short summers with brief intervening falls and springs, and unusually large annual ranges— these are the prime temperature characteristics of subarctic climate (Fig. 14.11). Subarctic thus is land-controlled climate at its maximum development.

Winter Winter, by reason of both its length and its severity, dominates the climatic calendar. Frosts may arrive in late August, and ice begins to form on ponds in September. At Yakutsk, Siberia, the average monthly temperature drops 37° (from 16 to

Climatic Data for Representative Subarctic Stations

	J	F	M	A	M	J	J	A	S	O	N	D	Yr	Range
Fort Vermilion, Alberta, Canada (58°27′N)														
Temp.	−14	−6	8	30	47	55	60	57	46	32	10	−4	27	74
Precip.	0.6	0.3	0.5	0.7	1.0	1.9	2.1	2.1	1.4	0.7	0.5	0.4	12.2	
Moose Factory, Canada (51°16′N)														
Temp.	−4	−2	10	28	42	54	61	59	51	39	22	5	30	65
Precip.	1.3	0.9	1.1	1.0	1.8	2.2	2.4	3.3	2.9	1.8	1.1	1.1	20.9	
Yakutsk, Siberia, Union of Soviet Socialist Republics (65°21′N)														
Temp.	−46	−35	−10	16	41	59	66	60	42	16	−21	−41	12	112
Precip.	0.9	0.2	0.4	0.6	1.1	2.1	1.7	2.6	1.2	1.4	0.6	0.9	13.7	

−21°) between October and November. Within an extensive area in northeastern Siberia, near the center of the great thermal winter anticyclone, the average January temperature is below −50° and minimum January temperatures of −76° and lower have been recorded. At Oimyakon, Siberia, the

FIG. 14.11 A cool summer, a severe winter, a large annual range of temperature, and modest precipitation concentrated in summer are characteristic of subarctic climate.

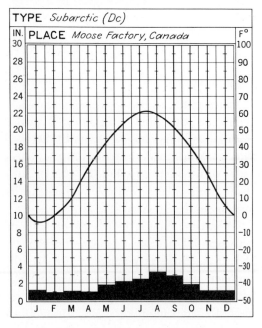

TYPE *Subarctic (Dc)*

PLACE *Moose Factory, Canada*

cold pole or region of lowest minimum temperatures, the thermometer has fallen as low as 95° below zero. However, these are the extremes in subarctic winters, for over most of the North American and European sectors average January temperatures of zero to 15° below are the rule. It is common, however, for the average temperatures of 6 or 7 months to be below freezing. The low temperatures combined with the long daily period of darkness (which is, obviously, partly responsible for them) make the winter weather depressing and hard to bear.

Summer The striking characteristic of the period of warmth in the subarctic is its briefness rather than its coolness. Typically the warmest month, July, has an average temperature in the 60s, which is no lower than that of many stations in marine climates farther south. Moreover, it is not uncommon for midday temperatures to reach 80° and above (Fig. 14.12). But July's modest warmth is very brief, for June and August averages are between 50 and 60°, and May and September are in the 40s. As a rule the period between killing frosts is only 2 to 3 months in length, and many stations experience freezing temperatures even in July and August in some years.

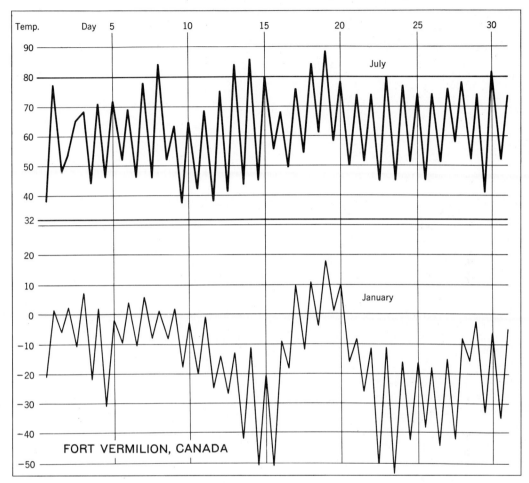

FIG. 14.12 Data from a subarctic station in Canada. Note the unusually strong nonperiodic air-mass control of temperature changes in winter. Summer shows greater diurnal regularity.

Somewhat compensating for the briefness of summer is the unusually long period of daylight in these higher latitudes. Thus at 60°N June days have an average 18.8 hr of possible sunshine.

PRECIPITATION

The characteristically meager annual precipitation, usually amounting to no more than 15 to 20 in., is related to (*a*) the great breadth of Eurasia and North America in subarctic latitudes, (*b*) low temperatures and associated low specific humidity, and (*c*) the well-developed thermal anticyclone of the colder part of the year with its settling air and diverging winds.

The year's precipitation is concentrated in the warmer months when the humidity content of the air is highest and atmospheric stability is least (Fig. 14.11). The especially low winter temperatures and the strong winter anticyclone mentioned above both operate to

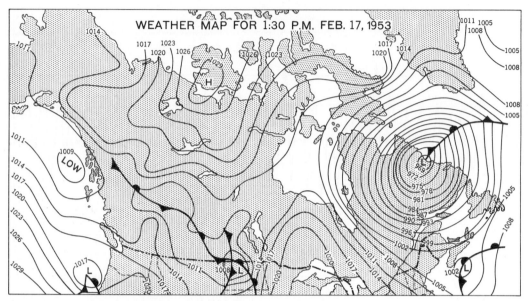

FIG. 14.13 A type of subarctic winter weather. A well-developed cyclone accompanied by strong winds and extensive snowfall prevails over the subarctic and tundra region of northeastern Canada. A cold anticyclone is conspicuous over northernmost Canada.

inhibit the processes making for precipitation. Over northeastern Siberia winters are especially dry, the precipitation ratio of the wettest summer month to the driest winter month being more than 10:1.

To a very great extent the year's precipitation originates in extensive disturbances, such as fronts and cyclonic storms. Thunderstorms are few. Disturbances are numerous enough at all seasons to give rise to marked nonperiodic weather changes, although in winter there is much settled anticyclonic weather (Figs. 14.2, 14.3).

RESOURCE POTENTIALITIES OF THE SUBARCTIC REALM

In spite of the fact that the subarctic realm is one of the most extensive of the earth's geographic realms, it is also one of the least productive. Like the dry lands and parts of

the wet tropics, the subarctic realm is coincident with relatively blank areas on the world-population map. The extractive industries, such as hunting, fishing, mining, and logging, which rank high in relative importance, are capable of supporting only a meager population. The landscape, therefore, is one composed predominantly of natural features: man has left but a modest imprint.

In productive capacity the realm is fundamentally handicapped by its niggardly climate, which sets very definite low limits upon agricultural development, the primary difficulties being associated specifically with (a) the briefness of the summers and (b) the relatively low summer temperatures. At present commercially successful agriculture is not likely in regions where the frost-free season is shorter than 80 or 90 days, and this condition prevails in all except the most southerly portions of the subarctic realm.

Subarctic Eurasia and North America are largely covered by primarily coniferous virgin forests. In their immensity and monotony these subarctic forests are like the sea, and travelers are impressed with their emptiness and silence. Even animal life is sparse. Conifers usually occupy in the neighborhood of 75 per cent of the forest area, with such deciduous trees as the birch, poplar, willow, and alder comprising most of the remainder.

Yet neither in the size of the trees nor in the density of the stand is the subarctic forest impressive, and in the ice-scoured Canadian subarctic extensive areas of lake, swamp, and bare rock are even practically without forest. As a result the subarctic forest does not represent nearly so great a potential supply of forest products as its area might seem to indicate. Most subarctic timber is more valuable for firewood and pulpwood than for good lumber. Moreover, the inaccessibility of these northern forests to world markets severely reduces their resource value.

An impoverished soil environment is characteristic of the subarctic realm, and this infertile soil, combined with a climate of low potentialities, causes the subarctic lands to offer what appear to be almost insurmountable difficulties to the agricultural settler. The needles from the coniferous forest provide a very meager supply of organic material for the soils, and the ground water, high in organic acids derived from the raw humus, leaches the soil minerals excessively.

Ranking after climate and soils as a third handicap to agricultural settlement within the subarctic realm is deficient drainage. Poorly drained land is prevalent, partly because of the permanently frozen subsoil which exists throughout the higher latitudes of the realm. Over most of subarctic North America and in Scandinavia, Finland, and western Soviet Russia the abundance of lakes and swamps is a consequence of continental glaciation.

POLAR CLIMATES

LOCATION AND BOUNDARIES

As the tropics lack a cool season, so do the polar climates (*E*) lack a genuine warm season. While monotonous heat characterizes the low latitudes, in the polar regions monotonous cold prevails.

Polar climates are confined to the high latitudes of the earth, largely poleward of latitude 60°. The poleward limit of forest growth is commonly accepted as the equatorward boundary of polar climates, and over the great continents this vegetation boundary coincides approximately with the 50° isotherm (line of 50° average temperature) for the warmest month. Here during much of the winter the sun is constantly below the horizon, so that darkness prevails and cold is intense and long-continued. Moreover, while in summer the sun may never set and constant daylight prevails, the sun is never far above the horizon, and its oblique rays deliver little energy at the earth's surface.

In the Southern Hemisphere the only extensive nonoceanic area with polar climates is the Antarctic Continent, the approximate center of which is at the South Pole. Since the Arctic is almost a landlocked sea, except for the frozen ocean, the polar climates there are confined to the northern borders of Eurasia and North America and to the island continent of Greenland.

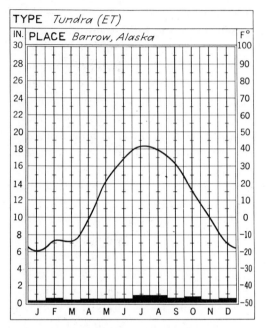

TYPE *Tundra (ET)*

PLACE *Barrow, Alaska*

FIG. 14.14 Data of a tundra station at a severe continental location. Note the large annual range of temperature and the meager precipitation.

TYPES

Polar climates may be divided into two types, *tundra* and *icecap*, with the *warmest-month* isotherm of $32°$ serving as the boundary between them. Where the average temperature of all months is below freezing ($32°$), vegetation is absent and a permanent snow-and-ice cover prevails. Such locations

have icecap climate. Where 1 or more months in the warmer period has an average temperature above $32°$ (but not over $50°$), there is tundra climate.

TUNDRA CLIMATE

Tundra climate (ET)[3] on land areas is almost exclusively limited to the Northern Hemisphere, for in the Southern Hemisphere oceans prevail in those latitudes where tundra climate normally would develop. The most extensive tundra areas are the Arctic Ocean margins of both Eurasia and North America and the coastal borders of Greenland (Fig. 11.2, Plate 2).

Temperature   A long cold winter and a very short and cool summer are the rule in tundra climate (Fig. 14.14). With the average temperature of the warmest month between 32 and $50°$ by definition, even the warmest months are raw and chilly, resembling March and April in southern Wisconsin, or January in the Gulf states. Killing frosts may occur at any time, although it does not freeze on most July nights (Fig. 14.15). The continuous but weak summer sun frees the land of its snow cover for a few months, but the subsoil remains frozen, so that the surface remains

[3] In the Köppen system T = warmest month below $50°$ ($10°C$) but above $32°$ ($0°C$).

Climatic Data for Representative Tundra Stations

	J	*F*	*M*	*A*	*M*	*J*	*J*	*A*	*S*	*O*	*N*	*D*	*Yr*	*Range*
Sagastyr, Siberia, Union of Soviet Socialist Republics (73°N, 124°E)														
Temp.	-34	-36	-30	-7	15	32	41	38	33	6	-16	-28	1	77
Precip.	0.1	0.1	0.0	0.0	0.2	0.4	0.3	1.4	0.4	0.1	0.1	0.2	3.3	
Upernivik, Western Greenland (73°N, 56°W)														
Temp.	-7	-10	-6	6	25	35	41	41	33	25	14	1	16	51
Precip.	0.4	0.4	0.6	0.6	0.6	0.6	1.0	1.1	1.0	1.1	1.1	0.5	9.2	

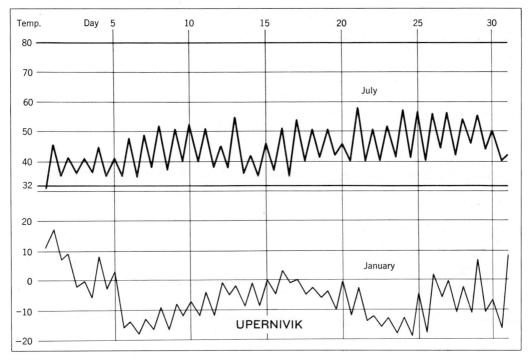

FIG. 14.15 Daily maximum and minimum temperatures for the warmest and coldest months at a tundra station in Greenland.

wet and poorly drained. Tundra vegetation consists of lichens, mosses, sedges, and bushes.

Precipitation Given the low temperatures of these high latitudes, the modest precipitation, usually less than 10 or 15 in., is not surprising. Likewise anticipated is the concentration of the year's precipitation, nearly all of it cyclonic in origin, in the warmer months of the year when the humidity content of the air is highest (Fig. 14.14). The meager winter snowfall is dry and powdery in character, so that the strong winds sweep the level surfaces bare and concentrate the snow in depressions and on the lee side of low eminences. It has been estimated that 75 to 90 per cent of the surface of the Arctic tundra lands is nearly free of snow at all seasons.

ICECAP CLIMATE

Icecap climate (*EF*),[4] the least well-known of the earth's climatic types, is characteristically developed over the great permanent continental ice sheets of Antarctica and Greenland and over the perpetually frozen ocean in the vicinity of the North Pole. Only fragmentary climatic data have been obtained from these deserts of snow and ice where the average temperature of no month rises above freezing.

Temperature The average annual temperatures of the icecaps are without doubt the lowest for any part of the earth. At Eismitte, located at nearly 10,000 ft elevation

[4] In the Köppen system F = warmest month below 32° (0°C).

Climatic Data for an Icecap Station (*EF*), Eismitte (Wegener),
Interior Greenland (70°54′N, 40°42′W, 9,941 ft)

	J	F	M	A	M	J	J	A	S	O	N	D	Yr	Range
Temp.	−42	−53	−40	−24	−4	4	12	1	−8	−32	−46	−37	−22	65
Precip.	No data													

on the ice plateau of interior Greenland, average winter-month temperatures are below −40° and the warmest month is about 12° (preceding table). During 9 months the averages are below zero. In all probability temperatures in inland Antarctica are even more severe.

Precipitation If little is known about temperature conditions of icecap climates, still less information is available about general weather conditions and precipitation. Certainly annual precipitation is meager (under 5 in., water equivalent), and all of it falls in the solid form. It appears to originate in cyclonic storms that pass over the ice plateaus or skirt their margins. One year at Eismitte, Greenland, there were 204 days with precipitation, and there was no conspicuous seasonal concentration.

HIGHLAND CLIMATES

There is no such thing as a highland *type* or clearly distinct types of climate. Instead, mountains exhibit an almost endless variety of climates depending on contrasts in altitude and in exposure to sun and winds. The valley contrasts with the exposed peak; windward slopes differ from leeward slopes; and southern exposures are unlike those facing north. And each of these climatic contrasts is in turn multiplied, as it were, by differences in latitude and continental location.

The resulting great complexity of the variety of climates within highlands has caused them to be grouped together under a single designation on Plate 2. Generally regions characterized by an elevation above 4,000 or 5,000 ft are included: lower regions are not so climatically different from the surrounding lowlands that they need to be differentiated from them.

ATMOSPHERIC PRESSURE IN MOUNTAINS

At low elevations the minor changes in air pressure from day to day, or from season to season, cannot be directly perceived by the human body. But the very rapid decrease in the atmosphere's weight with increasing elevation and the related very low atmospheric pressure that prevails on high mountains and plateaus cause the pressure element to be genuinely important in highland climates. Physiological effects (faintness, headache, nosebleed, nausea, weakness) of decreased pressure aloft are experienced by most people at altitudes above 12,000 or 15,000 ft. Sleeplessness is common and exertion is difficult. Yet mountain sickness is usually a temporary inconvenience that passes away after a week or so of residence at high altitudes.

SOLAR RADIATION AND TEMPERATURE

Solar energy Intensity of sunlight increases with elevation in the cleaner, drier, thinner air of mountains. This is to be ex-

Climatic Data for a Highland Station in the Tropics

	J	F	M	A	M	J	J	A	S	O	N	D	Yr	Range
					Quito, Ecuador (9,350 ft)									
Temp.	54.5	55.0	54.5	54.5	54.7	55.0	54.9	54.9	55.0	54.7	54.3	54.7	54.7	0.7
Precip.	3.2	3.9	4.8	7.0	4.6	1.5	1.1	2.2	2.6	3.9	4.0	3.6	42.2	

pected, since dust, clouds, and water vapor, the principal scattering, reflecting, and absorbing elements of solar radiation in the atmosphere, are concentrated at lower elevations. On a clear day probably three-fourths of the solar energy penetrates to 6,000 ft, but only one-half to sea level. This greater intensity of sunlight at high altitudes has an important effect upon soil temperature, and, both directly and indirectly, upon plant growth.

Air temperature   Most important of the climatic changes resulting from increased elevation is the decrease in air temperature (on the average, about 3.6° per 1,000-ft rise, as stated earlier) which occurs in spite of the increased intensity of solar energy. Quito, Ecuador, on the equator at an elevation of 9,350 ft (preceding table), has an average annual temperature of only 55°, which is 25° lower than that of the adjacent Amazon lowlands. Because the rare air at Quito is incapable of absorbing and retaining much solar energy, the air remains chilly. Yet for the same reason the sunlight itself is strong. The climate is therefore one of cool shade and hot sun.

Importance of vertical change   The vertical rate of temperature change along mountain slopes is several hundred times greater than the winter north-south horizontal gradient over continental lowlands, a fact that has important consequences. In the tropics, where the lowlands are characterized by continuous and oppressive heat, the cooler highlands may be so attractive to settlers that in some regions they become the centers of population concentration. Such is the case in much of Latin America. There is a striking vertical zonation not only of contrasting climates but also of agricultural and vegetation belts between tropical lowlands and highlands (Fig. 14.16). Thus in tropical valleys where there is a luxuriant rainforest such heat-requiring crops as rubber, bananas, and cacao thrive. Somewhat higher they may give way to an economy based on coffee, tea, maize and a variety of food crops. On the still higher and cooler slopes middle-latitude cereals and potatoes become more important, as does the grazing of animals, the natural pastures for which are terminated along their upper margins by the permanent snow fields.

By contrast, highlands in middle latitudes are less attractive climatically and have fewer vertical zones of contrasting vegetation and agriculture (Fig. 14.16). Here even the lowlands are none too warm, so that any reduction in temperature with altitude, resulting in a cooler summer and a shorter growing season, materially reduces the opportunities for agricultural production.

Diurnal and seasonal temperatures   The thin, dry air characteristic of mountains and high plateaus permits not only the entry of strong solar radiation by day but also the rapid loss of earth energy at night, resulting in rapid heating by day and rapid cooling

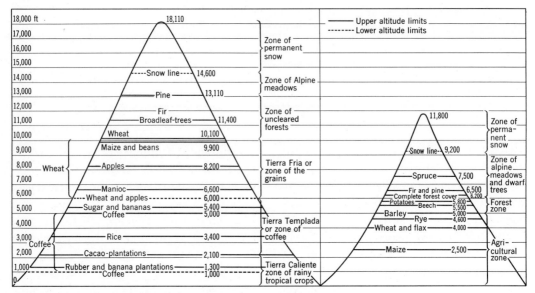

FIG. 14.16 Vertical temperature zones and the altitude limits of certain crops and types of vegetation on a tropical mountain (left) and a middle-latitude mountain (right). *(From Sapper.)*

by night. Thus large diurnal ranges of temperature are characteristics of highland climates (Fig. 14.17).

At high altitudes in tropical highlands this results in numerous days on which night freezing and daytime thawing occur, and this frequent and rapid oscillation between the two has a marked effect upon vegetation and soil characteristics. The great temperature difference between day and night in tropical highlands stands in contrast to the very small difference between the average temperatures of the warmest and coldest months, or the annual range. One of the distinctive features of high plateaus and mountains in

the tropics is this combination of a large daily and a small annual range of temperature.

Although the thermometer stands lower on a tropical mountain than it does on an adjacent lowland, the two locations are alike in having uniform daily and monthly mean temperatures and small annual ranges. Monotonous repetition of daily weather belongs alike to tropical highlands and plains (Figs. 11.5, 14.17). For instance, at Quito the temperature difference between the warmest and coolest months is only 0.7°, which is very similar to the difference in the Amazon lowlands in the same latitude (Fig. 14.18). Mexico City at 7,474 ft has an aver-

Climatic Data for a Representative Highland Station in Middle Latitudes

	J	F	M	A	M	J	J	A	S	O	N	D	Yr	Range
Longs Peak, Colorado (8,956 ft)														
Temp.	23	22	26	33	41	51	55	55	48	39	31	24	37	33
Precip.	0.7	1.2	2.0	2.7	2.4	1.6	3.6	2.2	1.7	1.7	0.9	0.9	21.6	

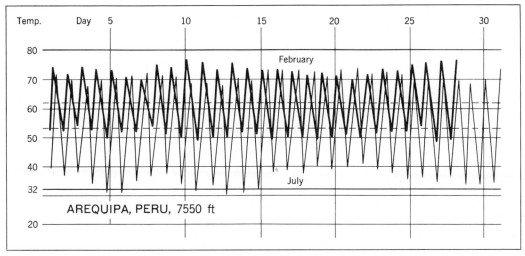

FIG. 14.17 Daily maximum and minimum temperatures of the warmest and coldest months at a tropical mountain station located at a moderate altitude. Note the diurnal regularity of temperature change indicating sun control. Diurnal range is greater in July, the dry season, when the least cloud is present.

age annual temperature 17° below that of Veracruz, in the same latitude but on the coast; yet their annual ranges are almost identical—11.5 and 11° respectively. One climatologist has tersely described this temperature relationship between lowlands and highlands as follows: "The pitch changes; the tune remains the same."

Highland climates in the tropics are unique among cool or cold climates in having a small annual range of temperature.

Farther away from the equator the annual range characteristic of highlands increases in magnitude, another similarity to lowlands. In fact, the annual range for highland stations and lowland stations in similar latitudes is approximately the same.

INCREASE OF PRECIPITATION IN MOUNTAINS AND ITS IMPORTANCE IN DRY CLIMATES

Precipitation is heavier in highlands than on the surrounding lowlands, as was ex-

plained in the discussion of orographic precipitation in Chap. 9. This is a fact of great importance, especially in dry climates. There, no matter what the latitude, this heavier precipitation (including snowfall) of highlands is critical. Not only are settlements attracted to the humid slopes and to the well-watered mountain valleys, but streams, descending from the rainier highlands, carry the influence

FIG. 14.18 A comparison of the annual marches of temperature at Iquitos, a tropical lowland station in Peru, and at Quito, a tropical highland station in Ecuador. Note the generally lower temperature at Quito. On the other hand, a small annual range of temperature is characteristic of both stations.

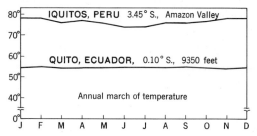

of highland climate far out on the dry lowlands. There the mountain waters (including meltwater from the snow fields) are put to multiple uses—irrigation, power development, and, in some places, transportation.

In addition, mountains in regions of drought, because they are "islands" of heavier precipitation, are likewise islands of heavier vegetation cover, and sometimes of more abundant agricultural production as well. In both arid and semiarid lands, highlands are likely to bear a cover of forest in contrast to the meager grass and shrub vegetation of the surrounding drier lowlands.

WINDS AND WEATHER

On exposed mountain slopes and summits, where the effects of ground friction are reduced, winds are strong and persistent. By contrast, protected mountain valleys may be particularly quiet areas. In general, highland areas are particularly subject to numerous local winds and accompanying weather, occasioned by the great variety of relief and exposure present. Common in valleys and along heated slopes is the upslope wind by day, when convection is at a maximum, and the downslope wind at night. Where well-developed cyclonic storms are present, as in the middle latitudes, the passing low-pressure system may induce a downslope wind, nondiurnal in character, known as the foehn or chinook. Such winds are characterized by great dryness and unseasonable warmth.

In highlands the weather changes within a 24-hr period are likely to be greater than on adjacent lowlands. Violent changes from hot sun to cool shade, from chill wind to calm, from gusts of rain or possibly snow to intense sunlight—these give the daily weather an erratic nature. Even in the tropics the complex sequence of weather within a day stands in marked contrast to the uniformity of the average daily and monthly temperatures.

SELECTED REFERENCES

Blair, Thomas A.: *Climatology: General and Regional,* Prentice-Hall, Inc., Englewood Cliffs, N. J., 1942.

Critchfield, Howard J.: *General Climatology,* Prentice-Hall, Inc., Englewood Cliffs, N. J., 1960.

Haurwitz, Bernhard, and James M. Austin: *Climatology,* McGraw-Hill Book Company, Inc., New York, 1944.

Koeppe, Clarence E., and George C. De Longe: *Weather and Climate,* McGraw-Hill Book Company, Inc., New York, 1958.

Miller, Arthur Austin: *Climatology,* 8th ed., E. P. Dutton & Co., Inc., New York, 1954.

Trewartha, Glenn T.: *An Introduction to Climate,* McGraw-Hill Book Company, Inc., New York, 1954.

Trewartha, Glenn T.: *The Earth's Problem Climates,* University of Wisconsin Press, Madison, Wis., 1961.

CHAPTER 15

Water and the seas

WATERS OF THE EARTH

Of all the substances that are familiar to man, probably none is more vital, more ubiquitous, or more changeable under ordinary conditions than water. Water covers more than two-thirds of the solid earth, it occurs in quantity beneath the solid surface, and it is a normal constituent of the atmosphere above the surface. Unlike any other substance that occurs commonly near the earth's surface, water may occur as a solid, liquid, or gas within the range of temperatures that are normal there.

THE HYDROSPHERE

It is sometimes convenient to refer to all occurrences of water on, above, or beneath the earth's surface collectively as the *hydrosphere,* in analogy to the *atmosphere,* or gaseous envelope of the earth, and the *lithosphere,* or solid crust of the earth. The term is not wholly satisfactory, for the three "spheres" interpenetrate one another. In this book, therefore, it has been felt proper to discuss much of that portion of the hydrosphere

277

which is ice as a part of the lithosphere, and most of that which is vapor as a part of the atmosphere. However, because water may pass freely from one place and form of occurrence to another, it is also valuable to consider the hydrosphere in its entirety as a distinct set of closely interlinked phenomena. The fact that consideration of the hydrosphere has, almost of necessity, been somewhat fragmented in this book in no way denies the importance or the fundamental unity of the hydrosphere. Instead it emphasizes the fact that each element of the earth's physical geography exists not by itself but in close relationship with the others, so that even in a survey study the individual elements cannot and should not be treated in complete isolation.

IMPORTANCE AND OCCURRENCE OF WATER

It would be difficult to overemphasize the importance of water in physical geography. It is one of the three major elements of weather and climate; it is the prime agent of degradation and aggradation; and it is an indispensable ingredient of the natural environment for the existence of life. Its place in the organic complex is well summarized as follows:

"Where there is life there must be water. There is no organism today, plant or animal, which is not highly dependent on it. . . . A seed will not sprout without water. Indeed the cells which make up a seedling . . . are largely water. Water has a basic role in the formation of the protein molecule, the fundamental material for all living matter, plant and animal. No less than light it is essential to photosynthesis, the biochemical process by which . . . plants obtain the principal raw materials for their growth. . . . Apart from fat, the tissues of all animal bodies are 70 to 90 per cent water."[1]

[1] Edward A. Ackerman, *Water Resources in the United States,* reprint 6, Resources for the Future, Inc. 1958, p. 2.

Man, being an animal organism, must of course have water to sustain his own life and to produce those organisms he uses for food. To these uses, man has added a long list of others. In our modern industrial and commercial society a large supply of water, far beyond that needed for drinking and for nourishing plants and other animals, has become a virtual necessity. There is no more important economic resource, and to meet all the demands on this resource a large, continuous supply must be available.

Even if the water held in chemical bond in the materials of the deep interior is ignored, there is a vast amount of water in the hydrosphere. In the outermost 3 miles of the earth there is three times as much water as all other substances put together, and six times as much as the next most abundant compound, feldspar.

As the table (p. 279) shows, most of the water near the earth's surface is in the great ocean reservoir. Less than 8 per cent exists elsewhere. An exceedingly small portion is in the atmosphere as vapor, as cloud-forming droplets, or as ice particles, and the remainder occurs as liquid or ice on and beneath the ground surface.

THE CYCLICAL BEHAVIOR OF WATER

The hydrologic cycle Practically all the water near the surface of the earth is in some sort of vertical motion, a result of a vast, continuous distilling process called the *hydrologic cycle.* (Though not named there, the hydrologic cycle was briefly discussed in relation to precipitation in Chap. 9.) Wherever water and the requisite energy meet, some of the water evaporates and enters the atmosphere. This happens at the soil surface,

Approximate Distribution of the Waters of the Earth in Cubic Miles of
Liquid Equivalent*

In the lithosphere:	
Above sea level	1,085,000
Below sea level to a depth of 2½ miles	1,255,000
In the subcrustal zone	19,400,000
On the lithosphere:	
In soil, plants, and animals	3,400
In lakes and streams	53,000
In icecaps and glaciers	9,200,000
In the ocean basins	315,000,000
In the atmosphere:	
In solid, liquid, and vapor	3,600
Total	340,000,000

* Estimated from various sources.

the surfaces of plants and animals, and the water surfaces of lakes and streams, but mostly at the ocean surface. Insolation is the ultimate source of energy for these processes, which together are called *evapotranspiration.* As a constituent of maritime air masses the vapor thus formed moves with the advectional and convectional currents of the atmosphere, wherein it condenses, sometimes as dew, but mostly aloft as water droplets or ice particles. Some of these coalesce and fall as precipitation. A portion returns to vapor again before it reaches the earth's surface. The rest falls directly back into the ocean reservoir or onto the land surface.

Much of the water that falls on the land is destined to return ultimately to the ocean reservoir, but its movement in that direction is not likely to be direct. Some falls upon lake or stream surfaces and thus starts back immediately, while some is shed on the ground and must find its way to a stream. In either case some of this surface water will be evaporated again before it returns to the ocean. The stream, responding to the pull of

gravity, may flow either toward the ocean or toward some enclosed basin on the land. In such a basin it may collect as a salt lake, from which it either evaporates again or sinks beneath the land surface. Where there is no such topographic interruption to its return to the ocean, the surface water continues on its way, sometimes being delayed in a fresh-water lake or swamp but always moving downward. On the way some may leave the stream by sinking into its bed.

A portion of the water that falls on the land neither evaporates again nor enters a stream, but instead sinks downward into the soil. Some of this is taken up by plant roots, passed upward through the stems, and evaporated from pores in the leaves, a process known as transpiration. A fraction may move upward by capillary force, but some continues downward to become part of the *ground-water,* i.e., the water that saturates the cracks and pore spaces of the regolith (unconsolidated surface material) and bedrock to the bottom of the fracture zone. Within this reservoir it moves in response to the pull

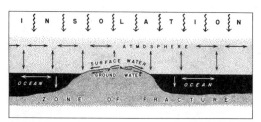

FIG. 15.1   The principal aspects of the hydro-logic cycle.

of gravity either directly or indirectly as a result of pressure differences, and consequently it may move laterally as well as vertically within the ground. Some of the ground-water reservoir discharges directly into the ocean, below sea level, but by far the larger part drains by seepages and springs to feed the streams and rivers that flow back to the ocean.

If, instead of summarizing the general functioning of the hydrologic cycle, a person tries to follow the history of a specific mass of water during a long period, he finds many complications. For example, a molecule may start life anew. A minute amount of new water escapes from the hot interior; this adds to the supply at the surface, since it is believed that none is lost to space. Again, some of the water may become locked up in ice masses or in mineral crystals, or be trapped in the pore spaces of sedimentary rocks being formed at the bottom of the sea, there to remain for uncounted years or perhaps even whole geologic eras. It may thus be held out of circulation for a time and consequently change to a small degree the relationship among the quantities of water in the surface portion of the hydrosphere enumerated in the preceding table. However, this does not greatly affect the short-term geographical operation of the hydrologic cycle, i.e., the movement of water via evaporation and pre-

cipitation from the sea to the land and back which is diagrammatically illustrated in Fig. 15.1.

Variations over the earth   The variations over the earth in the performance of the hydrologic cycle are very complicated as a result of the variations of all the factors that cause weather and climate to differ from place to place and from time to time, plus the variations of vegetation cover, soil and bedrock character, saltiness of water surfaces and many other factors. Nevertheless, some geographical generalizations are possible. It is estimated that some 60,000 cubic miles of water is evaporated into the atmosphere each year, the larger amount of it equatorward of the middle latitudes because the energy supply from the sun is greater there. In the higher latitudes, poleward from about 38°, it is thought that the total precipitation exceeds the evaporation. Thus there must be a net zonal transfer of atmospheric water from the lower to the higher latitudes that is compensated by return ocean flow.

Unfortunately, the measurement of the amount of water that evaporates from the land and sea surface is not as easy as the measurement of precipitation. Consequently an accurate world map of the distribution of actual evapotranspiration amounts cannot yet be made. When it is, it will bear a strong resemblance to a map of world precipitation. On the other hand, evaporation from the water surfaces of subtropical latitudes no doubt exceeds that from water surfaces in other parts of the earth, as a consequence of the greater surface receipt of insolation and the divergent surface airflow characteristic of these regions.

At any given latitude those land areas that have more water on the surface or in the soil and a denser vegetation cover will furnish proportionately more water to the atmosphere. Likewise, the clearer, windier, and warmer an area, the greater will be the possibility of transfer. Thus the climatically dry land areas, generally being clear, windy, and warm, have a high *potential* evapotranspiration, but, because of having little surface or soil water and meager vegetation, naturally have a relatively low *actual* rate.

THE SEAS

SIZE AND SIGNIFICANCE

The land surfaces upon which man lives and from which he derives the greater part of his sustenance in reality occupy what may seem a surprisingly small fraction of the whole surface of the globe. Nearly 71 per cent of the earth is covered by the oceans, and all of the land masses are completely surrounded by water, forming huge islands in the continuous sea. Moreover, the wide sea is also deep, its volume being many times as great as that of the portions of the continents that lie above sea level. It is the sea, not the land, that is the prevalent environment on the earth, foreign though this is to the human point of view. Though man does not live in the sea, he has much to do with it, for it serves him as a route of transport, as a source of food and, increasingly, of minerals, as a modifier of his climate, and as a partitioner of his lands. A study of the earth as the home of man cannot properly neglect so great and so significant a part of that earth.

NATURE OF SEA WATER

Sea water is a substance of highly complex composition. To be sure, only 3.5 per cent of the substance, by weight, is anything but pure water, and the greatest part of this small amount of impurity is common salt (sodium chloride) which is present in solution, with most of the small remainder being dissolved salts of magnesium, calcium, and potassium. But there are minute quantities of an immense number of other substances—so many that a complete listing here is impossible. Most of these impurities have probably been brought into the sea at a very slow rate by streams, though some may be derived from other sources. Since evaporation leaves the salts behind, a gradual concentration of soluble materials in the sea is occurring.

The degree of concentration of dissolved salts, called the *salinity* of the water, varies somewhat from place to place, being affected principally by the relative rate of precipitation and evaporation. Heavy rainfall lowers the surface salinity by dilution; strong evaporation raises the salinity by removal of water and concentration of salts.

The highest salinities in the open sea are found in the dry, hot subtropics, where evaporation is great. Nearer the equator salinities decrease because of heavier rainfall. In the cooler middle latitudes salinities are relatively low because of the decrease in evaporation and the considerable rainfall. But the variations are small in the open sea, generally less than 5 per cent on either side of the mean.

In coastal waters and nearly enclosed seas, on the other hand, the salinity often departs greatly from the mean. In hot, dry, nearly isolated seas such as the Red Sea and Persian Gulf, the salinities reach very high figures because the water in them is subject to strong evaporation but cannot mix freely with less saline waters from the depths of the open sea. On the other hand, in the neighborhood of the mouths of large rivers or in nearly enclosed seas into which large rivers flow, such as the Black Sea and the Baltic Sea, the dilution by fresh water reduces the salinity to relatively low figures.

The mean density of sea water is slightly higher than that of pure fresh water because of the presence in sea water of dissolved salts, and the density becomes greater with increasing salinity, as well as with decreasing temperature. Therefore very saline or very cold surface water tends to sink and to be replaced by water from beneath. Thus in middle-latitude waters, where winter cooling of the surface is extreme, there commonly occurs during the winter an "overturning," with the chilled surface waters becoming cold enough to sink, while slightly warmer waters from below come to the top. Where warm and cold surface waters meet, the colder sinks beneath the warmer.

MOVEMENTS OF OCEAN WATERS

WAVES

Waves are the smallest and most localized of the several kinds of movements in which the ocean waters are involved. Most waves are originated by the wind, though they may continue to travel beyond the area stirred by the wind and long after the wind has ceased to blow. The importance of waves lies chiefly in their effect upon the operation of

seagoing ships and, more pertinent to the present discussion, in their function of eroding along the coasts and distributing the eroded material.

In deep waters, with low or moderate wind velocities, wave movements are smoothly progressive, with each water molecule describing essentially a circle as the wave impulse passes. The water rises on the front of the wave, moves forward as the crest passes, drops down the rearward slope, and moves backward in the succeeding trough (Fig. 15.2). However, with high wind velocities the crest of the wave is tipped forward and breaks, forming a whitecap.

The height of waves in the open sea appears to depend upon the velocity of the wind, the length of time the wind has blown, and the distance the wind has driven the waves across the surface. Up to a certain point, the height becomes greater with increasing values of each of these controls.

Near the shore, where the depth of water decreases, an approaching wave is slowed by friction from below. The crest rises, steepens, and finally crashes forward as a breaker, which may hurl tons of water against the bottom or, if close enough inshore, against the land (Fig. 3.31). It is here that the erosional effect of the waves, which was described in Chap. 3, is greatest.

THE TIDES AND THEIR CAUSES

Nearly all shores of the open seas experience the distinct periodic rises and falls of sea level known as the tides. Like most familiar natural phenomena, they have been known and studied from very early times, and along the way have become a symbol of the certainty and inflexibility of natural processes. But understanding of how and why the tides vary from place to place has

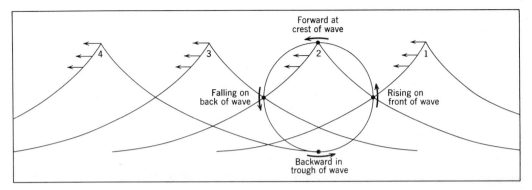

FIG. 15.2 How a water particle moves in a circle during the passage of a wave in the open sea.

been slow in coming, and even now it is not securely grasped. The basic factors that produce the tides are not especially obscure, but the actual mechanism of tidal activity on the earth is exceedingly complex. A full discussion of the causes of the tides is beyond the scope of this book, but they will be briefly summarized here.

The moon and the tides The principal tide-producing forces are (*a*) the gravitational attraction of the moon and (*b*) the centrifugal force of the earth's revolution about the center of gravity of the earth-moon system. It may be shown that the first of these forces is directed toward the moon and is strongest on the side of the earth toward the moon, while the second force is directed away from the moon and has the same strength at every point on the earth. At the center of the earth the two forces are in balance. On the side toward the moon, the lunar attraction exceeds the centrifugal force, producing a net pull toward the moon. On the opposite side of the earth, the centrifugal component exceeds the gravitational, producing a net force directed away from the moon (Fig. 15.3). As the earth rotates within this field of forces, the waters of each small area of the oceans are subjected to successive pulls away from

the center of the earth which reach maximum strength at intervals of about 12 hr, 25 min, the time it takes for earth rotation to carry a point on the surface from a position facing the moon to a position opposite the moon.

Because the seas are not continuous but form a series of interconnected basins of many shapes and sizes, the tides do not actually behave as simple progressive bulges moving westward on the earth as it rotates toward the east. Instead, this type of movement appears to be combined with various oscillatory or swashing movements of the sort that may be produced by tilting or swinging a basin full of water. Each major ocean basin and bordering sea has its own pattern and style of tidal movement, and movements set up in each of two adjacent seas may, in the zone between them, interfere with and affect one another. The result is extreme variety from place to place in height of successive tides, intervals between tides, amount of rise and fall, and various associated phenomena.

In most places there are two high tides per day, at approximately the expected 12 hr, 25 min interval, and the amount of change is usually a few feet. Along most Atlantic shores successive high tides are roughly of equal height, while in the Pacific every second

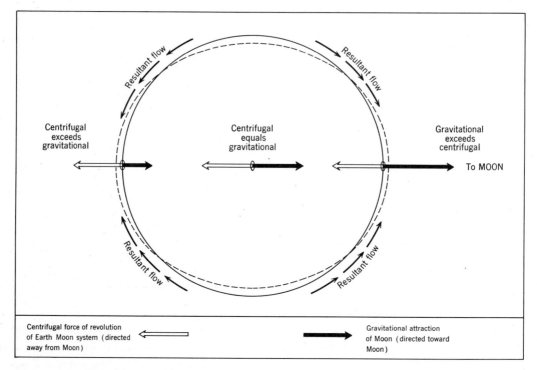

Centrifugal exceeds gravitational

Centrifugal equals gravitational

Gravitational exceeds centrifugal

To MOON

Centrifugal force of revolution of Earth Moon system (directed away from Moon)

Gravitational attraction of Moon (directed toward Moon)

FIG. 15.3   The principal forces involved in the production of tides.

high tide is distinctly lower than the preceding one (Fig. 15.4). On some shores, notably parts of southern Asia and the Caribbean and Gulf Coasts of North America, there is but one high tide per day.

Tidal range   The average difference in water level between low and high tide at a given place is called tidal range. Common tidal ranges on exposed coasts vary from 5 to 10 ft. In sheltered waters, such as the Gulf of Mexico and the Caribbean Sea, the range is usually less than 2 ft; and in nearly enclosed seas, such as the Mediterranean and the Baltic, the tides are so slight as to be negligible. In a few localities, mostly in funnel-shaped bays and estuaries, remarkably high ranges occur, increasing toward the head of the inlet. Liverpool has a range of 29 ft, and the head of the Bay of Fundy,

Nova Scotia, sometimes experiences tides of more than 50 ft.

The sun sets up tides in precisely the same manner as the moon; however, these solar effects are much weaker, and in fact appear not as separate tides but simply as modifications of the lunar tides. At times of new moon and full moon, when the earth,

FIG. 15.4   The intervals and amounts of rise and fall of the tide at Honolulu during a 48-hr period. Note the alternation of smaller and larger tidal rises.

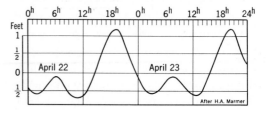

After H.A. Marmer

moon, and sun are nearly in line, sun and moon tides reinforce one another, producing unusually high tidal ranges. These tides, referred to by the misleading term of spring tides, recur every 2 weeks. At intervening times, when the sun and moon tides are at odds with one another, unusually low tidal ranges, called neap tides, occur.

Tidal phenomena are important to the use and development of harbors. Currents of considerable strength are often set up by the tides in narrow inlets and bays, and these may cause hazards to the handling of ships in harbor entrances and about docks. In ports where the tidal range is large it is sometimes necessary to construct docking basins with lock gates to maintain water levels high enough to keep moored vessels afloat at low tide, as well as to decrease the inconveniences of change of level in loading and unloading.

OCEAN DRIFTS AND CURRENTS

The waters of the oceans, even if wave movements are neglected, are not stationary, but take part in a broad system of continuous circulation that involves practically the entire water mass. The pattern of movement is three-dimensional, but the deeper parts of the system will not be considered here.

Much the larger part of the surface movement of ocean waters is in the nature of a slow, relatively inconspicuous transfer, at an average rate of 2¼ miles per hour, that affects only shallow depths. The slowest movements are more correctly spoken of as *drifts,* in contrast to the deeper and more rapidly flowing *currents* that sometimes attain velocities two or three times the above average. Such rapid currents are usually confined to localities where discharge takes place through narrow channels. An example is the Florida Current, which achieves velocities of 4 to 6 miles per hour in making its exit from the Gulf of Mexico through the narrow strait between Florida and Cuba.

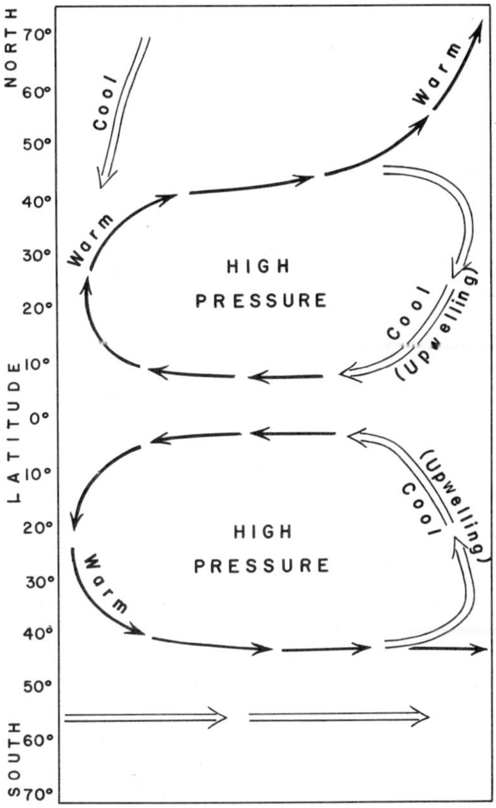

FIG. 15.5 Generalized scheme of ocean currents.

General scheme Except for the polar seas, there is a tendency for all the great oceans to exhibit similar general patterns of surface currents and drifts. This is because surface ocean currents are fundamentally related to the direction of the prevailing wind, though temperature and salinity differences and the shape and depth of the ocean basins also affect the pattern.

The most conspicuous elements of the circulation of surface waters are great, closed elliptical whirls about the subtropical oceanic high-pressure cells (Fig. 15.5). The trade winds on the equatorward sides of the subtropical highs in both hemispheres tend to drift the surface waters westward before them across the oceans in what is known as the Equatorial Current. (There are really two equatorial currents, separated in the eastern part of the oceans by a minor countercurrent setting toward the east.) Checked in its westward progress by a continent, the Equatorial Current is divided, part of it flowing northward and part of it southward. Because of the rotational deflection and the trend of the coast line, and because of the wind direction around the western end of the subtropical high, the warm poleward-moving current gradually is bent more and more to the east.

At about latitude 40° the warm surface waters move slowly eastward across the ocean as a west-wind drift. In the eastern part of the sea the drift divides, a part of it being carried by the winds equatorward along the coast until it again joins the Equatorial Current and thus completes the low-latitude current circuit. In the Northern Hemisphere, however, a considerable portion of the westwind drift is carried poleward by the stormy southwesterlies, its relatively warm waters washing the west coasts of the continents and eventually entering the Arctic Ocean. The Arctic, compensating for this receipt of warm water, produces an outward flow of cold water that passes down the western side of the ocean into the middle latitudes. In the Southern Hemisphere much of the westwind drift continues clear around the earth in the unbroken belt of ocean that occupies the southern middle latitudes.

It should be emphasized that this picture of surface currents and drifts is greatly simplified, for superimposed upon this generalized average pattern are numerous eddies and surges, together with changes in direction and strength of currents following the seasonal shifts and reversals of winds.

Yet if the idealized pattern is compared with a somewhat generalized map of actual surface currents, it will be seen to correspond fairly closely (Fig. 15.6). In the Atlantic and Pacific Oceans the subtropical whirls, westwind drifts, and Arctic currents are clearly distinguishable. In the Indian Ocean, though, only the Southern Hemisphere pattern is well developed.

Warm and cool currents   If it is kept in mind that poleward-drifting surface waters, since they come from lower latitudes, are inclined to be warmer than the surrounding waters, while those from higher latitudes are likely to be cooler, the following generalizations will be understandable. In the latitudes equatorward from about 40° warm ocean currents tend to parallel the eastern sides of continents, cool ocean currents the western sides. In the latitudes poleward from about 40° the reverse is more often the case, warm ocean currents affecting the western sides of land masses, and cool ones the eastern sides. Along east coasts (western sides of oceans), therefore, there is likely to be a convergence of contrasting currents, while along west coasts currents tend to diverge.

A part of the cool water along west coasts in lower latitudes—those of Peru and northern Chile, northwest and southwest Africa, and southern California, for instance—is the result of upwelling from depths of several hundred feet along the coast. In these areas equatorward-moving winds from the subtropical whirls drive the surface waters toward lower latitudes and away from the land. Colder water from below, therefore, rises to replace the surface water.

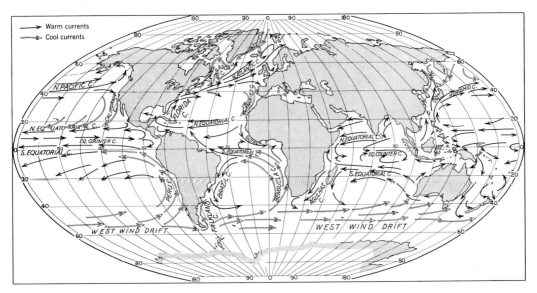

FIG. 15.6 Surface currents of the oceans. *(After G. Schott.)*

SEA-SURFACE TEMPERATURES

Surface temperatures of the seas range from about 28.4°, which is the approximate freezing point of sea water, to about 86°. This is a much smaller range of values than is experienced on the lands, very low temperatures not being present in the seas (unless temperatures of the polar ice be included). In addition, changes in the temperature of the sea surface during the year are remarkably small, amounting to no more than 2 to 7° in tropical waters and 9 to 15° in the upper middle latitudes; and variation in the surface temperature between day and night is no more than a fraction of a degree. This considerable variety of temperatures, combined with the slight change from day to day and the only modest variation during the entire course of the year, constitutes a fact of great importance to the earth's climate.

The heating process The chief process by which the sea is heated is absorption of radiation from the sun and the atmosphere; cooling of the sea is accomplished largely by radiation from the surface and by evaporation of water from the surface. Since incoming radiation decreases from the tropics toward the poles, and since the greatest cooling of the seas by radiation occurs in the higher latitudes, especially during the winter, it is not surprising to find that the ocean temperatures follow essentially a latitudinal pattern (Fig. 15.7). The tropical seas are warm, with only small variations from place to place. Poleward of the tropics, however, temperatures fall off rapidly with increasing latitude.

The fact that the sea-surface isotherms do not strictly follow the parallels of latitude indicates, of course, that radiation, which does have a clear latitudinal pattern, is not the only control. Prevailing air temperatures have an effect also, particularly in lowering

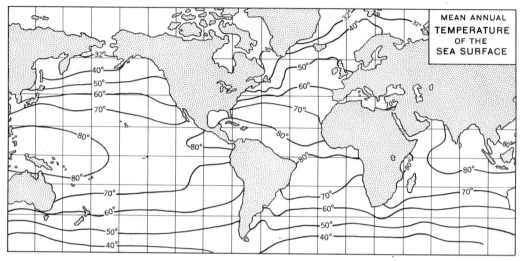

FIG. 15.7   Surface temperatures of the oceans. *(After G. Schott.)*

sea temperatures near the eastern coasts of the continents in the middle latitudes during the winter.

Much more important, however, is the circulation of ocean water in the great surface-current systems previously described, by which warm water is brought into the middle latitudes on the western sides of the oceans and moved across to the eastern sides, and by which cool water is brought equatorward on the east sides of the subtropical oceans and on the opposite sides in the high latitudes.

The effects of these movements of the ocean waters may be seen in Fig. 15.7. As there shown, the average sea temperature on the coast of southern Japan, washed by a warm current, is nearly 10° warmer than that in southern California, in the same latitude but washed by a cool current reinforced by upwelling. Between Labrador, flanked by a cold Arctic current, and the northern part of Ireland, in the path of the warm west-wind drift, the difference is more than 15° in August, and during the winter it is nearly twice that.

Ocean temperatures and climate

While the relationships between the oceans and the various climatic elements have been discussed earlier in the book in the chapters dealing with specific climates, certain of the more significant connections may conveniently be recalled and treated generally here.

Because of the great width of the oceans, air masses passing across them are in contact with the water surface for considerable periods of time. This gives the surface layers of the atmosphere a good opportunity to assume temperatures that are approximately those of the sea surface itself, or at least the temperature of the air will tend toward that goal. When air that has been so modified by a long sea crossing passes onto an adjacent continent, it carries the sea temperatures along with it.

Since the ocean temperatures tend to be relatively mild and to change but little from winter to summer, a corresponding mildness is a distinguishing characteristic of the temperatures of those land areas into which sea air is regularly carried. This effect is especially noticeable on west coasts in the middle latitudes, where the prevailing onshore movement of marine air imparts much warmer winter and cooler summer temperatures than are characteristic of the interiors or eastern sides of the continents. Thus at San Francisco the average temperature of the warmest month is only 60°, and that of the coldest no lower than 49°.

The more or less foreign temperatures brought by ocean currents to any given latitude are variously reflected in coastal climates. Thus in northwestern Europe, where westerly winds carry the effects of the warm North Atlantic Drift far into the continent, coastal temperatures in January are 30 to 40° warmer than the average for those latitudes. Where currents of contrasting temperatures converge, as along the middle-latitude east coasts of Asia and North America, the sharp gradient in sea temperature is to a small degree reflected in a similarly abrupt gradient in air temperature along the coast. Cool-water coasts in the subtropics are often foggy because warm air from over the ocean proper is chilled to below the condensation point by passing over the cool current near the shore.

PRINCIPAL CLASSES OF SEA LIFE

The myriad forms of life that exist in the sea may, for present purposes, be divided into three major groups according to their mobility. Most familiar are the free-swimming forms, which include the larger fish, Crustacea, and sea mammals that are able to move about over considerable distances in search of food. A second group is made up of the sessile forms, those plants, shellfish, corals, etc., that are more or less permanently attached to the bottom. The third and perhaps least familiar group is the *plankton*. These are small, sometimes microscopic organisms, both plant and animal, that, either because they have no means of locomotion or because they are so very small, are incapable of self-determined movements of any significant scale. Instead, they drift with the water in which they live.

Plankton The plant plankton are the most fundamental source of food for sea life in general. The animal plankton and all other forms of sea creatures feed either directly upon these tiny plants or include in their food other sea animals which do feed upon the plants. Remove the plant plankton from the sea and all other forms of life would soon perish. Thus where the plant plankton are concentrated, there also will be found the greatest numbers of sea animals, feeding upon the plants or upon one another. Any localized conditions favoring the concentration of plant plankton will tend to concentrate animal plankton, fish, shellfish, and sea mammals as well.

The needs of plant plankton are the same as those of plants in general: light, and certain mineral and organic nutrients. The first requirement confines them to the surface layers of the sea, into which light can penetrate. The second is manifest chiefly in a need for constant replenishment of the nutrients, to make up for the supply that has been removed from the waters by the earlier-existing generations of plankton.

This renewal of nutrients must come largely from the waters below. Hence any process that brings deeper water to the surface will favor the maintenance of a dense plankton growth. This is significantly accomplished by (*a*) turbulent mixing of water by wave action in shallow coastal waters, (*b*) upwelling of cold waters along subtropical west coasts,

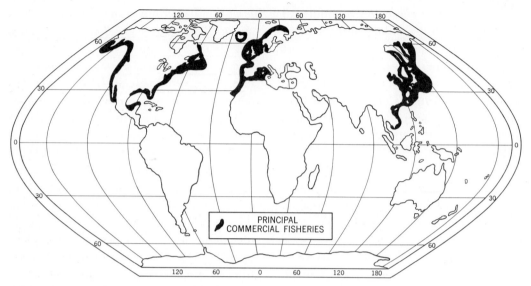

FIG. 15.8 The principal commercial fisheries are found in the cool seas of the Northern Hemisphere, especially along the broader continental shelves.

and (*c*) winter overturning of waters in the higher middle latitudes. The surface waters in areas where one or more of these processes occur appear to be the centers of plankton concentration and therefore of sea life generally.

Fish and sea mammals Following the pattern of occurrence of plankton, fish appear to be relatively strongly concentrated on the continental shelves, in areas of upwelling, and in waters of the higher latitudes. The great commercial fisheries line the margins of the North Atlantic and North Pacific Oceans, where fish exist in unparalleled abundance and where there are also populous markets on the adjacent lands (Fig. 15.8). In these waters occur such species as the herring, cod, haddock, halibut, mackerel, salmon, sardine, tuna, and menhaden. Herring, the most important of all food fish, occur here in great numbers and sometimes in remarkable concentration. In the same areas are found

other forms of sea life—including oysters and other shellfish, crabs and sponges—that are also valuable to man.

The corresponding waters of the Southern Hemisphere also appear to be rich in sea life, but the large human populations that are the other necessary component of commercial fisheries are wanting. Also, certain of the most abundant fish of the Northern Hemisphere are not found in southern waters, though conditions are favorable for them. Herring have been introduced into the Southern Hemisphere in recent years and appear to be thriving.

It is commonly believed that the tropical seas are generally less densely populated by fish than are the cooler waters of the globe. Yet while this may be true, the disparity is not as great as once thought; at least the resource is sufficient to permit many peoples of the tropical coasts to derive much of their living from the sea. It seems clear that in the warm waters of the low latitudes there is a much greater variety of species than in the higher latitudes, but that the number of individuals in any single species is likely to be much smaller. There are, for example, no known tropical counterparts of the tremendous schools of herring and of sardines that are found in cooler waters. Interestingly enough, similar contrasts between tropics, with more species, and middle latitudes, with more individuals per species, characterize both the animal and plant kingdoms on the lands.

Most of the large sea mammals, such as the whales and seals, stay in no one latitudinal area but are wanderers, ranging from Arctic to Antarctic. Since they, like fishes, live chiefly upon fish or plankton, they too seek out the areas where these are concentrated. Because of their value for furs, skins, or oil, many of these animals have been ruthlessly hunted and their numbers greatly reduced, especially in the Northern Hemisphere. The whale fishery is now largely in Antarctic waters, and the Arctic fur-seal fishery is closely regulated to prevent extinction.

The "deserts" of the sea are the interiors of the great subtropical high-pressure whirls. In these areas the high evaporation and low rainfall lead to unfavorably high salinities, and these saline surface waters converge and sink. There is a low supply of nutrients at the surface, and therefore the plankton population is low, and there is no basis for sustenance of a significant population of fish.

CHAPTER 16

The waters
of the land

The occurrence and properties of water Excepting the water that lies below sea level beneath the continents and that portion presently locked up in glaciers, only about 0.3 per cent of the earth's water is on or within the land. This tiny fraction of the total amount of water, moreover, is the only fresh, liquid water available to the organic life of the continents, including the life of man.

There are variations over the earth in the occurrence of this water of the land, and, because water has extraordinary properties and is, indeed, indispensable to organic life, a great share of the differences in physical environment from place to place is a direct consequence of these variations.

Water is one of the few naturally mobile substances on the earth, and in consequence it functions as a great conveyor, moving massive amounts of material from one place to another on the land. It can do this because (*a*) water can dissolve a larger number of substances in larger amounts than any other agent, and (*b*) its high specific gravity and internal friction enable it to pick up and transport materials easily.

Dissolving power Pure water scarcely occurs in nature, for as soon as liquid water forms in the atmosphere it dissolves carbon dioxide and becomes weak carbonic acid. When this acid then reaches the surface of the earth, it instantly begins to dissolve other compounds, and these move with the water, either downward or across the land surface. Because of this uniquely high solvent power of water billions of tons of dissolved materials are constantly in transit. Also, this quality is ultimately responsible for the chemical characteristics of the sedimentary rocks mantling most of the earth—the rocks which provide sustenance, in the form of mineral foods, for a large share of the organic complex on the land, again through the medium of solution. The land form itself is even in large measure a result of this solvent quality, for a considerable share of the processes of gradation is carried on through the medium of solution.

Movement of solids   Water is also the primary agent moving solids over the surface: it is estimated that roughly three times as much material is moved in suspension in running water as is carried in solution in it, and atmospheric and glacial transportation of suspended material is considerably smaller. The high surface tension of water allows it to be held in the regolith by capillary force, the more finely divided solid aggregate being able to retain more water than the coarser. This makes the mass become "liquid" and potentially mobile. Thus water, functioning with the force of gravity, acts as an important agent in the mass movements of the land.

An accurate summation of the total transport activity that may be ascribed to the direct and indirect action of water is beyond our ability, but the estimates that have been made of it probably lie in the correct order of magnitude. It is reasonable to suppose that an annual average of some 250 to 300 tons of solid sediment and 80 to 100 tons of dissolved material per square mile of the earth's land surface are transported to the ocean by water. No doubt a much larger amount is simply moved, i.e., temporarily picked up and deposited again on the land, shifted laterally through mass movements, or merely relocated vertically in the regolith. Certainly, moving water is the most universal and significant agent affecting the ever-changing land surface.

The distribution over the land surface of the earth of these activities of water varies in somewhat direct proportion to the quantities of water available on the land. Although many other factors are involved at each locality, a map of average annual precipitation portrays the basic pattern of the variations in the activity of water as an agent in the movement of materials.

Water as a resource   Simply as a visible and invisible constituent of his natural environment that affects his comfort and enjoyment water is, of course, of great interest to man, but man's concern is greater than that. In the first place, the very existence of life requires water, and consequently, little if any life can exist where only negligible quantities of it are available. But beyond this, water, while only one of a long list of minerals used by man, *exceeds all others* in the urgency of its need and in the quantity used.

Increasing needs   Until recently a relatively small amount of water was required to supply the consumptive needs of man and the other land-based organisms—needs that are clearly the most important but do not require large quantities. Beginning with the Industrial Revolution, however, water steadily increased in significance, until today it is cer-

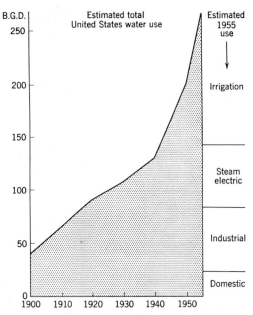

FIG. 16.1   Estimated total United States' water use from 1900 to 1955, in billions of gallons per day (B.G.D). *(Based upon estimates of the U.S. Department of Commerce in the "1955 Annual Report of Resources for the Future," 1955).*

Figure 16.1 shows, for example, that in the United States the requirements for water have increased more than five times since 1900, although the population has little more than doubled.

Withdrawal and nonwithdrawal.   When water is made use of in place, the uses are classed as *nonwithdrawal;* when it is diverted from its source the uses to which it is put fall in the category of *withdrawal.*

Water for withdrawal use must meet rather stringent purity requirements, and for most purposes it must be fresh (free of objectionable mineral content); and only the water precipitated from the atmosphere is generally of that quality. Thus regions of abundant precipitation usually, although not always, have ample sources of fresh water close at hand, and inhabitants may use it lavishly; in dry regions, on the other hand, sources

FIG. 16.2   Estimated withdrawal use of water in the United States in 1950, in billions of gallons per day (B.G.D.). Water used for hydroelectric power is not included. The municipal value includes water supplied to industry from municipal water works; the industrial value is that obtained from private sources only. *(From U.S. Geological Survey Circular 115, 1951.)*

tainly the most used material in our complex modern life. Quite apart from its uses in place, that is, for such things as outdoor recreation and surface transportation, it is sought and utilized for a large variety of home and industrial needs. It is our major industrial and home solvent, coolant, and waste carrier; virtually all manufactured electricity requires water; and almost all industrial production requires amazing amounts of it. For example, a steel mill uses perhaps 65,000 gallons of water for each ton of steel it produces; each gallon of gasoline requires some 10 gallons of water for its preparation, and at least 2,000 gallons of water is used in producing each pound of rayon. As the population of the earth grows and industrial and irrigation needs increase, the use of water is increasing at a considerably faster rate than population.

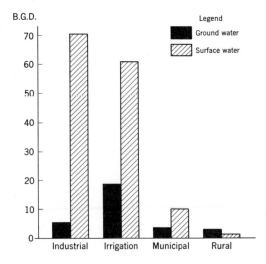

are not ample and it may not be used lavishly, which is a fact of critical significance.

The actual amount of withdrawal water used by man naturally varies from place to place, depending in part upon this varying availability and in part upon technologic development and density of human occupance. The total amount used is a meaningless figure, but some idea of the magnitude may be gained from knowing that the average domestic use of water in the United States is nearly 65 gal per person per day, and that even the most primitive living conditions anywhere on earth require at least 5 gal per person per day. Although domestic use always has the highest priority, it accounts for only a minor portion of the total amount used. Withdrawal uses for irrigation, industry, and steam-power production require vastly more.

Withdrawal supplies are obtained from the surface water in streams and lakes, and from the ground water that exists below the surface of the land. Surface water is by far the more important supplier since it is usually easier to obtain. The proportion obtained from each source for the United States is illustrated in Fig. 16.2.

SURFACE WATER

As indicated in the preceding chapter, in the operation of the hydrologic cycle some of the water that results from precipitation spends part of its stay on the land as surface water, either in temporary storage close to the surface or as running water in the streams that drain a watershed; the remainder departs from the surface by evapotranspiration processes or by sinking to lower depths to become incorporated in the ground-water reservoir; and in turn, some of the water in the ground-water reservoir drains into the surface water. Figure 16.3 shows in a diagrammatic fashion these important relationships.

In considering these relationships, it should be borne in mind that the timing of the hydrologic cycle is a complex matter, Thus, since the hydrologic cycle is in continuous operation, it is difficult to estimate the volumes of water that are in each segment of the cycle at any one time. Also, it is known that there are significant variations in (*a*) the total amount of water involved in the operation of the cycle at particular times, (*b*) the proportions in each part of the cycle at specific times, and (*c*) the annual regime, i.e., the timing of the functioning of the cycle, during a year. Yet just as the variations of the climatic elements result in geographical patterns, so are there general spatial patterns in the functioning of the cycle. Our knowledge of these is much scantier; nevertheless, they constitute a fundamental part of the physical geography of the earth.

WATER STORAGE

If a person were able to add with accuracy the amounts of water that at a particular time were (*a*) in the ocean reservoir, (*b*) in the ground-water reservoir, (*c*) in the atmospheric reservoir, and (*d*) actually in the process of draining off the land, and if he then compared this sum with the total amount of water on the earth, he would find that there

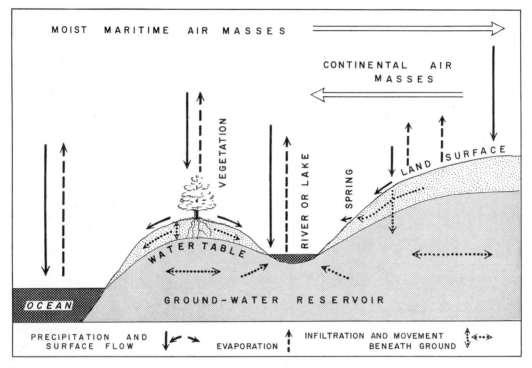

FIG. 16.3 Some of the major relationships of the surface-water portion of the hydrologic cycle.

was a significant residual unaccounted for. The difference consists of the surface water that is temporarily held in storage on and in the upper portion of the land, including (*a*) the water in the regolith *above* the saturated ground-water reservoir, (*b*) the water in ice and snow on the surface, and (*c*) the water in the tissues of plants and animals. Some of the surface water is always in such storage on and in the land, for shorter or longer periods; this water in storage is always distributed unevenly over the earth; and at each place the amount varies from time to time.

The study of this storage-water balance of the earth is very complicated. There are good records of the areal and seasonal distribution of precipitation from which the stored water is derived; but there are not good records of the amounts in other portions of

the cycle which, if taken together and subtracted from precipitation distribution, would show how the storage remainder is distributed. Nevertheless, enough is known to indicate the general pattern.

Figure 16.4 shows in a generalized fashion the average distribution by latitudinal zones of water temporarily detained on the land. The figure might be said to show the latitudinal variation of the "average wetness" of the land. The symmetrical distribution shown there for the two hemispheres is to be expected, but the latitudinal variations within a hemisphere show well the effects of (*a*) the heavy precipitation of the tropics, and (*b*) the marked effects in the higher middle latitudes of lessened evaporation at all seasons and of the storage of snow and ice in winter.

The variations during the year of the

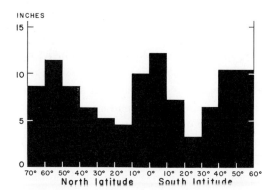

FIG. 16.4 General distribution of the amount of water detained in temporary storage on and near the surface of the land at various latitudes, expressed in depth per unit area. Values are the averages of computed monthly totals. Since the storage water of one month may be carried over to the next, the graph does not reveal the total amount of water involved. *(Data from van Hylckama.)*

amount of water detained on and in the land areas at the various latitudes also are symmetrical; i.e., similar latitudes have similar variations. Figure 16.5 shows diagrammatically for each latitude the season of the year when most water is detained. In the higher latitudes late winter and spring are the seasons of maximum storage, since winter evaporation approaches nil because of low temperatures, causing a large volume of water to be locked up in snow and ice. In the lower latitudes the maximum occurs during and shortly after the wet season.

SURFACE RUNOFF

Sources and measurement The drainage in streams, called surface runoff, comes from three immediate sources: (*a*) the rainfall that remains after losses due to evapotranspiration and infiltration, (*b*) the water released from storage, and (*c*) the water that emerges from the underground (ground-water) reservoir. Considerable variation from place to

place and from time to time occurs both in amounts of runoff and in the proportion supplied by each source. Short-term minor variations result from individual storms, while seasonal differences result from variations in the regimes of annual precipitation and the release of storage water. The proportion of runoff that is discharged from the ground-water reservoir is subject to the least fluctuation.

The annual runoff of a watershed (a landform drainage area) is measured by the discharge accomplished by its streams, which is expressed as a volume per unit of time. The total annual volume may then be divided by the drainage area to obtain a quotient that may be expressed as a depth of water, just as precipitation is expressed, and annual averages of these values may be mapped. It should be borne in mind, however, that maps of average annual runoff provide an even more generalized picture of variations from place to place than maps of average annual precipitation, since the volume of runoff for

FIG. 16.5 Highly general diagram of the season of maximum water detention on the land at the various latitudes in the hemispheres. *(From van Hylckama.)*

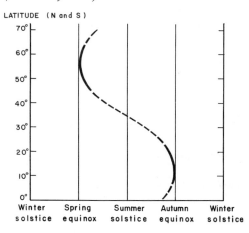

an area can only be obtained from a point, viz., a stream-gauging station, and the total runoff is then equally apportioned to all parts of the watershed. Consequently, a map of runoff shows only the general pattern of variation, not the actual amount that drains at every point. Figure 16.6 is a map of the average annual runoff of the United States. The major differences shown on a map of annual runoff are, of course, associated with variations in annual precipitation, as a comparison with a precipitation map will show.

Stream flow Much of the time surface runoff is largely fed by emerging ground water. However, the ground-water proportion of runoff is lower at the time of rainfall or snow melt. Then, when there is a large supply of water on the land surface, it follows the pull of gravity and most of it quickly collects in channels. One recognized listing of these channels separates those that contain flowing water only a portion of the time and those that do so continuously; the former, if they contain water with some regularity, are called intermittent streams; the latter are termed permanent streams.

Generally, the variations in stream flow are tied closely to variations in precipitation, evaporation, infiltration, and storage-water release; and the interrelations vary from place to place and from time to time.

Unchannelized movement of water in a thin layer over a surface, called sheet wash, occurs when the accumulation of water on a sloping surface is greater than the channeling and water-infiltering capacity of the surface forms and materials. Heavy rains and snow melt, relatively gentle slopes, and a surface material with a slow infiltration capacity, such as a "tight" clay or frozen soil,

FIG. 16.6 The average annual runoff in the United States. *(Generalized from a map by the U.S. Geological Survey.)*

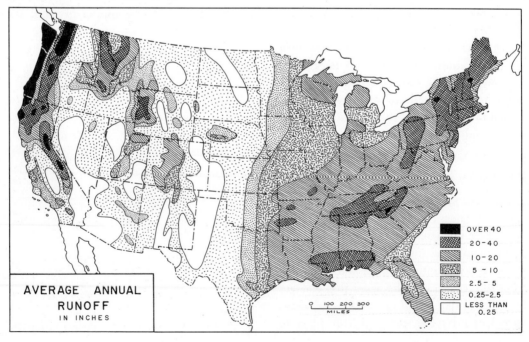

AVERAGE   ANNUAL
RUNOFF
IN INCHES

0 100 200 300
MILES

■	OVER 40
▨	20-40
▨	10-20
▨	5-10
▨	2.5-5
▨	0.25-2.5
☐	LESS THAN 0.25

favor sheet wash. Where there is not enough slope to draw off the water, it simply collects as temporary "standing water" in swamps, marshes, and shallow lakes.

Regime of runoff As everyone knows, creeks and rivers fill up after a heavy rain. But there is a lag between the time of rainfall and the rise of stream levels, resulting from the facts that (*a*) it takes time for the surface flow of water to reach the streams, and (*b*) a share of the water filters downward and then moves laterally to seep out again where runoff channels have cut below the temporarily water-filled upper soil layers. This water moves more slowly because of friction.

Since all this direct surface runoff increases after a rain, and drainage from the underground reservoir fluctuates relatively little, one might expect that the annual runoff regime would likewise reflect seasonal variations in precipitation amounts. But the annual variation in runoff is much more closely regulated by the release of storage water, and peak runoff generally is associated with the period of peak storage. In the tropics this period nearly coincides with the rainy season, but for a large part of the middle and higher latitude areas this period is around the time of the spring equinox in each hemisphere.

Figure 16.7 is a composite graph illustrating the average regime of runoff for two areas in Ohio. As winter wanes and spring advances, temperatures, and consequently evaporation, are still relatively low, and the top layer of soil is likely to be frozen. Rainfall and storage water from melting snow contribute considerable direct surface runoff. As temperatures rise farther and plants begin to grow, an increasing proportion of the precipitation and storage water is subtracted through evapotranspiration. Thus, even though the precipitation reaches a maximum

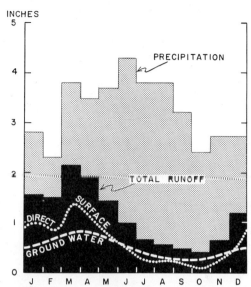

FIG. 16.7 Twenty-five-year (1921–1945) combined averages of the precipitation and total runoff as measured at the Hocking and Mad Rivers, near Athens and Springfield, Ohio, showing the proportions of the total runoff supplied from direct surface runoff and from ground water. *(From U.S. Geological Survey.)*

in the summer, surface runoff decreases, and ground water, an equalizing influence, provides an increasing proportion. In the autumn the decrease of both plant growth and air temperatures allows an increase in direct surface runoff as well as a steady replenishment of the ground-water reservoir. The concentration of surface runoff in the early part of the warming season tends to increase poleward; floods and soggy ground are common springtime phenomena in the areas of humid climates in the middle and higher latitudes.

Factors affecting the amount of annual runoff Figures 16.6 and 16.9 show for the United States and the world, in a highly generalized fashion, the annual amount of runoff as determined in the manner outlined on page 297.

Climatic factors It is clear from these

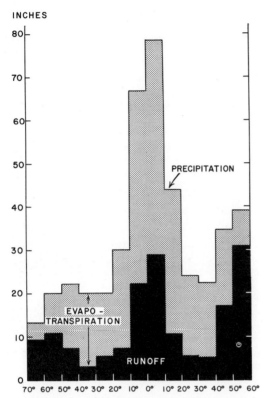

INCHES

FIG. 16.8 Relationship of the average annual total runoff to average annual total precipitation on the land per unit area according to latitude. The vertical difference between the two represents the loss through evapotranspiration. North latitude is to the left. *(From L'vovich and Drozdov.)*

ground-water reservoir, is merely delayed, not lost as a potential source of runoff; on the other hand, any water that is evaporated is lost. Consequently total runoff is the amount of precipitation minus the loss due to evapotranspiration.

Because potential evapotranspiration is primarily a function of temperature one would expect, other things being equal, that the lower latitudes would have low runoff in proportion to their precipitation, and this general relationship obtains to a degree. But as Fig. 16.8 shows, actual runoff is heavy in the tropics in spite of the high evapotranspiration there, because rainfall is proportionately even heavier. The subtropical areas, because of their generally high temperatures and low precipitation, are zones of low annual runoff. The middle and higher latitudes, where evaporation rates are relatively low, have the highest ratios of annual runoff to annual precipitation.

Land-surface effects   The land surface, including the bedrock on which it has developed, adds complexity to the general pattern of annual runoff that basically results from the climatic pattern. This is primarily a result of variations in permeability. Large areas of the continents are covered with surface materials that permit rainfall quickly to percolate to considerable depths, where the water is beyond the reach of plant roots and the evaporation process. This water becomes a part of the ground-water reservoir and eventually feeds into streams. Thus surfaces underlain by pervious lavas and limestones are capable of absorbing rapidly vast quantities of water, and these areas are commonly notoriously low in surface-runoff amounts. Also, sandy areas and the alluvial plains, small and large, which fringe many mountainous areas, particularly in dry climate

maps that over the world as a whole, average annual runoff tends to vary directly with precipitation, the ultimate source of surface runoff. But some variations result from differences in the nature of the precipitation. Where rainfall occurs primarily in the form of heavy or very frequent showers, a greater proportion of the fall will immediately become runoff because other factors come into play, such as a decrease in the rate of ground infiltration, as a consequence of saturation or compaction of the soil.

Water held in storage near the surface, as well as that which percolates down to the areas, are likely to have porous surface materials, and thus low runoff. On the other hand, there are many areas of very low permeability in marginal sections of dry climates that have unusually low runoff amounts for quite a different reason. The collection of the water in surface depressions here may allow a large proportion to fall victim to evaporation. In general, there is likely to be more variability in annual runoff from place to place in the dry areas of the earth than elsewhere.

World map of annual runoff   The world map of average annual runoff (Fig. 16.9) is necessarily crude because stream gauging, from which it is derived, is not widespread, nor have such data been gathered for long periods. Nevertheless, the pattern displayed is not likely to be far from reality.

The map shows certain general relationships that are to be expected; for example, the areas of copious precipitation generally have the heaviest runoff. Such areas are of two major types: (*a*) the areas of heavy tropical rainfall where runoff is high despite the high evapotranspiration, and (*b*) the areas of marine climates where relatively heavy precipitation is combined with cool temperatures. In many of the latter areas the precipitation is augmented by orographic precipitation, but not always: the lowlands of Europe stand out as high runoff zones in spite of moderate amounts of precipitation. Low runoff zones extend into humid climatic areas well beyond the climatic dry boundaries, for in many of the moister areas precipitation comes in the high-sun season and much of it is quickly lost to evapotranspiration. Notable also are the rapid transitions from regions of high to low runoff. Rapid gradients are characteristic of maps of runoff at any scale (Fig. 16.6).

The world map and the following table, derived from the data used to prepare the map, show that the continents differ greatly in runoff amount. It will be seen that South and North America are the most favored and that Australia is the least.

Lakes, swamps, and marshes   Surface runoff, in the course of its movement in response to gravity, is, as previously mentioned, sometimes delayed enough for quiet, sluggish bodies of water to result. If such water bodies are shallow enough to allow vegetation to grow through the thin layers of water, they are called swamps, marshes, or boglands. Where water in them exists in an unbroken sheet, they are called lakes or ponds. By definition any such body of water, as distinguished from a stream, must lie in a basin-

Annual Runoff by Continent

Continent	Average annual runoff, inches*
South America	17.7
North America	12.4
Europe	10.3
Africa	8.0
Asia	6.7
Australia	3.0

* Estimate by M. I. L'vovich.

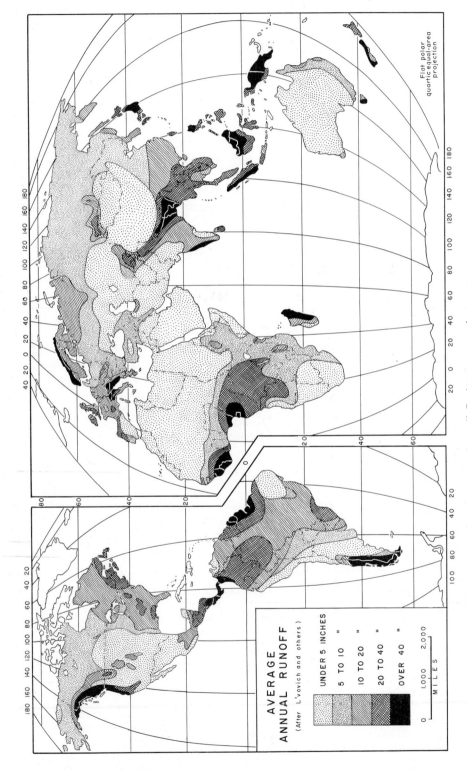

FIG. 16.9 Highly generalized world map of average annual runoff. For large areas only meager data are available.

like depression of the land surface. How any particular low-lying area of this type may have come to be is not the major interest here, but the fact that the majority are created by only a few kinds of processes helps to account for their location.

Regions of occurrences The majority of lakes, swamps, and marshes occur in regions of the world where the degradational and aggradational processes have not—for the moment, since basins, like all other land forms, are transitory—been able either to fill the basins with solid materials or integrate them into "normal" stream channels. The most obvious examples of such areas are those that have been subject to recent glaciation, especially continental. In large areas in northern North America and Europe there are literally tens of thousands of major and minor basins that are perennially or intermittently inundated by sluggish surface water. Swamps and marshes are also common in these areas. Many lakes occur on floodplains along the courses of sluggish meandering streams where new surface patterns are continually being formed by gradational processes. Similar swampy areas are found in coastal areas of unusually gentle pitch. In all these kinds of areas the drainage of the land is poor; that is to say, whatever the amount of surface runoff may be, the rate is slow enough that there is an abundance of standing water.

In some areas underlain by soluble limestone (karst areas), the sinks may intersect the saturated ground-water zone and so contain lakes, or the free drainage of the sinks may have become plugged so that water collects in them. Many limestone areas, on the other hand, show little or no surface water even in streams, their drainage being primarily beneath the surface.

In dry regions most basins, whether formed by tectonic or gradational process, are not filled to overflowing by the meager surface runoff; hence they are not quickly integrated into stream drainage. These are bolsons, or basins of interior drainage, which may contain temporary lakes. Tectonic forces, especially deformation, have created numerous lake basins, including some of the more notable of the world. Lakes Tanganyika and Nyasa in Africa, as well as the Dead Sea, are examples of lakes that have developed in great down-dropped trenches (Fig. 3.6).

The occurrence of lakes in a surface-runoff system in humid areas changes the character of both the water and the runoff process. Silts brought into a lake by stream flow are deposited in the quieter water, so that water leaving a lake is usually clear. Water flowing out of a lake also tends to have a more uniform temperature, and its mineral and organic character has usually been affected by the biological processes at work in the lake.

But the most significant effect of a lake upon the runoff process is its regulation of the rate of flow; a lake acts as a reservoir, collecting and detaining water during times of heavy surface runoff and releasing it later at a more uniform rate. This is of great utility to man in at least two ways: (*a*) it reduces both the incidence and severity of downstream flooding, and (*b*) it raises the volume of the stream, at the time of minimum flow, above what it would otherwise be. The maintenance of higher volume is in many ways advantageous to water supply for withdrawal uses, and even more so for nonwithdrawal uses. Two of the nonwithdrawal uses, the production of hydroelectric power and navigation, are generally limited by the minimum flow—the former by its volume, the latter by its depth.

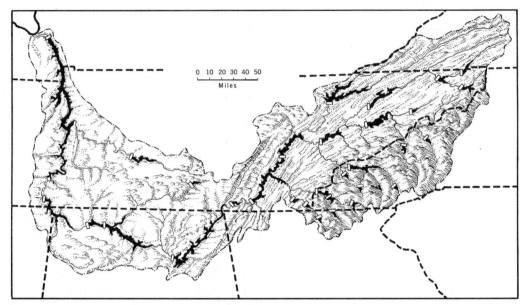

FIG. 16.10 Highly generalized diagram of the Tennessee River drainage basin, showing the numerous reservoirs which have been integrated into the scheme of natural surface runoff. Projects of this nature are being carried out in many parts of the world where surface runoff is subject to great fluctuation. *(Norman J. W. Thrower.)*

Man-made basins Where natural lake basins are absent in the scheme of surface runoff and regulating effects are still desirable, man may construct artificial basins. A steadily increasing number of these reservoirs is being constructed in those surface runoff areas where the regime is characterized by a large range between maximum and minimum flow. In the aggregate these constitute, without doubt, the most notable man-made change that is reflected in the maps of his physical environment (Fig. 16.10).

Man-made lake basins are subject to the same forces as natural basins. Thus, although man can easily prevent the outlets from eroding deeper and draining the reservoir, it is difficult to control the silt content of the inflow in order to prevent the lake from filling with solid material. To do this requires careful planning and regulation of the land use in an entire drainage basin, and such a complex, long-range program is not easily accomplished except with governmental aid.

SURFACE WATER AS A RESOURCE

The large quantities of water required for withdrawal use by modern urban and industrial centers are in some instances obtained from wells and springs, but usually from large lakes, large rivers, or small streams the drainage of which is stored behind dams to create municipal reservoirs. Only about one out of four of the principal American cities obtains its water supply from wells. Most of the remainder, especially the large cities, use surface water. Indeed, over half of the communities in the United States having more than 10,000 inhabitants are supplied from surface water.

As the cities of the world grow in size the problems of obtaining sufficient surface water also grow. For example, New York City uses about 1 billion gal of water per day, and, because it is not located near a large lake or a usable river, must obtain this tremendous supply from a variety of areas. New York City depends on seven different stream watersheds that gather water from a combined area of about 2,000 square miles, an area half again as large as Rhode Island (Fig. 16.11). The water is taken from more than 1,000 streams, small and large; it is stored in 27 artificial and natural reservoirs, some of which are as far as 120 miles away; and it is brought to the city by means of more than 350 miles of aqueducts and tunnels (Figs. 16.11, 16.12).[1]

In many areas of the world cities have grown up without an adequate, easily obtainable, supply of surface (or ground) water, and water must be brought great distances by aqueduct. For example, Los Angeles brings water from the Owens River–Mono County area on the eastern side of the Sierra Nevada, nearly 300 miles away, and from the Colorado River on the California-Arizona border. In some parts of the world sea water is distilled, but this is costly: the unit cost of distilling is directly related to the mineralization of the source water, and sea water has from

[1] Anastasia Van Burkalow, "The Geography of New York City's Water Supply: A Study of Interactions," *Geographical Review*, vol. 49, 1959, pp. 369–386.

32,000 to 36,000 parts per million of total dissolved solids. In the light of present technology it appears that, even with atomic or solar energy providing the power requirement, it will be cheaper for some time yet to transport fresh water great distances than to distill sea water.

Surface water differs from ground water in a number of important respects as a resource. Generally, surface water is less mineralized than the ground water of the same region, because surface water is derived in part from the runoff of rain water which has not been so long in contact with the minerals of the ground. However, surface water is likely to contain larger quantities of sediment and organic matter, including bacteria, than ground water. For this reason many cities find it necessary to purify and filter their water supplies. For example, nearly half the population of the United States uses water that has been treated in some way. Water used for irrigation must not have too high a mineral content, and many industrial uses, ranging from boilers to canning, require water having specific mineral qualities.

The large industrial and municipal withdrawal uses of water occasion complex problems of pollution when the effluent (the water that has been used) is returned to surface drainage. This affects recreation and wildlife, as well as communities downstream that may also use the surface water. Surface drainage through streams and lakes is related also to other water uses which are matters of great public concern, such as soil erosion, flood control, power production, and inland transportation. Out of these varied uses of surface water grow conflicts of human interest which lie beyond the scope of physical geography.

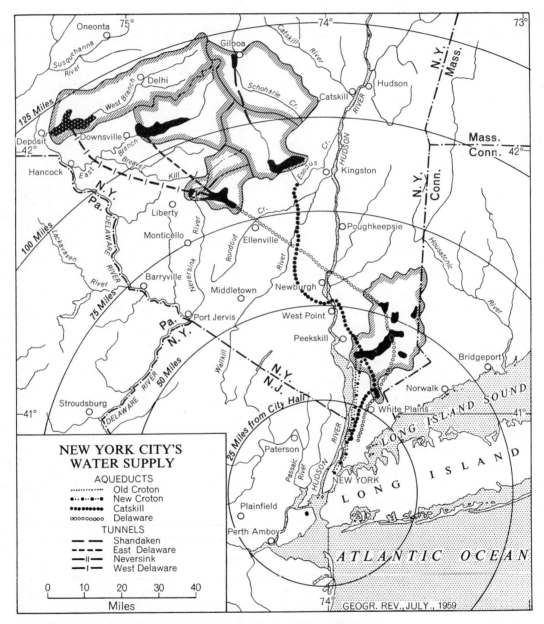

FIG. 16.11 Map showing the situation of the sources of New York City's water supply. Watershed areas are bounded by the shaded line and reservoirs are shown in black. The Cannonsville Reservoir, the site of which is shown in Figure 16.12, is indicated by the stippled black. *(Adapted from map in Geographical Review.)*

GROUND WATER

THE GROUND-WATER RESERVOIR

Wherever more water is supplied to the surface than immediately runs off or is evaporated, the remainder sinks beneath the surface of the land. Generally, water beneath the surface is called ground water, as distinguished from surface water. Yet, as indicated in the preceding discussion of surface water, a portion of the water that seeps downward does not go far, but instead is stored temporarily in the upper section of the ground. Much of this water never penetrates deeper, and may shortly be lost by evapotranspiration processes or in runoff. This water was considered, for purposes of explaining surface water, as part of it. More accurately, however, this water near the surface, at least in humid areas, is in a sort of transition stage between surface water, ground water, and atmospheric water. Its groundwater aspects will be considered now.

Water responds to the forces of gravity and molecular attraction. The former pulls water directly downward and acts indirectly through atmospheric pressure. Molecular attraction, through surface tension and capillarity, causes water to adhere to surfaces in a thin film or creep into crevices and tiny channels in the regolith, and so to remain suspended in spite of the force of gravity. As a volume of water moves downward from the surface of the ground, a portion is left behind as a consequence of molecular attraction. The upper portion of the ground is therefore commonly damp, although by no means saturated. On account of (*a*) the interaction of the forces of gravity and molecular

FIG. 16.12 Site of the Cannonsville Reservoir and dam (white line) before construction. *(Board of Water Supply of the City of New York.)*

attraction, (*b*) the amounts of water available, (*c*) the unevenness of the land surface, and (*d*) the vertical variations among the surficial materials, several zones or layers of ground-water character are observed.

Zones Figure 16.13 illustrates the several different recognizable sections in the earth's reservoir of ground water. Each is a

FIG. 16.13 Zones of subsurface water occurrence. In many places not all the zones occur; in some places none occur.

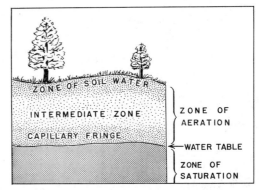

zone into which ground water may move during its stay in the ground-water portion of the hydrologic cycle. Water from immediate precipitation, from melting snow, or from the surface runoff of some other area first passes into the zone of soil water. This upper section of the regolith usually consists of finely divided materials having a large admixture of organic substances. This zone can absorb a considerable quantity of water and retain it for a time until it passes into another stage of the hydrologic cycle, by evaporation directly, or through the roots and transpiring surfaces of plants.

Water that enters the zone of soil water in excess of the amount that can be retained there, may percolate through and into the intermediate zone, which is below the reach of most plant roots. Here surface tension causes the water to adhere to the surfaces of rock particles and the sides of cracks and other openings. Although these voids may be temporarily filled during a time of heavy ground-water recharge, usually they are not. Air also circulates among these spaces.

The intermediate zone and zone of soil water above it are collectively called the zone of aeration. As a consequence of the circulation of air in the zone of aeration, water may be removed by evaporation, causing some fluctuation of the amount of water there.

The downward-moving water that does not remain in the zone of aeration enters the zone of saturation, where all the pore spaces, cracks, and other openings among the particles of the regolith or the bedrock are filled with water.

The top of the saturated zone, or the contact surface between the zones of aeration and saturation, is called the *water,* or *ground-water, table.* Immediately above the water

table and thus at the bottom of the zone of aeration is a zone called the capillary fringe. Here surface tension holds the water above the saturated zone in interconnected voids or "tubes" that are so small that water cannot drain out of them. These extend some distance into the zone of aeration. Water may creep upward from the water table into the capillary fringe, but the fringe is primarily supplied from above by the downward movement of the water. The thickness of the capillary fringe depends upon the sizes of the voids; the smaller they are the thicker it will be. Thus, in sandy areas the thickness may be a foot or less, while in clay areas it may be three or more feet. The capillary fringe is significant because it often brings a source of water within reach of deep-growing plant roots.

The water table . If the land were suddenly to become transparent so that the water table at the surface of the saturated zone could be seen, it would be noted that it undulates in much the same way that the land surface does. It would be apparent, however, that its configuration is more subdued than that of the land surface; that is, the water table actually coincides or even intersects with the surface in some low places or valleys. Although it rises beneath hills it is proportionately farther from their surfaces at their summits.

There is no need here to go into detail concerning the physical laws governing the movements of ground water, but one factor that basically accounts for much of the configuration of the water table is worth considering. In order for water to flow, either above or below ground, it requires a slope, and the rate of flow varies with the slope. The slope of the water table is called the hydraulic gradient, and it is expressed as the

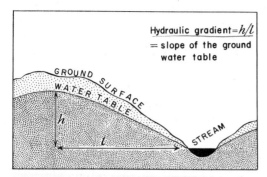

FIG. 16.14   The hydraulic gradient.

ratio of the head (vertical height or "fall" of the water) to the horizontal distance between the intake and discharge points, i.e., the points where water enters and leaves the table (Fig. 16.14). Therefore, if a constant rate of flow is specified, the greater the distance between the place where the water enters the ground and where it discharges, the higher the head must be. Consequently, water in the saturated zone near a discharge point can escape with little head, while that farther away will pile up higher until the rate of addition to the saturated zone balances the rate of flow.

As the rate of addition to the saturated zone changes from time to time the elevation of the ground-water table changes significantly being higher during periods of net ground-water recharge and lower during periods of net discharge (Fig. 16.15). The regime of surface runoff considered on page 299 is likely to be strongly correlated with the elevation of the water table but with somewhat of a lag, since it takes time for the water to move through the ground.

Factors which affect the occurrence of ground water   Ground water near the land surface is vitally significant just in the fact that almost all land vegetation derives its sustenance from this water and the minerals dissolved in it. In many rural areas and in

Precipitation and Evaporation   The major influences on the occurrence of ground water are generally precipitation and evaporation. The heavier the precipitation and the less the evaporation, the more water is likely to percolate downward to enter the saturated zone, and consequently the higher the ground-water table is likely to be. It is these two factors that, in combination, maintain the ground-water table in some areas at such a level that it commonly intersects the undulations of the land surface, creating numerous lakes, swamps, and streams. In such areas the zone of aeration is likely to be thin even in the higher and drier land. Of course, as local relief becomes higher, the zone of aeration becomes thicker beneath the hilly areas because of the greater lateral drainage of the water of the saturated zone. In dry climates and areas where meager precipitation occurs at a time of high temperatures, the water table is likely to be buried deeply everywhere except in the deepest valleys.

Porosity   The term porosity refers to the ability of the regolith and bedrock to absorb variable quantities of water in response to the force of gravity. This depends upon many factors, but primarily upon the abundance and the size and shape of the spaces within the materials. Unconsolidated or loosely cemented sands and gravels, some limestones and lavas, and greatly fractured bedrock are porous because the sum of the spaces between the particles is large.

Permeability   The term permeability includes porosity but refers to the ease with which water can move. Permeability, or conversely impermeability, depends primarily on molecular attraction, which, acting mainly through surface tension, tends to retard the movement of water. The average size of the particles in a mass affects the amount of surface area inversely; namely, the smaller the particles, the larger the total surface area. The larger the surface area, the greater the volume of water that can be held by surface tension; hence, fine-textured materials tend to be relatively impermeable. For example, the surface area of the particles in a given volume of clay may be five thousand times that of the same volume of gravel, making the permeability of the gravel much the greater, while the porosity of the two materials is the same.

The permeability of the *upper* surface material (the soil) is in general independent of the average size of the particles in the regolith of which it is composed. Instead, the permeability of the soil is greatly affected by its content of organic material, and in general, the more organic material there is, the more water the zone of soil water can absorb and transmit.

Rock formations and deposits which hold large supplies of water and allow it to move easily are called *aquifers*. These may range from fractured but otherwise solid rocks to those with many pore spaces, such as sandstone, that allow water to move. The most permeable formations are beds of gravels and loose sands. These are relatively widespread since they are normal products of the gradational processes.

DISCHARGE AND RECHARGE OF GROUND WATER

Source and timing of recharge   The ground-water reservoir in any area is recharged primarily from two sources: (*a*) direct infiltration from precipitation, and (*b*) infiltration from streams and other bodies of water that receive drainage from other areas. There are important regional contrasts in the relative dominance of these suppliers and in the time when most recharge occurs.

Since precipitation is the ultimate supplier of almost all the water on the land, it might be surmised that recharge from that source would ordinarily occur at the time of highest amounts of precipitation; but it is more complicated than that. Over much of the earth the maximum precipitation occurs during the time of high sun when air temperatures, incident sun energy, and vegetation growth are all at a maximum; therefore, much of the precipitation that occurs during this period is lost through evapotranspiration. Consequently maximum recharge of the ground water occurs, rather, when the balance of these factors is favorable for it. This depends primarily upon the timing of the climatic elements, particularly precipitation and temperature.

Regional variations In humid areas recharge usually begins and reaches a maximum in the early part of the rainy season. Here, where the rainy season generally coincides with high sun, the increasing temperatures soon turn the tide in favor of losses by evapotranspiration, so that even where amounts of rainfall increase to a maximum during summer, the recharge of the ground water tends to decrease. Only in the humid tropics where potential evapotranspiration rates are relatively constant and in the humid mesothermal areas with low-sun precipitation does maximum recharge ordinarily coincide with the time of maximum precipitation.

The recharge of ground water in arid regions follows a similar regime, closely tied to the annual variations in precipitation amounts. But there is one major difference between arid and humid regions with respect to recharge: recharge in humid areas usually occurs locally, that is, where the precipitation occurs, while the recharge area in arid regions is commonly displaced from the area of precipitation. The scanty precipitation at low elevations of arid regions is quickly lost by evaporation, but that which falls on the cooler, higher areas is not so subject to loss by evaporation and there is usually more of it. Thus it collects in stream channels and flows to the edges of the uplands, where it is likely to encounter marginal alluvial deposits made up mostly of highly permeable gravels. The water quickly sinks and while doing so also moves laterally beneath the surface, sometimes for considerable distances.

Effluent and influent streams Water that enters the ground and moves beneath the surface as ground water must ultimately leave the ground water. It may do so in two ways: by emergence into the surface-water supply or by evapotranspiration. In humid areas the loss of water from the saturated zone is usually by outflow to streams; in dry areas the loss is more often by direct evaporation.

Streams may be classed as either effluent or influent in their relationship to ground water. Effluent streams are those that are fed by a water table above their level; here the stream channel intersects the water table, and water drains into it from the ground-water reservoir. Influent streams are those from which water feeds into the ground; here the water table lies beneath the bottom of the stream channel (Fig. 16.16). The streams of humid climatic regions tend to be effluent streams, and because of the steady addition of outflowing ground water, tend to increase in volume downstream; dry-land streams tend to have opposite characteristics. A small stream that is situated where its valley is in a variable relationship with the fluctuating water table, changes from time to time, being

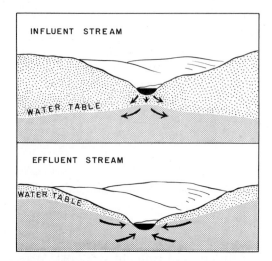

FIG. 16.16   Cross sections of an influent and an effluent stream.

effluent when the water table is high and being influent, or even drying up entirely, when the water table is low.

Springs   Where ground water discharges onto the surface instead of at or below the level of a flowing stream, a spring exists. A spring may flow either continuously or intermittently, and its water may be either cold or warm, hard or soft (page 313).

Springs result from a variety of conditions involving the position of the water table, the configuration of the land surface, and the nature and structure of the rock materials. Figure 16.17a illustrates the occurrence of springs on the sides of a valley which has eroded below the usual level of the water table. Springs of this type are common, and often they are the main water sources for small brooks at the headwaters of rivers. If the level of the water table is lowered after a period of protracted drought, such a spring will cease to flow until the water table is again raised by the downward seepage from further rains.

Figure 16.17b illustrates the site of a spring

caused by the movement of water downward through porous formations and then horizontally along the top of an impervious layer. Permeable formations of gravels, sandstones, or other porous materials underlain by compact shales often produce many such springs in an area. Figure 16.17c illustrates how water from a wide area of rocks, even rocks of low water-holding capacity, may converge upon a spring site that results from a fault.

GROUND WATER AS A RESOURCE

Ground waters are not used as a source of water supply to the extent that surface waters are. Nevertheless, the ground-water reservoir is extensively utilized, especially (a) where surface supplies are limited or have unde-

FIG. 16.17   Some of the many possible conditions of surface, material, and structure that are related to the occurrence of springs.

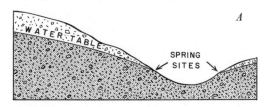

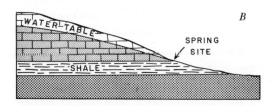

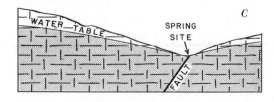

sirable qualities, and (b) in smaller cities and villages, in suburban areas, and on farms. The approximate proportions of ground waters and surface waters taken for the major withdrawal uses in the United States are shown in Fig. 16.2.

Almost no water is free from dissolved or suspended material, but the nature and quantity of such materials varies widely from region to region. Ground water ordinarily has been filtered through the earth, sometimes for many years, before it again comes or is brought to the surface; it is therefore relatively free from mud and other suspended materials. On the other hand, ground water commonly contains dissolved minerals, and some of these, such as sulphur or iron, may impart to water a disagreeable taste or render it unfit for certain industrial processes. Some minerals give tonic, laxative, or other medicinal qualities to the water.

Among the most abundant of the soluble salts found especially often in ground water are compounds of calcium (lime), sodium, and magnesium. In desert regions, for instance, seepage waters are commonly charged with compounds of these elements and other salts to a degree that retards or prevents their use. In the United States these are known as alkali waters. In humid regions most of the readily soluble sodium compounds have long since been removed from the upper portion of the ground. However, limestones and lime-cemented sediments furnish calcium and magnesium compounds which, although they do not much affect the taste of water, give it a quality which does affect its domestic and industrial utility.

The amount of mineral in solution usually is expressed in terms of the parts of dissolved mineral per million parts of water (ppm). Regions underlain mainly by crystalline rocks or by highly siliceous sands or sandstones may contain as little as 5 or 10 ppm. These are the naturally soft waters. Water containing as much as 60 ppm still is considered soft, but if water contains more than 120 to 180 ppm it is considered hard water. In regions of lime-containing sedimentary rocks, well waters in common use contain 300 to 500 ppm and, in a few places, as much as 700 to 800 ppm. Hard waters, if not "softened," may cause serious problems in the home and in certain industrial processes. This is because of their chemical reactions and especially the formation of undesirable precipitates. It is estimated that use of hard water for municipal supply costs the homeowner well over $100 per year directly and indirectly. The ground waters that supply some 10 per cent of the urban population in the United States are twice as hard as the surface waters used for that purpose (160 ppm compared with 80 ppm, approximately).

The use of wells and spring waters Throughout the world there are no doubt thousands of farmhouses and not a few villages that are located upon sites originally chosen, long ago, because spring water was found there. Large numbers of these springs, most of them on valley slopes, still are flowing and still supply water. Yet the substitution of tilled crops for forest and grassland has tended to increase the rate of runoff and so to decrease the proportion of the precipitation that infiltrates. The consequent lowering of the water table has had the effect of rendering the supply of spring water less dependable, and at the same time the growth of population has tended to make this source of supply less adequate and more subject to pollution. In the more heavily occupied areas the withdrawal of ground water by artificial

soluble mineral – hard water
crystaline rock formation – soft water

means (wells) has also greatly depleted the ground-water supply.

Kinds of wells   Wells are holes that penetrate below the water table where ground water may drain into them from an aquifer and then be brought to the surface. Formerly, many wells were made by simply digging a hole below the level of the water table, and they seldom were many feet deep. Millions of such dug wells still are in daily use in nearly all parts of the world, although this shallow and open construction makes them particularly subject to surface pollution. Since most dug wells cannot easily be extended far below the water table, the normal rising and falling of the water table with periods of recharge and discharge makes them also a relatively undependable source of water supply.

A driven well is obtained by forcing a point (a pointed length of pipe with screened holes in it) into the ground, adding successive sections of pipe in the process. If the point enters an aquifer, the water will enter the holes and may be pumped out. Since the pipe forms a casing all the way to the aquifer, there is less likelihood of pollution than in the case of a dug well. But driven wells are usually shallow also, and can only be put down in unconsolidated materials.

A drilled well is made by boring a hole into the bedrock until a bedrock aquifer is pierced. The hole is cased, at least in its upper portion. The hole may be drilled until the rate of flow of water into it provides the supply desired. Ordinarily only drilled wells extend very far beneath the surface and merit the term deep wells.

The quantity and the quality of water from deep wells depend upon the nature of the aquifer and its structural relationships. If the wellhole terminates in a thick, porous aquifer such as a porous sandstone, it may provide an abundant and continuous supply of water. Where the rock beneath a locality is the massive crystalline type, the water yield may be continuous but not abundant, since such bedrock has little pore space. The rate of flow into a well in dense rock is sometimes increased by using explosives at the bottom of the hole to shatter the surrounding rock and thus make numerous crevices through which the water may flow. However, some hard crystalline rocks are so low in water content that no operation can bring about enough flow to justify the very high cost of drilling deep wells in them. Shale rocks, although not hard, are commonly compact, impervious, and dry, but they are usually closely associated with other sedimentary rocks which are porous.

Wells in regions of fractured limestones draw water primarily through fissures, such as joints and other fractures that have been enlarged by solution, and they may yield abundant supplies. On the other hand, since the water may enter the system of fissures directly from the surface drainage, some of it through sinkholes, it may not have the benefit of much natural filtering, and therefore possibly be polluted when withdrawn. It may be little safer than the surface waters of the region, which have at least been exposed to the bacteria-destroying power of sunlight.

Effects of wells on water table   The surface of the ground-water reservoir (the water table) is in a natural state of equilibrium with respect to its discharge and recharge. These rarely remain constant, and the water table rises and falls in response to their natural fluctuations, but the rises and falls offset each other, over a period of time. When man extracts water from the reservoir, he upsets this natural balance by adding an unnatural

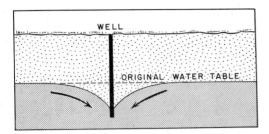

FIG. 16.18 Development of a cone of depression around a well. When withdrawal exceeds the rate of movement, the cone will ultimately reach the bottom of the well.

discharge. The water table therefore falls until a new balance is reached, either by an increase in recharge or a decrease in natural discharge. When water is withdrawn from a well at a rate greater than lateral movement of ground water can supply it, a *cone of depression* forms around the well, and as long as the withdrawal exceeds the rate that water can be supplied, the cone steadily deepens and grows laterally (Fig. 16.18). Obviously, if discharge continues to be faster than the lateral movement of water, the cone will deepen until it reaches the bottom of the well. The cone may even intercept the cones of other wells, reducing their yield; but in any case the natural discharge will be decreased somewhere. The gradual lowering of the water table involved will, of course, increase the costs of pumpage. If the well is located near the sea, the development of the cone may reverse the direction of ground-water flow, causing salt water to move toward the well, as has happened in numerous places.

Artesian wells Any well in which water rises above the level of the tapped aquifer is commonly referred to as an artesian well. Formerly, the term was restricted to wells that flowed freely without pumping. Artesian wells are possible under any one of several sets of conditions of underground structure,

two of which are illustrated in Fig. 16.19. But the favorable situation must include the following conditions: (*a*) the aquifer must be of some permeable material; (*b*) the aquifer must outcrop, or be exposed at the surface, in a region of sufficient precipitation to fill it with water; (*c*) the formation must dip beneath a capping layer of some impermeable material such as shale; (*d*) it must lead toward a region where the land surface is lower than it is at the exposed end of the pervious formation; and (*e*) there must be partial constriction (or total blockage) of exit sufficient for the water that collects in the higher portion of the aquifer to be placed under pressure. Water will then rise in a well, or even flow from the opening, as long as the rate of recharge exceeds the rate of loss through withdrawal from the well and natural seepage. In a few regions saucerlike structural basins contain aquifers which outcrop at the edges of the basin and incline from all sides, underneath other rocks, toward its center, where artesian water may be had in abundance. Artesian conditions also occur on a smaller scale in constricted layers of gravel

FIG. 16.19 (Above) A structural artesian condition such as that described in the northern Great Plains of the United States. (Below) A local artesian condition that might occur in an area of glacial deposition.

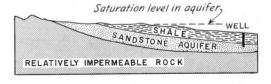

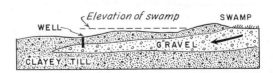

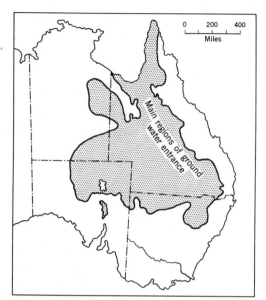

0   200   400
Miles

Main regions of ground water entrance

FIG. 16.20   The great artesian basin of Australia. *(From James E. Collier.)*

or sand, called lenses, in the otherwise clayey drift of glacial deposition.

Notable artesian structures underlie some areas of truly great extent. One is the northern Great Plains region of the United States. There porous formations, especially sandstones, outcrop at considerable elevation near the Rocky Mountains and incline eastward, under suitable capping layers, toward the lower plains. They yield artesian waters far out in the eastern part of the Dakotas. Parts of the dry lands of Australia also are blessed with artesian structures. One of these structures is deservedly called the great artesian basin (Fig. 16.20).

The effect of excessive artificial discharge through wells drilled into artesian structures is ultimately similar to the effect of withdrawal upon the level of the water table. Thousands of flowing wells in the Dakotas and hundreds in Australia, because of careless waste of water through them, have decreased the pressures in both regions until many wells now require pumping, and the flow of others is much reduced.

SUGGESTED READING

Kuenen, P. H.: *Realms of Water,* translated by May Hollander, John Wiley & Sons, Inc., New York, 1955.

Langbein, Walter B., et al.: *Annual Runoff in the United States,* U. S. Geological Survey Circular 52, 1949.

McGuiness, C. L.: *The Water Situation in the United States with Special Reference to Ground Water,* U. S. Geological Survey Circular 114, 1951.

Thomas, H. E.: *The Conservation of Ground Water,* McGraw-Hill Book Company, Inc., New York, 1951.

Thornthwaite, C. W., and J. R. Mather: "The Water Balance," *Publications in Climatology,* Drexel Institute of Technology, Philadelphia, vol. 8, no. 1, 1955.

U.S. Department of Agriculture: "Water," *Yearbook of Agriculture,* 1955.

van Hylckama, T. E. A.: "The Water Balance of the Earth," *Publications in Climatology,* Drexel Institute of Technology, Philadelphia, vol. 9, no. 2, 1956.

CHAPTER 17

Natural vegetation

NATURAL VEGETATION AS A GEOGRAPHICAL ELEMENT

The plant cover which varies greatly in kind and in density from region to region over the earth is one of the most striking features of the land surfaces, for the visual landscape is to a significant degree the product of the vegetation mantle. Forested areas stand in marked contrast to grasslands; the green woodland in leaf gives a totally different scenic effect to that provided by the somber grove which has shed its leaves; and some woods of middle latitudes which are spectacular in their beauty during the period of rich and varied autumn colors are beauti-

ful in an entirely different way in spring. Indeed, natural vegetation takes high rank among those elements which serve to differentiate regions in appearance and attractiveness, and for this aesthetic contribution alone is a feature of great geographic importance.

But in addition to its aesthetic qualities, native vegetation has important resource value. In the preagricultural stage of human development it was the only source, besides animal life, of the essentials for food and clothing. Since then, as civilization has advanced and population multiplied and spread, the original vegetation over huge areas of the continents has been consumed or destroyed, leaving behind a greatly altered landscape consisting of a modified vegetation cover, as well as human settlements, tilled fields, and other signs of land utilization. Nevertheless, even in this twentieth century forest products, in the form of lumber, fuel, and pulp, and natural pasture lands for animal grazing continue to make an important contribution to economic well-being. As a resource in another form, the enduring attraction of woods and forests with their wildlife gives many of the most popular summer and winter playgrounds their special lure.

Since the natural vegetation is an expression of the whole physical environment, and reflects the integration of all environmental conditions, past as well as present, it likewise serves as an indicator of the potentialities of an environment for human use; thus the suitability of a soil for certain types of farming is often clearly shown by the density and composition of the vegetation cover. Moreover, even in those parts of the earth where the original vegetation has long since disappeared and agriculture is of long standing, the soil continues to bear the imprint of the type of plant cover under which it developed.

CAUSES OF REGIONAL VARIATIONS IN THE PLANT COVER

The character of the earth's present cover of natural, or wild, vegetation reflects chiefly the present physical environment, whose principal conditioning elements are climate, soils, and organisms. Unlike animals, plants do not have the power of locomotion, cannot construct shelters, and do not generate heat;

so they are unable to escape the effects of the surrounding environment to the same degree. All the factors of the environment act collectively and simultaneously upon plants, and the action of any one element is conditioned by all the others.

In part, however, the present cover of vegetation is the product of time processes—and not only the previously mentioned occurrences of human history, but also evolutionary process involving modifications and regional shiftings of plants which result from past environmental changes.

Climatic effects   In its broader pattern, the distribution of natural vegetation over the earth reflects present climatic conditions more strikingly than the effects of any other single factor. Plant geographers have long recognized this fundamental relationship, which is evidenced by the approximate agreement between general climatic characteristics, on the one hand, and the general characteristics of vegetation, on the other. This relationship, moreover, extends deep into the past. Vegetation, being basically dynamic, not static, has responded to long-term changes in world climate: when climate has changed in the past so has the world pattern of vegetation.

But because world climates have been stabilized now for at least several millenniums, the present arrangement of the great vegetation grouping represents a relatively enduring situation. In this grouping the areally extensive vegetation types, corresponding to the major types of climate, are called *climaxes* or *plant formations*. Illustrations of important climaxes are the tropical rainforest of the constantly wet low-latitude climates and the coniferous (needle-leaf) forests of the subarctic climates. "The climax communities are considered to be the highest types of vegetation that can develop under the different aspects of climate, and are in dynamic equilibrium with the climate." [1]

Heat and water are the two climatic elements that most importantly affect plant growth and vegetation characteristics. No plants can live entirely without water, and for every species of plant there appear to be three critical temperatures: (*a*) lower and (*b*) upper limits beyond which it cannot exist, and (*c*) an optimum temperature in which it grows most vigorously.

Different species resist cold in different ways. Some adjust by halting certain functions during the period of low temperatures. This may be evidenced by a marked external change, such as occurs in fall when certain trees and shrubs shed their leaves to remain bare in winter. These are the previously mentioned *deciduous* (seasonally leaf-shedding) plants, so called to distinguish them from the *evergreens,* those plants that retain some foliage through the year. In the tropics, lacking a cold season, seasonal leaf fall where it occurs is induced by a dry season. Most coniferous trees belong to the evergreen group, and lapse into a dormant period without an apparent outward change. In some species of plants the vegetative parts are caused to die by the cold season, and the plant is perpetuated only by a seed which is resistant to cold. These are the *annuals,* and they stand in contrast to *perennials,* whose vegetative parts live on year after year.

Water, taken in at the roots of plants, is the principal ingredient of sap, in which mineral matter in solution is carried to all parts of the plant. Transpiration of water takes place through the leaves, the process being associated with chemical changes by which the sap ingredients are prepared for assimilation by plant tissues.

Plants that are at home in wet climates or in wet, swampy locations are called *hygrophytes*. These plants usually have long and relatively fragile stems containing a minimum of woody fiber, and leaves are large and usually thin. Roots are likely to be shallow. The banana tree, characteristic of the wet tropics, is a hygrophyte. At the opposite extreme are the *xerophytes,* which are adapted to drought conditions. The roots of xerophytes are deep or widespread, which increases the depth or area from which water can be obtained, while stems are likely to be short and strong. Leaves are smaller and thicker, their stomata (openings for transpiration) fewer to protect them against rapid transpiration; leaves may even be replaced by thorns. A hairy undercover is common. A thick, corky bark or a coating of wax may further protect against transpiration. Certain desert species—one being the fleshy-stemmed cactus—adapt themselves in a different way, viz., by accumulating supplies of water within their vegetative structures.

Soil and organisms Although climate, especially through temperature and precipitation, sets the broader outlines of the earth's vegetation groupings, modifications and variety within the larger plant formations are usually the result of secondary factors, chiefly soil and organisms.

Soil is not a completely independent element of the environment, for general soil character is greatly influenced by climate as well as by the vegetation cover. But nonclimatic factors —such as the nature of the bedrock, quality and depth of parent soil materials, drainage conditions, angle of slope, and exposure— cause many regional and local variations in soils; and it is these variations which cause

[1] Stanley A. Cain, *Foundations of Plant Geography*, Harper & Brothers, New York, 1944, p. 11.

much of the variety within the larger climaxes of vegetation. The soil environment specifically modifies plant life chiefly through its temperature, chemical composition, and water retentiveness.

Further variety is added to the vegetation mantle through the effects of organisms—effects achieved in a variety of ways. Man, one of the more important organisms, has left a strong mark. Thus overgrazing, involving other animals but also fostered by man, may change the native vegetation of a region, as it has, in all probability, on the North American Great Plains; and man-set fires have been a major modifier of vegetation over extensive areas. Indeed, over extensive parts of the earth, man, as previously stated, has so greatly modified the original vegetation through his use of the land that at present it bears little resemblance to what it was in its native state. Other kinds of organism influence are associated with the work of pollinating insects and the relations between hosts and parasites.

Classification of the earth's vegetation The classification and brief description of the earth's native vegetation which follows is plant geography in its broadest aspects—an attempt to describe the principal plant associations, show their relationships to the environmental complex, and indicate their world distribution (Plate 5).

The broad outline of plant geography here presented is possible because of the fact that —in spite of the incursions of man—over extensive areas covering scores and even hundreds of thousands of square miles the vegetation cover maintains a considerable degree of similarity, provided the climatic environment is fairly homogeneous. Even more impressive, similar environments on widely separated continents appear to have plant formations which are much alike in general aspect, even though they are not composed of identical species. Thus the plants found in the tropical rainforests of the Amazon River Basin in South America and in the Congo River Basin in Africa are fairly similar in general appearance and type; and the same plant similarity exists in the grasslands of Argentina, the United States, and Hungary. Thus, on a basis of common physical needs, certain plants genetically unrelated to one another repeatedly grow in intermingled fashion in similar environments.

It is these plant associations, prevailing over extensive areas and occupying characteristic physical environments, that are the topic to be emphasized in this chapter.

THE GREAT PLANT ASSOCIATIONS

No widely accepted geographical classification of the earth's plant cover has as yet been evolved, partly because of a lack of reliable information on the nature of the vegetation mantle over extensive areas. The classification that follows of the great plant associations into classes and types of natural vegetation is therefore tentative in character.

1. Forest associations
   - a. Tropical forests
     - (1) Tropical rainforest
     - (2) Lighter tropical forest (including semideciduous, deciduous, scrub-and-thorn forest)
   - b. Middle-latitude forests
     - (1) Mediterranean woodland and shrub

(2) Broadleaf forest *Willamette Valley*

    (*a*) Deciduous

    (*b*) Evergreen

(3) Needle-leaf or coniferous forest

(4) Mixed broadleaf–needle-leaf forest

2. <u>Grassland associations</u>

  a. Tropical grasslands (wooded savanna and savanna)

  b. Middle-latitude grasslands

3. Desert shrub

4. Tundra

Plant geographers commonly recognize four principal classes of natural vegetation: (*a*) forests, (*b*) grasslands, (*c*) desert shrub, and (*d*) tundra, which is composed chiefly of herbaceous plants other than grass. Without doubt the distribution of these major classes of vegetation over the earth's land areas is environmentally controlled, largely the result of climate in fact, but it is by no means easy to make broad generalizations about the specific qualities of the environment of each class.

As a general rule forests are characteristic of relatively humid climates. Because of its deep or extensive root system, the tree is better able to tap deep-lying supplies of water than grass, so that how precipitation is distributed through the year is not as important to trees as to grass. Normally trees do not thrive in climates with cold, dry winters where there is a prevalence of strong or continuous winds, with resulting excessive transpiration.

Grassland associations dispute the possession of the land with woodland and are likely to prevail where the environment discourages luxuriant tree growth. Thus, in the middle latitudes grasslands occupy drier climates than do forests. A winter climate that is cold, dry, and windy does not adversely affect grasses as it does trees. But in the tropics grasslands and woodlands appear to occupy a wide range of climates, and trees and grass are frequently intermingled. Admittedly, the origin of tropical grasslands is a highly controversial question.

TYPES OF FORESTS AND THEIR DISTRIBUTION[2]

LOW-LATITUDE FORESTS

Tropical rainforest The most luxuriant type of woodland community, the tropical rainforest, is the climax vegetation of tropical lowlands and slopes where rainfall is heavy and well distributed throughout the year, there being no marked dry season. Distribution of this type of forest is imperfectly known. Certainly the Amazon River Basin, in northern South America, and west central Africa are the two largest areas of tropical rainforest, although it is found along many rainy coasts and on numerous islands in the tropics as well (Plate 5).

The tropical rainforest has three principal characteristics: (*a*) A great variety of different species of trees is present, in contrast to most middle-latitude forests, where one or at most a few species may form almost solid stands. But rainforest trees, although species are numerous, are rather similar in appearance. (*b*) There exists a strong vertical stratification in the forest, the many species arranging themselves in several groups, each having a particular height limit (Fig. 17.1). The result is a forest with a number of tree tiers, each with its own height level and each lower one reflecting an increasing tolerance for the shade imposed by the canopy above. (*c*) The num-

[2] In addition to their previously stated classification as deciduous and evergreen (p. 319), trees are classified as either (*a*) broadleaf or (*b*) needle-leaf (coniferous). Some broadleaf trees are evergreen, some deciduous; coniferous trees (conifers) are predominantly evergreen.

FIG. 17.1 Tropical rainforest in the Amazon River Basin of Brazil. Note the density of the stand and the variability in the size and height of individual trees. *(Hamilton Rice Expedition of 1924–1925.)*

ber of lianas, other kinds of climbers, and epiphytes, is unusually large. The giant lianas have the appearance of great cables interlacing the branches of the forest crown and binding the individual trees together.

External and internal appearance In external appearance the rainforest presents a richly varied mosaic of many shades. The mature leaves are a deep green, but young leaves are highly colored, resembling autumn foliage in middle latitudes. The result is a forest in which the fresh green of middle-latitude woodlands is absent. Just as the climate exhibits little seasonal change, so does the vegetation: there is no general dormant period when the forest is bare of foliage. Different species drop their leaves at different times, and trees without leaves may be observed at any time.

Viewed internally, the tropical rainforest is seen to be composed of trees which vary greatly in height and diameter growing close together. Trunks are rather slender and have branches only near the top. The bark is thin

and smooth. The mass of vines and creepers appears almost to suffocate the trees that support it. Because of the heavy shade produced by the almost impenetrable canopy of tree foliage, the undergrowth is usually not dense. The typical jungle with its thick undergrowth generally occurs just in areas where light reaches the forest floor, as along rivers and coasts or in abandoned clearings.

Lighter tropical forest The lighter tropical forest includes a variety of woodland vegetation types—semideciduous, deciduous, scrub, and thorn—whose distinctive characteristics and precise distributions are not well enough known to permit localizing them individually on a small-scale, generalized vegetation map such as Plate 5. As a rule, where soils and drainage do not interfere, tropical rainforest gives way at its climatic limits to semideciduous and deciduous forest, and as rainfall continues to decline this in turn passes over to wooded grassland and finally to scrub-and-thorn woodland and desert shrub.

Compared with the rainforest, the lighter tropical forest is composed of small trees widely spaced, with a dense undergrowth of shrubs or grass (Fig. 17.2). Also, more of the trees are deciduous in character. Not all species are leafless during the drier dormant season, but enough are to make the season of drought the time when contrast with the rainforest is most marked.

The scrub-and-thorn forest found in parts of the lighter tropical forest varies in density from an open, parklike growth of low stunted trees and thorny plants to dense thickets of the same. The trees composing this dry forest are small in diameter, rarely exceeding 1 ft. No other type of tropical forest equals this forest in tolerance of physical conditions.

Utilization of tropical forests Although

tropical forests occupy nearly 50 per cent of the earth's total forest area, they at present only supply the limited needs of local populations and furnish to world commerce small quantities of special-quality woods, such as dyewoods and cabinet woods. Nevertheless these low-latitude forests, especially the tropical rainforest, represent one of the world's great potential timber sources. The problems involved in their utilization—labor supply, sanitation, the need for new logging technologies, how to utilize the great variety of species composing the tropical forest—are serious, but none appears to be insurmountable.

MIDDLE-LATITUDE FORESTS

Mediterranean broadleaf evergreen woodland and shrub The Mediterranean broadleaf evergreen woodland and shrub is characteristic of subtropical locations with mild rainy winters and long, dry, and usually hot summers. The largest region of this forest is the Mediterranean borderlands; smaller areas exist in California, middle Chile, southern Australia, and the Cape Town region in southernmost Africa. It is an unusual woodland, for seldom are trees broadleaf and evergreen and at the same time adapted to serious summer drought. Instead

FIG. 17.2 Lighter tropical forest (semideciduous) in central Africa. The trees are sufficiently far apart that they do not create a dense shade. Coarse grasses mantle the forest floor. *(American Geographical Society.)*

FIG. 17.3 Mediterranean woodland in California. An open stand of dwarf oak and shrub. *(U.S. Forest Service.)*

of dropping their foliage in the dry season, as trees of many tropical deciduous forests do, the trees in this woodland adjust to drought through protective devices—thick bark and small, thick leaves with hard shiny surfaces—which reduce the loss of water by transpiration.

Where climatic and soil conditions are most favorable, the Mediterranean woodland consists of low, or even stunted, widely spaced trees with thick trunks and gnarled branches (Fig. 17.3). Between the trees the ground is partly covered by bush vegetation or bunch (tufted) grass. Seemingly more widespread is a vegetation cover consisting largely of shrubs and bushes in which there may be stunted trees. The chief economic importance of this bush thicket lies in its protection of slope lands from the injurious effects of rapid runoff.

Temperate broadleaf forest   Within the more humid parts of the middle latitudes are found two great groups of forests: (*a*)

forests of broadleaf trees, and (*b*) forests of needle-leaf trees, or conifers. Over large areas these trees are mixed in conifer-broadleaf forests. As a general rule, but with important exceptions, the coniferous forests occupy the colder locations and thus are usually on the poleward side of the broadleaf woodlands. In regions of porous, sandy soils where water is deficient, and on steep mountain slopes where soils are thin or rocky and temperatures lower, conifers may supplant broadleaves even in the lower middle latitudes.

Temperate broadleaf forests vary widely in composition, the dominant tree species differing from one region to another. In some areas, especially along their poleward margins, there are numerous conifers among them—so many, in fact, that some plant geographers designate such forests as mixed rather than broadleaf (Fig. 17.4). In the eastern United States two general broadleaf-forest areas are distinguished: (*a*) a northeastern area including northern Wisconsin and Michigan, New York, and southern New England, where birch, beech, and maple predominate but there is a large infusion of hemlock and other conifers; and (*b*) a central and southern area lying south of the first and terminating at the northern and western boundary of the sandy Atlantic and Gulf Coastal Plain (Fig. 17.5). In this latter forest, which was originally the finest and most extensive area of broadleaves anywhere in the world, the broadleaves oak, chestnut, hickory, and poplar predominate, but the coniferous pines become prominent toward the Coastal Plain margins. The greater part of the original American broadleaf-forest belt, lying as it does in an environment eminently suited for agriculture, has now been cleared and turned into farm land.

By far the greater part of the temperate broadleaf forest is deciduous in character, the trees dropping their leaves in fall and remaining without foliage during the winter season (Fig. 17.4). Except in the dormant season, this forest is rather uniformly bright green in color. Along the humid subtropical margins of the middle latitudes evergreen broadleaf forests are to be found, but these are not nearly so extensive in the middle latitudes as the deciduous variety. These subtropical forests, in many respects akin to those of the wet tropics, occur principally in southern Japan and in southern and southeastern Australia.

Needle-leaf forest Coniferous trees are predominantly evergreen, the addition and fall of the needles being continuous rather

FIG. 17.4 Broadleaf deciduous forest (oak and hickory) in northern Indiana. Much of this type of woodland occupied potentially good agricultural land, and as a consequence was destroyed in the process of settlement. *(U.S. Department of Agriculture.)*

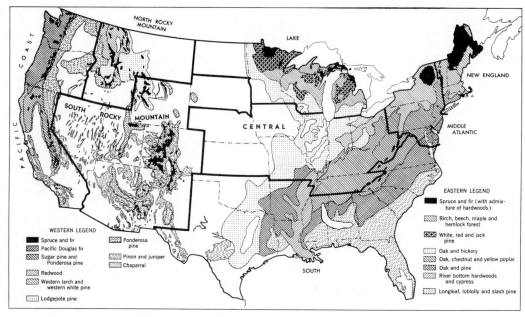

FIG. 17.5 Natural-forest types of the United States. *(U.S. Forest Service.)*

than confined to any particular period or season. Unlike broadleaves, the needles of conifers are xerophytic in character, so that shedding is not necessary to protect against a cold or a drought season. On the whole, the crowns of coniferous forests do not intercept so much sunlight as the crowns of broadleaf woodlands, and yet less sun actually reaches the earth in coniferous forests, because (*a*) they lie predominantly in higher latitudes where there are longer periods of low sun, and (*b*) they are never without foliage. As a result there are usually less surficial vegetation, a minimum of bacterial activity, and smaller accumulations of humus in the soil.

Subarctic conifers Conifers are most extensively developed in the severe subarctic regions of North America and Eurasia, where they form wide and continuous east-west forest belts stretching from coast to coast (Fig. 17.6). The name *taiga* has been given

to the subarctic coniferous forests. On their northern frontiers they make contact with the tundra, a region thoroughly hostile to trees. The Eurasian taiga forms the largest single continuous forest area on the earth (Plate 5).

Conifers (larch, spruce, fir, pine) predominate in the taiga, although broadleaf trees (alder, willow, aspen, birch, mountain ash) are scattered throughout, individually as well as in thickets or clusters. Species are few in number. Trees are small in size, usually not over 1½ ft in diameter, and growth is slow (Fig. 17.7). On the shaded forest floor vegetation is meager, mosses and lichens being the most common plant forms, and sometimes even these are stifled by the thick blanket of slowly decomposing needles. Little organic matter is made available to the soil, for needle leaves are a poor source of humus to begin with, and the low temperatures and deep shade act to retard decomposition and discourage the activity of soil fauna.

FIG. 17.6 In many parts of ice-scoured subarctic Canada the coniferous-forest cover is thin and patchy. *(Royal Canadian Air Force.)*

FIG. 17.7 Side view of subarctic coniferous forest in Canada. Note the small diameter of many of the trees. *(U.S. Forest Service.)*

Conifers in lower middle latitudes South of the great belts of subarctic conifers are other, less extensive areas of needle trees which are more valuable forest regions (Plate 5). This is because they are composed of larger trees and superior timber species, and also are more accessible.

In western North America broken belts of conifers extend southward from the taiga following the rainier highland chains—the Pacific Coast mountains and the Rocky Mountains—to beyond the Mexican border (Fig. 17.5). These forests of the American Pacific Coast states, western Canada, and Alaska constitute the most extensive area of fine coniferous forest anywhere in the world. Large trees, dense stand, good-quality timber —all contribute to this high rank (Fig. 17.8).

East of the Rockies conifers extend southward from the taiga into southeastern Canada

seems somewhat out of place, for rainfall is abundant, and the growing season long. However, the poor, sandy, droughty soil and the high evaporation are offsetting factors, creating an environment that is generally hostile to broadleaf varieties. Open, parklike character, with the ground covered by a mantle of coarse grasses or low shrubs, is typical. During the last few decades this southern pine forest has been one of the principal sources for American lumber, although the peak of its production has been passed (Fig. 17.10). Extensive areas of low-grade cutover land are now one of the most conspicuous features of the southern pine region. On the poorly drained floodplains of the Coastal Plain, pines give way to a con-

FIG. 17.9   Southern pine forest of the United States, composed of longleaf, loblolly, and slash pines, typical of the Atlantic and Gulf Coastal Plain. *(U.S. Forest Service.)*

FIG. 17.8   Interior view of Douglas fir forest in the Pacific Northwest of the United States. Trees are tall, of large diameter, and form a dense stand. *(U.S. Forest Service.)*

and the northern portions of the northeastern tier of American states—Minnesota, Wisconsin, Michigan, New York (the Adirondacks), and much of Maine. The most valuable timber trees from this eastern forest have been removed, leaving behind extensive areas of cutover waste-land of little value. South of the taiga in Eurasia valuable coniferous forests occupy the slopes of the Alps, the Carpathians, and other highland regions, as well as certain sandy areas of coastal and outwash plains.

The southern pine forest of the Atlantic and Gulf Coastal Plain in the United States, separated from the northern conifers by an extensive broadleaf forest, is composed of 10 different species of pine, of which the longleaf pine is most abundant (Plate 5; Fig. 17.9). Climatically this subtropical needle-tree forest

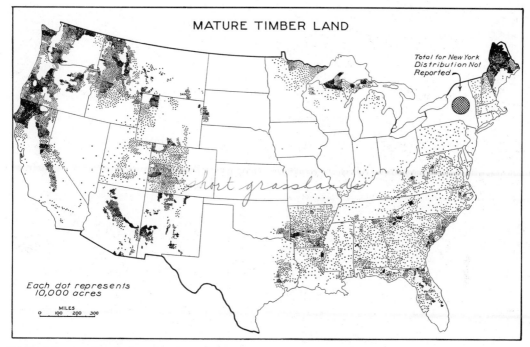

FIG. 17.10   Distribution of land with timber large enough to be currently merchantable. It does not include second growth cut primarily for chemical distillation, firewood, posts, ties, mine props, etc. *(U.S. Forest Service.)*

trasting type of forest composed of such trees as the tupelo, red gum, and cypress.

TYPES OF GRASSLAND AND THEIR DISTRIBUTION

Tropical grasslands: wooded savanna and savanna   There is at present too little reliable information on the various types and gradations of tropical grasslands and their distribution to permit a satisfactory classification and mapping. Therefore the various low-latitude grasslands, or savannas, are here grouped together under one general heading. The reader should be forewarned, however, that this grouping must not be interpreted to indicate uniformity of species and appearance. There are open savannas, with only occasional trees, and there are others in which trees or shrubs are so numerous that it is difficult to decide whether the vegetation is more properly classified as grassland or woodland. There is also regional variety in the height and spacing of the grasses.

Until recently tropical grasslands were believed to be definable as the climax, or plant formation, of areas where precipitation was intermediate between the heavy year-round rainfall of the tropical rainforest and the constant drought of the desert. But this climatic explanation has been seriously questioned in recent years. It now seems doubtful whether tropical grasslands are a plant formation in equilibrium with a specific type of climate at all. Since with declining rainfall tropical rainforest frequently gives way to semideciduous

FIG. 17.11 Tall, coarse grass, studded with low trees, in the wooded savanna of Africa north of the equator. *(American Geographical Society.)*

and deciduous forest, and finally to scrub-and-thorn forest, perhaps a tropical-grassland climate is nonexistent. Thus it has been fairly well established that the tropical grasslands of Latin America are fairly coincident with areas of flattish or slightly rolling terrain where, because of the mild relief and an impermeable subsoil, drainage is poor. In such areas the vegetation may be subjected to standing water in the rainy season and a parched soil at other times, and repeated burnings may help in establishing and expanding the grasslands.

Character of vegetation Savannas of both the wooded and the open variety are common. As previously stated, the trees are few and widely scattered in some places, while in others they are so numerous they form thickets (Fig. 17.11). Clumps of trees intermingled with patches of open grassland also are a very common arrangement. Throughout the tropical grasslands dense forests usually occupy the river floodplains. Tall trees are not absent from tropical grasslands, to be sure, but low and dwarf varieties are more common. Usually they have twisted and gnarled trunks, a thick corky bark, and leathery leaves.

Savanna grasses are variable in height. In Africa there are high savannas where the grasses range from 5 to 15 ft in height, but these do not seem to exist in Latin America. Much more common are the tall bunch grass (1 to 2 ft high) and the short bunch grass (under 1 ft high). Both grow in slender tufts with much bare earth between individual tufts, so that the grass may occupy not more than 60 per cent of the soil surface. The blades of mature savanna grasses are stiff and leathery, and only the fresh young shoots are palatable to most grazing animals. Among the natives of tropical grasslands it is a common practice to burn off the grasses in the dry season in order to make room for new growth at the beginning of the rains.

Middle-latitude grasslands The grasslands of middle latitudes appear to be the climax vegetation of subhumid and semiarid regions, and in this they stand in contrast to the savannas of the tropics. An additional contrast is the general absence of trees in the grasslands of middle latitudes, except along their contact zones with forest and in the vicinity of streams.

In the grasslands of interior North America east of the Rocky Mountains three large subdivisions are recognized: (*a*) the short grass occupying much of the semiarid Great Plains, (*b*) the transitional mixed-grass prairie coinciding with a somewhat more humid belt to the east of the short grass, and (*c*) the tall-grass prairie, or true prairie, typical of the better-watered lands between the mixed prairie and the eastern forest (Fig. 17.12). This tall-grass prairie originally extended eastward as far as western Indiana in the form of a wedge driven into the forest. West of the Rockies, there still exist extensive areas of short bunch grass in parts of Washington, Oregon, Idaho, and California. Almost all of the original prairie of interior North America east of the Rockies has been converted into agricultural land of high quality. Originally, the native wild grasses in this region attained

FIG. 17.12   *(From map by J. Richard Carpenter.)*

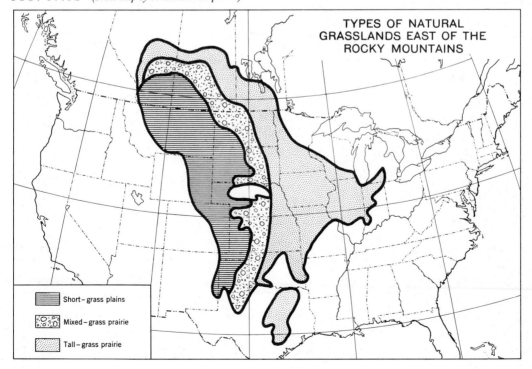

heights of 3 to 8 ft, and were intermingled with many colorful flowering plants.

Although North American grasslands have been subdivided into several groups and their distributions shown on Fig. 17.12, this same degree of detail has not been possible for the remainder of the earth's middle-latitude grasslands. For this reason, on Plate 5 all middle-latitude grasslands have the same legend. This should be interpreted to mean that insufficient information is available to permit a more detailed system of classification and of distribution similar to that for North America.

PLANT COVER OF DESERTS AND TUNDRA

Deserts   A few deserts or parts of deserts are extensive areas of rocky plain or sand and almost wholly without plant life. But most arid regions of both low and middle latitudes have some vegetation, even though

FIG. 17.13   Desert shrub, chiefly sagebrush, in Nevada. This type of vegetation cover is of little value for grazing. *(John C. Weaver.)*

it is sparse. It may be low bunch grass, with widely spaced bushes, or fleshy water-storing plants such as cacti; but much more commonly it is the perennial xerophytic shrub. In the United States, for instance, the latter type of vegetation predominates over a large part of the area west of the Rockies, interrupted here and there by bunch grass, or, at higher elevations, by forests. Rainfall over much of this region is under 12 in. per year.

The perennial shrubs of desert areas grow far apart, with much bare soil showing between them—a response to low rainfall (Fig. 17.13). Growth is very slow. Desert shrubs, exemplified by such American types as sagebrush and creosote bush, are physiologically equipped through special forms of roots, stems, and leaves to withstand drought. Some are deciduous, others evergreen in character.

Unlike the perennial shrub, the desert annuals do not show drought-resistant characteristics. Their stems and leaves are delicate, roots are thin and relatively shallow, and flowers are conspicuous. They adapt to drought through a very short life cycle: the dormant seeds germinate after a shower, the plant grows and makes its seed rapidly, the plant dies forthwith.

The vegetation of the desert proper is scanty and pale green, and so stands in contrast to the rich verdant color and luxuriance of vegetation around oases, where water is abundant—a contrast that is striking when, as frequently, almost knife-edge boundaries separate the two.

Tundra   Genuine tundra is composed largely of such lowly forms as mosses, lichens, and sedges, the whole of this vegetation incompletely covering the ground. In places there is much bare, stony soil with only the most meager plant life. On the southern margins of the tundra, where it merges with the taiga or coniferous forest, the vegetation cover is more complete, and stunted and creeping forms of trees and bushes are conspicuous. Grasslands exist on the marine margins of the tundra.

The coldness and acid character of tundra soil retards water absorption, and in the long winter period of physiological drought the soil moisture is locked up in solid form; so most tundra plants appear xerophytic, having stiff, hard, leathery leaves with thick cuticle. The short period between frosts makes the vegetative period in the tundra as short as 2 months, or less, and for this reason plants are compelled to hurry through their vegetative cycle. Even so, many of them are frozen while still in flower or fruit.

Dry tundra is composed principally of lichens interspersed with coarse, grasslike sedges—the predominance of lichens resulting in a dull, gray landscape tone. Wetter flooded areas along streams and shallow basins on higher ground are characteristically moss swamps. The southward-facing drier slopes are flower oases, where in summer brilliant colors are in evidence in a great variety.

SELECTED REFERENCES

Borchert, John: "The Climate of the Central North American Grassland," *Annals of the Association of American Geographers,* vol. 40, 1950, pp. 1–39.

James, Preston E., and Clarence F. Jones (eds.): "Plant Geography," in *American Geography: Inventory and Prospect,* Syracuse University Press, Syracuse, N. Y., 1954.

Küchler, A. W.: "A Geographic System of Vegetation," *Geographical Review,* vol. 37, 1947, pp. 233–240.

Rand McNally & Company: "World—Natural Vegetation," colored map in *Goode's World Atlas,* Chicago, 1960, pp. 16–17.

Richards, P. W.: *The Tropical Rainforest: An Ecological Study,* Cambridge University Press, New York, 1952.

Schimper, A. F. W.: *Plant Geography upon a Physiological Basis,* English translation, Oxford University Press, New York, 1903.

U.S. Department of Agriculture: "Climate and Man," *Yearbook of Agriculture,* 1941.

U.S. Department of Agriculture: "Grass," *Yearbook of Agriculture,* 1948.

U.S. Department of Agriculture: "Trees," *Yearbook of Agriculture,* 1949.

U.S. Government Printing Office: "Natural Vegetation," *Atlas of American Agriculture,* sec. E, 1924.

Weaver, John E.: *The North American Prairie,* Johnsen Publishing Company, Lincoln, Neb., 1954.

————, and Frederic E. Clements: *Plant Ecology,* 2d ed, McGraw-Hill Book Company, Inc., New York, 1938.

CHAPTER 18

Soils

The nature and significance of soil
The outermost rocks of the earth's crust are continuously being decomposed by mechanical and chemical weathering processes, and as a consequence, most areas are covered by the thin layer of more or less finely divided material called the regolith. Some of this is residual, that is, it accumulates on top of the bedrock from which it forms; while some of it is moved by agents and deposited in other areas, for example as loess, glacial drift, or alluvium. In any case, most of the earth's land surface is covered with exposed, loose rock debris; only in limited localities does the bare bedrock protrude or ice cover the surface.

Except when frozen, this superficial mantle of regolith is relatively porous, so that air and water circulate between the mineral particles. The top of the layer, being exposed to sunlight, is regularly bathed with energy, and the interaction of all the components supports various forms of life, adding yet another element to its character. This exceedingly thin layer where the solid, liquid, and gaseous inorganic and organic ingredients are integrated is called "soil." Only when all of these components are present is the mixture true soil.

In most places this complex, life-supporting veneer extends downward from the surface only a few feet. In this narrow zone where inorganic and organic materials interact, innumerable processes are continually at work developing layers, or *horizons,* with different chemical and mechanical characteristics. A vertical slice through a particular soil cutting through the soil horizons is called the *profile* of that soil.

It would be difficult to overemphasize the significance of soil. The variety of chemical elements on which human life depends are primarily needed in the form of organic compounds, such as proteins, fats, carbohydrates, and vitamins; and these come from the soil either by way of plants man consumes directly or as animal products derived from plants. Some areas are covered with soils that under natural conditions can support a large and healthy human population, but the reverse seems to be true of even larger areas. If the qualities of a soil are nutritionally deficient, so will be the food derived from it, and consequently the health of people who attempt to subsist upon that food.

THE CONTROLS OF SOIL FORMATION

The soil anywhere represents a stage in a continuing evolutionary process, and its characteristics develop as a result of the interaction of many controls. The individual controls vary in their effects and relative importance from place to place, and some of the variations are quite systematically arranged over the earth, such as those deriving from climatic factors, while others are not, such as those primarily dependent upon the character of the bedrock or the land form. The general world pattern of soil regions is more subject to internal variation than the pattern of climatic variation because some of the important soil controls do not exhibit a patterned distribution. The major controls that combine to produce a soil are parent material, climate, living organisms, land form, and time.

Parent material Each kind of regolith —and there are many kinds, such as the sediments of old lake bottoms, the accumulation of glacial drift, the new alluvium on floodplains and deltas, aeolian deposits of volcanic ash and loess, and, especially, the residual mantle weathered in place from bedrock— contains a combination of mineral grains of particular chemical character which have weathered to a particular array of fragment sizes. Although the processes of development may impart new characteristics to the soil, they are not likely to erase completely the distinctive effects deriving from this parent material. Some regoliths may modify rapidly, whereas others may be highly resistant to change. Some are highly complex aggregations of mineral compounds; others are simple.

The fragment sizes derived from the weathering of the parent material are of great importance because they affect the degree to which water and air can circulate in the soil layer. The importance of the mineral content lies in the fact that the chemical character of the soil is largely the source of the soil's fertility. A mineral element not in the parent material will be missing from the soil. Thus the parent material may be thought of as a limiting factor with respect to some of the soil's mechanical and most of its nutrient characteristics.

Climatic factors   Soil formation is influenced both directly and indirectly by the climate. Climate directly affects the rate of weathering of rocks and the amount of water percolating through or evaporating from the soil. Prevailingly high temperatures promote rapid weathering and other chemical changes in the soil, while cold temperatures slow them; and alternating seasons of rain and drought develop soil compositions and colors differing from those of continuously rainy regions. Water—more prevalent, of course, in humid regions than in dry lands—acts to remove the lime and other soluble salts from the soil.

Climate also affects the soil character indirectly through its influence upon the organic content of the soil. Most organisms can flourish only within certain temperature and moisture ranges, and partly as a consequence of such restrictions, there are definite zones of plant life on the earth. The vegetation has, in turn, a marked effect on soil character, and as a result, soil forms vary with the different organic forms they support. Because the vegetation of an area is dependent to some degree upon the climate for the form it takes, the soil of the area also is controlled by the climate.

Plants and animals   Various kinds of organisms and their tissues affect the soil character in a variety of ways. For example, when plants and animals die their remains become a part of the soil complex, and the microorganisms (bacteria, protozoa, fungi, etc.) in the soil are primary agents affecting the manner in which the decomposition of plant and animal remains takes place. Some

microorganisms also can change atmospheric nitrogen into a form that can be utilized by plants. The soil is modified by burrowing organisms and plant roots because by penetrating the soil they add to its porosity. Deep-rooted plants too, bring minerals up from the subsoil and hold them in their tissues; when the plants die and decay, these minerals are returned to the upper soil layers.

Land form   Slope characteristics are important factors in soil formation because slope differences affect, sometimes greatly, the moisture and air conditions within the soil and, even more significantly, the rate of its surface erosion. Maximum soil development will most likely take place on undulating but well-drained uplands with free underdrainage and only slight surface erosion. On such sites surface materials are removed at a rate slow enough to allow a relatively deep penetration of the effects of the soil-forming processes. Soils formed under such circumstances become fully developed and possess well-defined profiles. The soils of steep slopes, on the contrary, generally fail to develop these characteristics because accelerated surface erosion restricts the profile development in several ways, such as thinning the horizons and restricting the vegetative cover and consequently lessening the organic content. Soils of poorly drained or marshy areas develop quite different profiles, but in these cases it is primarily because they remain waterlogged and air cannot penetrate them.

Time   Because the other soil-forming processes do not proceed at the same rates in different environments, time is not a constant control either. Thus there is no specific length of time in which a soil develops its own particular characteristics. Some may reach a condition of relative balance in a comparatively short period, possibly in a few hundred years or even much less; others may require thousands of years.

If the usual soil-forming processes of an area have been locally restricted in any way, the profiles will show the effects of these modifications. Since there are a great many ways in which this can happen, it is to be expected that some soils of a region will not have the typical mature profile. In fact, in many regions there is little, if any, mature soil. Because farming modifies a soil, it is also likely that nearly mature soils are restricted to untouched soils. Many regions of high agricultural development have remaining only a few scattered remnants of the virgin soils. On the other hand, it is important to keep in mind that the immature soils of an area commonly have distinctive qualities closely related to those of the actual or hypothetical mature soil of that region.

THE ELEMENTS OF SOIL CHARACTER: COMPONENTS OF SOIL

The soil cover varies from one place on the earth to another, so that generalizations regarding the geographical occurrence of soils on the basis of similarities in their qualities and profile characteristics may be made in much the same way atmospheric phenomena are categorized, leading to a system of climatic types, groups, and regions. Because the factors affecting the formation of soil vary systematically from place to place just as the climatic controls do, the soils of the earth also vary systematically. In order to understand the world pattern of soil regions, it is first necessary to define and describe the essential characteristics that make one soil similar to another but different from a third. The more important of these are (*a*) *fertility,* that is, the chemical characteristics affecting nutritional quality, (*b*) *texture* and *structure,* or the sizes and arrangements of the inorganic particles, (*c*) *organic* components, both plant and animal, included as integral parts of the soil, (*d*) *water* and *air* relationships, (*e*) *color,* and (*f*) *soil profile.*

Fertility All plants and animals living on land, including man, ultimately obtain their sustenance from the soil. Animals are nourished by plants or by other animals which feed on plants, and plants obtain from the soil the elements required for their photosynthetic construction of carbohydrates and their biosynthetic production of protein and other essential foods.[1]

Many chemical elements are required to sustain life; but some are needed in relatively large amounts, such as oxygen, carbon, hydrogen, nitrogen, sodium, calcium, potassium, phosphorus, sulphur, magnesium, and iron, while others are required only in very small amounts, such as manganese, copper, zinc, iodine, and boron. Although some are supplied directly from the air as gases, others are obtained through the water in the soil, others, such as nitrogen, are supplied through the organic material in the soil, and still others, such as the metallic elements calcium, potash, and phosphorus, are derived from the soil's inorganic matter.

[1] W. A. Albrecht, "Soil Fertility and Biotic Geography," *Geographical Review,* vol. 47, 1957, pp. 87–105.

fertility

The available supply of the critical chemical elements is referred to as a soil's fertility.

The earth's crust, and consequently the soil, is in large measure composed of only a few elements, with the other life-giving elements occurring relatively rarely. The most abundant components, which constitute the bulk of the soil, are the elements oxygen, silicon, aluminum, and iron as they are combined in the common minerals and their weathered derivatives. The major fertility elements, excepting carbon and nitrogen, are provided from the same source.

Reduction of fertility and remedies
The supply of essential minerals in a soil may be reduced in several ways: by erosion; by excessive use, or overcropping; and, especially, by leaching, the dissolving of elements by water percolating downward. In arid regions the rate of removal of the fertility elements by leaching is low. In fact, the accumulation of soluble minerals in the soil may be large enough to be even harmful. In humid regions, however, the loss by leaching is generally heavy. The slowness with which chemical elements are supplied by natural processes often results in soils of humid lands being deficient in one or more of the critical elements. The deficiency may be partially remedied in several ways: by appropriate mineral fertilizing; by fallowing, leaving the land idle so that natural decomposition provides an additional supply; and by manuring, returning a major proportion of the plant growth to the land in the form of animal excreta and plant refuse.

Factors affecting fertility Plants obtain their mineral nutrients only from the supply of minerals dissolved in the water in the soil. The transfer is made by means of an ion exchange between the plant roots and the solution.[2] Each plant species has a certain set of nutrient requirements, and a plant's ability to obtain these nutrients as well as the soil's capacity to make them available—assuming that the elements are in the soil—is greatly affected by the soil solution.

One of the more important indicators of the availability of nutrients, but by no means a complete index of a soil's potential, is the acidity or alkalinity of the soil. With all other aspects being favorable, this does provide an indication of the kinds of plants that will grow in a particular soil and the food elements the plants will contain. In some localities organically derived acids and abundant rainfall tend to reduce the availability of the basic compounds as well as to remove those compounds from the soil by leaching. The soil solution then is likely to have an acid reaction favorable to the production of excessive amounts of bulk carbohydrates, such as starches, sugars, fats, and cellulose, as compared to the nutritionally more significant proteins. In less humid regions, where there is less leaching, soils normally have a neutral or somewhat alkaline reaction, and there is likely to be a greater supply of calcium, magnesium, and the other essential elements conducive to the production of proteins as well as carbohydrates.

It is apparent that the most universal factor affecting the fertility of a soil is the degree of leaching to which the soil is subjected. This,

---

[2] The processes by which a plant obtains its nourishment are very complex and as yet not completely understood. A root takes in water from the soil by capillary pressures and the osmotic pressures of the solution. The soil's nutrient value is dependent upon the exchange of the plant's ions (electrically charged particles in solution) for the nutrient ions available on the surfaces of the soil particles in contact with the root.

in turn, depends largely upon the rainfall, though also, to some extent, on temperature, vegetation, and other factors. Thus humid regions tend to have less fertile and more acid soils than do dry regions.

Texture and structure Assuming favorable climatic conditions, of course, the productivity of a soil depends upon several physical characteristics in addition to its inherent fertility. Among the more important are its texture, or the proportional sizes of the various inorganic particles, and its structure, the manner in which these particles tend to clump or aggregate.

Texture The inorganic particles of a soil commonly occupy nearly one-half the volume of the upper part of the profile, and most of the chemical reactions within a soil, such as those that make nutrients available to plants, take place on the surfaces of the particles. The smaller the soil particles, the more specific surface, or total surface per unit mass, there will be. Consequently, the reactivity of a soil, which is the soil's ability to react chemically and thus provide an ionic food supply, varies in direct proportion with the specific surface (Fig. 18.1). The sizes of the particles also affect markedly the movements of water and air within a soil. Very large particles, which allow free drainage, have poor water retention, making soils dry out quickly after rains. Conversely, very small particles inhibit drainage and air movement.

Particle sizes are grouped in classes ranging from sands (the largest) to clays. The table shows the class limits assigned by soil scientists.

Since the inorganic mass of a soil usually contains fractions from more than one class, various combinations of percentages are given

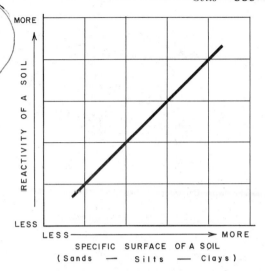

FIG. 18.1 The general relationship between the specific surface of a soil and its chemical reactivity.

specific names, loam being the general term assigned to combinations that include moderate amounts of all three (Fig. 18.2). The most significant fraction of a soil as far as reactivity is concerned is the clay because clay particles are the smallest. In addition to the sand, silt, and clay particles, however, there are very much smaller particles of either organic or inorganic origin called colloids. The role of colloids in the physical and chemical processes of the soil is known only imperfectly, but it is suspected that one of their functions is the formation of gelatinous films on soil particles that affect the clumping of the particles.

The soil's texture usually varies from

Texture Classes

Name	Diameter, mm
Sand	2.0 to 0.05
Silt	0.05 to 0.002
Clay	Less than 0.002

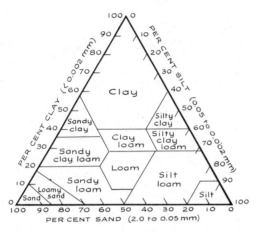

FIG. 18.2 The textural triangle used by the soil scientists of the U.S. Department of Agriculture. In order to find the textural class, the percentages of sand, silt, and clay are entered on the appropriate scales and the hatch lines are followed to the intersection of the three lines.

horizon to horizon. Downward-moving water may wash with it the smaller particles, mostly the clay and colloidal fractions, and thus reduce their proportion in the upper part.

This mechanical removal is called eluviation. The load removed by eluviation may be deposited lower in the profile. Such charging of a layer with fine particles from above is called

illuviation. Because this shifting of particles is accomplished by moving water, the soils of humid lands tend to be eluviated as well as leached.

Structure Not all the important physical characteristics of a soil depend only upon its texture. For example, soils that consist largely of clay particles are not necessarily compact and impervious to water and air, as might be expected. Instead, in many clayey and silty soils the individual particles are arranged together in tiny clumps, which, as a result, have some of the physical characteristics associated with larger particles. This property of a soil, its structure, is beneficial for the

soil's productivity because it may permit considerable pore space to develop. Thus an internal structure can develop in which the pore space among the structural units available for air, water, and root penetration is much greater than in a soil of the same texture but with a less favorable structure (Fig. 18.3). In some soils the amount of pore space may be less than 20 per cent of the soil volume, whereas in highly structured clays it may exceed 60 per cent. Most agricultural soils include amounts of pore space comprising from 35 to 50 per cent of the soil volume.

Good structural arrangements including a high percentage of pore space commonly are found in soils of fine texture that have considerable organic content, but sandy soils are essentially without structure, with each sand particle acting as an individual unit. A favorable structure is promoted by the presence of lime, colloids, and organic material that form gluey films which help the soil particles to stick together. On the other hand, a good soil structure may be destroyed by improper treatment.

Organic components The organisms and partially decomposed organic matter

FIG. 18.3 Individual particles in a soil with a structure may be arranged in clumps, thus affecting the pore space.

make the soil complex essentially different from raw regolith. Dead organic matter derived from plant and animal tissues provides the major food for bacteria, fungi, and protozoa. These soil microorganisms, which may constitute so large a part as to total 1,000 lb per acre, perform many useful functions: they rot organic matter; they promote good soil structure; they make nitrogen available to the plants; and they produce antibiotics that promote the quality and health of plants.

The organic fraction of the soil is constantly being used by the plants, but under natural conditions a fresh supply of raw organic matter is added each year to the soil. Partially decomposed plant remains are called humus. In the natural course of soil variation from place to place some soils have relatively small amounts of humus and others are richly supplied. Some, such as peat soils, are made up largely of slightly decomposed organic matter which has not yet reached the condition of humus.

The part played by the humus and the living microorganic population within the soil in maintaining soil quality includes the following: (*a*) the organic material, when dissolved, directly supplies food for plants, including nitrogen and some quantities of the essential mineral elements, such as calcium, magnesium, and phosphorus; (*b*) the dead organic tissues are the major food source for the living microorganisms of the soil, which in turn affect the health and quality of the higher forms of organic life supported by the soil; (*c*) the process of organic decomposition yields complex organic acids which contribute to further weathering of mineral matter; (*d*) the humus has a high water-holding capacity, which helps the soil retain a supply of water for the soil solution and at the same time retards the leaching of dissolved minerals until the plants can use them; (*e*) the humus promotes the development of a structure favorable to water and air circulation, plant cultivation, and root development.

Nitrogen is essential to plant growth and protein production. The supply in the air is not directly available to plants, but is transformed, largely through the work of microorganisms, into the soluble form of nitrates which the plants can use.

The activity of the higher forms of life, such as many kinds of insects and, especially, earthworms, is extremely favorable for soils. Insects are responsible for a considerable portion of the processing of plant residue into humus; together with worms they affect the porosity of soil with their burrows and galleries; and they do extensive transporting and overturning of the soil. The several million earthworms which may inhabit an acre of soil can bring as much as 20 tons of material to the surface in a year. This is an important aid in the vertical mixing of the soil materials.

Water and air relationships Although the proportions vary from soil to soil, perhaps 50 per cent of the volume of an average, good-quality surface soil consists of inorganic particles, organic materials, and living organisms; water and air circulating within the pore spaces make up the remainder of the complex. Water and the gases of the air take part in the inorganic and organic chemical reactions that occur in the soil, and hence are just as much integral constituents of soil as the solids. Although plants derive their food from the soil solutions, only a few types of plants are able to thrive in soils in which the pore space is always filled with water; most of them require soils containing both air and water.

Forms of occurrence of water The water

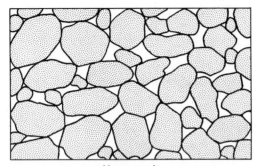

Hygroscopic

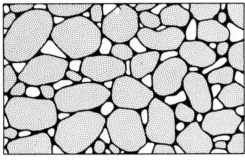

Capillary

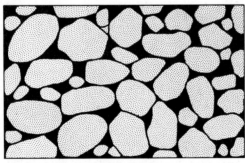

Gravitational

FIG. 18.4 Forms of soil water. Stippled areas indicate individual soil particles or structural units; blackened margins, water; and white areas, air spaces.

in the soil is supplied by the atmosphere. Even in regions that are nearly rainless, there is a molecular film of water on the surfaces of the soil particles that is called hygroscopic water (Fig. 18.4). It adheres firmly, does not move from one place to another, and is very resistant to both evaporation and the absorbing power of plant roots.

Soil particles that are moistened more frequently have thicker films of water, called capillary water (Fig. 18.4). This water, which also tends to be held upon the soil particles by surface tension, is absorbed by the soil colloids, causing them to swell and giving them their jellylike consistency. The capillary film does not fill the pore spaces, thus allowing the soil air to circulate. Capillary water, with its dissolved materials, is readily absorbed by plant roots.

When the supply of capillary water is abundant, it moves slowly downward under the pull of gravity. When the supply is diminished by plant use or direct evaporation, it may move horizontally, or even creep upward, under the pull of its own surface tension. In fine-textured soil, water may move in this fashion with relative ease, although in periods of extreme drought it may not do so fast enough to furnish plants with a sufficient water supply. In soils of coarse texture, both the usual supply and the movement of capillary water are limited.

Immediately following a rain the pore spaces of a soil may be filled with water displacing the air. In this condition there is water in excess of that which can be held to the soil particles by surface tension, and the surplus will move downward to the saturated zone of ground water. This is called free or gravitational water.

Variations in soil-water supply   Other things being equal, the regional variations in the supply of soil water depend directly upon the ratio of precipitation to evapotranspiration. Where precipitation is relatively high in proportion to evapotranspiration, there will be more gravitational water and hence more leaching. Less gravitational water may be expected where precipitation is low and evapotranspiration is high. There may be other complicating factors, however, such as the intensity of precipitation, or the water-retention ability of the ground cover. Nevertheless, in general, the humid areas of the earth are regions of net downward water movement.

In sites where the ground-water table coincides with the land surface, or in localities where there is an impervious layer in the subsoil, there may be a more or less permanent supply of gravitational water near the surface. This creates a waterlogged or swampy soil in which most cultivated plants will not grow. Where free drainage conditions exist, the gravitational water continues downward, quickly in soils of coarse texture or open structure and slowly in those fine and compact. In arid regions gravitational water may move downward only for a few feet, carrying with it dissolved salts, and the water may then be lost through evapotranspiration. In this way lime and other salts may accumulate in definite horizons of dry-land soils, while in humid-land soils they are leached out and carried away in the underdrainage.

Soil color Because the soil color is significant as an indicator of physical or chemical conditions, many soils have color terms as parts of their names. Among the commonest colors found in soil horizons are shades of red, brown, and yellow caused by the different forms, degrees of hydration, and concentrations of the oxides of iron and aluminum usually forming a considerable proportion of the inorganic fraction of soils. Black and dark-brown colors in soils usually, but not always, denote considerable organic content. Gray layers in an otherwise dark soil indicate poor drainage and waterlogging. While in some humid regions a whitish color may show a lack of the iron oxides and organic matter, the same color in arid regions may denote a harmful concentration of soluble salts. In many soils two or more color-forming ingredients are present, giving rise to intermediate colors, such as yellowish-brown and grayish-brown. It is commonly assumed—with good reason—that the darker soils are more productive than the light-colored ones (red to white).

Soil profile It was previously noted that soils are characterized by an internal vertical arrangement of layers, or horizons, with different thicknesses and different chemical and physical properties. These are designated as A, B, and C horizons, reading from the top down. The thicknesses of the horizons vary greatly, so that in some types of soil the horizons are thin and in others so thick and irregular that, for purposes of better description, each horizon is further subdivided as A_1, A_2, A_3, etc. (Fig. 18.5).

The horizons within a profile are distinguished from one another in texture, structure, and so on. In the A horizon organic life and debris is most abundant, but some soils have only a thin surface layer of the organic material. In humid regions the A horizon is characterized generally by leaching and eluviation and is left poorer in soluble substances and coarser in texture as a result. The B horizon may be, in contrast, one of illuviation and also a zone of nutrient enrichment. In it may be deposited some of the materials carried in solution from the layer above. The C horizon is the little-changed parent material from which the solid fraction of the soil derived.

Pan layers One of the commoner and less desirable features of a soil profile is that known as a pan layer. This is a dense, im-

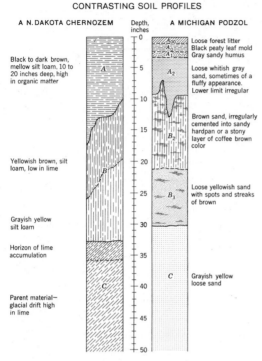

FIG. 18.5 The characteristic elements within the profiles of two different soils.

penetrable zone that interferes with root penetration and water movement and is unfavorable from the point of view of soil use and management. Pan layers develop as a result of a variety of factors, but the usual causes are excessive gravitational water in humid regions and precipitation of carbonates

in dry regions, both of which result in a strongly illuviated or even cemented horizon. There are many kinds of pan layers grouped into several general types; only the most important can be mentioned here: [3]

1. Claypan is a compact layer of uncemented clay resulting either from a high concentration of clay in the original subsoil or from illuviation. Claypans are relatively widespread, occurring in very smooth or flat lands of arid regions and of the humid middle latitudes. Because the nutrients in claypans do not differ much from those of the soils in which the claypans occur, the aspects which limit crop productivity are mostly poor permeability and other unfavorable physical properties.

2. Hardpan is a layer of chemical cementation, the commonest kind being the iron oxide crust, or laterite, which occurs widely in humid tropical soils in a variety of physical forms. Other hardpans, which are not so widespread as those in the tropics, occur in humid areas of the middle and high latitudes and also in several warmer regions. The latter, sometimes called *caliche,* are the result of calcareous cementation. Generally, hardpans are unfavorable to plant growth, sometimes because of their relatively low nutrient qualities, but primarily because their density prevents root and water penetration.

SOIL CLASSES AND REGIONS

SOIL CLASSIFICATION

As the foregoing discussion of the components of soils and the factors involved in their development has indicated, a soil is similar to a living organism: some of its characteristics are, in a sense, hereditary, such as

those derived from its inorganic ancestry (parent material), while others have developed more as a result of environmental factors. Although the soil-forming controls of climate and organisms (especially vegetation)

[3] Eric Winters and Roy W. Simonson, "The Subsoil," *Advances in Agronomy,* vol. 3, 1951, pp. 31–45.

generally tend to produce dominant soil characteristics, the numbers of different combinations of important qualities that can occur is very large. Consequently, there are a great many kinds of soils, and in order to consider how they vary from place to place it is necessary to classify them. Fortunately, the soil scientist has devised a system that may be used to study their geography, or their systematic variation over the earth.

The basic unit in the classification is the soil *series*. Each series includes all soil bodies that have closely similar horizons and profiles developed from similar parent material.[4] Several soil series may differ in detail but may yet have the same number and arrangements of horizons in their profile. Such a collection of related soil series is called a great soil group. There are less than 100 great soil groups, and each may be assigned to one of three soil orders, the highest category in soil classification.

The three orders are *zonal, intrazonal,* and *azonal.* Zonal soils include all those soils that have well-developed and mature profile characteristics largely resulting from the dominance of climate and vegetation among the soil-forming controls. Intrazonal soils also have clearly developed profiles, but unlike those of zonal soils their profiles reflect the dominance of some other more localized soil-forming factor, such as poor drainage or a particular parent material. Azonal soils, such as are found in dune sand or recent alluvium, do not have much profile development. Figure 18.6 illustrates for portions of the United States how the various categories in the classification system can be mapped.

[4] There are hundreds of soil series, and each can be further subdivided into types, usually on the basis of surface textural differences, and the types into phases, on the basis of some quality significant in their utilization.

REGIONALIZATION OF SOILS

In order to study the general pattern of soil variation over the earth, it is desirable to recognize regional soil associations that show primarily the broad effects of the major soil-forming controls. Some of these controls vary over the earth in a relatively systematic fashion, such as climate and vegetation, but others do not, such as parent material and land form. Consequently, the characteristics of the zonal soils are used to describe the major soil regions. It is to be expected that azonal and intrazonal soils may commonly occur within such regions, and to the degree they do, the broad generalizations are less applicable than one would wish.

Basic categories   The many great soil groups of the zonal order have here been sorted into eight general categories to which have been added the categories of alluvial soils (azonal), because alluvial areas are significant regions of human use, and the mountain soils, because mountainous areas show tremendous internal variety in soils, as in climate. The following outline shows the 10 basic categories:

1. Soils of the humid lands
   a. Latosolic soils
   b. Podzolic-latosolic soils
   c. Podzolic soils
   d. Podzol soils
   e. Tundra soils
2. Soils of the subhumid lands
   a. Chernozemic soils
   b. Chernozemic-desertic soils
   c. Desertic soils
3. Other soils
   a. Alluvial soils
   b. Complex soils of areas of high local relief

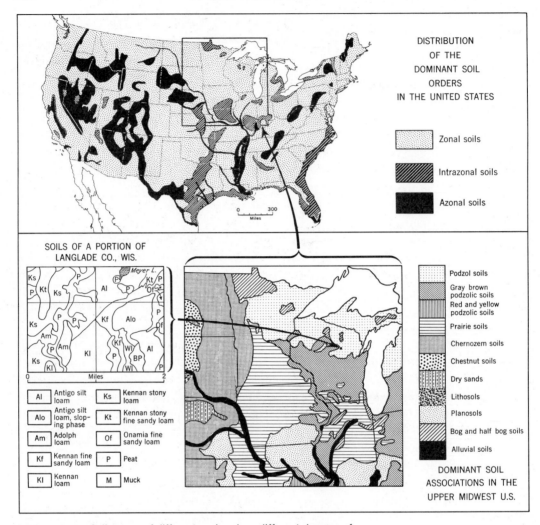

FIG. 18.6 Soils maps of different scales show different degrees of detail in the classification of soils. The lower left-hand map shows the soil series (identified with names such as "Antigo") and some of their types and phases. The right-hand map shows the great soil groups; the top map shows the soil orders. Note the area covered on one map in relation to the scale on the adjacent map. *(Generalized from maps of the U.S. Department of Agriculture Wisconsin Soil Survey.)*

The eight classes of zonal soils are shown on a hypothetical continent in Fig. 18.7 in order to clarify their typical positions and arrangements. Similarly, Fig. 18.7 is intended to show in a highly schematic manner the relationship between climate (with its commonly associated vegetative cover) and these broad regional soil categories. The diagram represents a land mass extending northward from the equator to the high latitudes and grading from a humid east to an arid west.

Differences between humid and dry land soils Fundamental differences exist between zonal soils found in humid lands

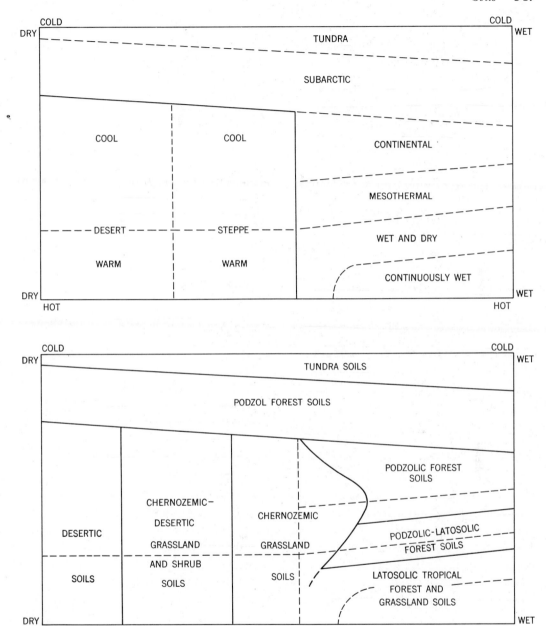

FIG. 18.7 Highly generalized relationship between major climatic zones and broad descriptive soil categories.

and those found in dry lands. The soils of humid lands have generally developed under natural vegetations of forest or woodland in areas of generous precipitation. In such regions organic matter is incorporated only slowly and there is a net downward movement of soil water. Therefore, the mature soils of humid regions as a whole are much leached and relatively infertile, prevailingly light-colored, usually acid, and characterized by a comparatively low content of organic matter. From a fertility standpoint they tend to support bulky plant life that has a high content of carbohydrates in comparison with the protein and mineral content.

The soil-forming processes and the profiles that result in warm humid regions are notably different from those in cool humid regions. The dominant factors affecting the development of soils in the humid tropical and subtropical regions are abundant precipitation and warm temperatures, which combine to produce a latosol.[5] In these soils the basic soil minerals and even silica are dissolved and leached away, leaving a concentration of reddish iron and aluminum oxides in both the A and B horizons. In the higher latitudes, on the contrary, the dominant factors are abundant moisture associated with cool temperatures, which combine to produce a podzol. In podzols iron and aluminum are removed from the A horizon and deposited in the B horizon. Silica, left behind in the A, forms a relatively light gray horizon beneath a dark surface layer of humus and above the brown B horizon. Intermediate between these lower and higher latitudinal areas the soils show some of the effects of both the latosolic and podzolic processes.

Soils of the drier lands are not greatly leached, because of the lack of water, and consequently have a considerable, and in some places excessive, content of soluble alkaline compounds. Calcium and magnes-

ium may be plentiful in these soils, and they are likely to have a neutral or basic reaction. Where there is enough moisture, they are likely to support a less woody, grassy vegetation, with a high mineral and protein ratio in proportion to the carbohydrates. Because of the high evaporation characteristic of these areas, an actual horizon of lime concentration often develops. Although there are some significant differences between the soils of the warm dry regions and those of the cool dry regions, these differences are not so marked as are those between the soils of the very arid or desert regions and the subhumid margins of the dry regions. The typical desertic soil of the very dry region is light-colored, high in saline or alkaline minerals, and low in organic matter, while the chernozemic soil of the barely subhumid region is black or dark brown in color, neutral or moderately alkaline, and high in organic content.

The world pattern of soil distribution is shown in a generalized way on Plate 6. Several circumstances act to exclude detailed charting on a map such as this, including the following: (a) There is no abrupt change from one soil category to another, as there usually is not from one climatic type to another, but rather there tends to be a gradual transition. (b) The small scale of the map necessitates drawing only a general picture of the soil variations, in spite of the fact that the details of soil distribution are highly complex. (c) Large areas of some of the continents, especially in the lower latitudes, are not completely surveyed. (d) The categories are made up largely of great soil groups in the zonal order, but in many areas intrazonal and azonal soils abound and are intimately linked with the zonal soils.

[5] The term latosol is preferred by the soil scientist to the term laterite, which is now more often reserved for certain extreme clayey concentrations rich in iron and aluminum oxides that are commonly associated with latosols.

SOILS OF THE HUMID LANDS

Podzol and tundra soils The typical zonal soils of the higher-latitude regions that have humid climates are the podzol and tundra soils. Podzols occur in areas covered largely by forest vegetation, while tundra soils lie in the more poleward treeless areas. Tundra soils are generally associated closely with areas of tundra climate, while podzols are found mostly in the cool-summer micro-thermal and subarctic climatic regions. Like the associated climatic areas, these soil categories are essentially confined to the Northern Hemisphere.

The mature podzol develops under a needle-leaf or mixed broadleaf–needle-leaf forest. The relatively low temperatures, combined with the substantial forest litter, retard bacterial action. The spongy, often soggy, dark layer of raw humus, or half-decomposed organic remains, that accumulates becomes highly acid as the result of fermentation, similarly affecting the downward-moving soil solutions. The strong acidity is unfavorable to earthworms and other small, burrowing, soil-mixing organisms. Partly for this reason there tends to be a comparatively sharp separation between the layer of raw surface humus and the horizon beneath it (Fig. 18.8). Moreover, the strongly acid solutions remove much of the iron and aluminum from the A horizon, making it appear as if it had been bleached to a grayish-white color. Consequently, beneath the layer of raw humus, the A horizon is strongly leached and through eluviation has lost most of its clay and finer constituents. It is, therefore, generally infertile and nearly structureless (Fig. 18.8). The B horizon is strongly illuviated, typically brown, and may contain a pan layer. In large sections

of Europe and North America, the C horizon is composed of sandy glacial drift.

Unimproved podzols are poor soils for most farm crops. As a consequence of cultivation and cropping, the supply of organic matter is soon lost, and the grayish surface soil requires lime, fertilizer, and good management to keep it productive. Although some food plants for man can be grown on typical podzols, much of their nutrient productivity for humans must be obtained by way of animals that are better able to subsist on the

FIG. 18.8 Profile of a podzol soil in Ontario. Note the typical heavy leaching of the lower A horizon and the strongly illuviated B horizon. *(G. A. Hills, Ontario Department of Lands and Forests.)*

FIG. 18.9 Profile of a podzolic forest soil. Compare this with Fig. 18.8. Note that in this gray-brown podzolic soil the organic matter is better mixed and the effect of bleaching in the A horizon is not so marked. *(G. A. Hills, Ontario Department of Lands and Forests.)*

vegetative production of these soils. Good yields of some grasses, potatoes, oats, rye, and numerous vegetables are obtained from finer-textured podzols after lime and fertilizers are applied.

In the treeless region of the tundra soil profiles show evidence of excessive moisture, because of the low rate of surface evaporation in the cold climate and the permanently frozen subsoil. A brown peaty surface layer is commonly underlain by a grayish horizon that is characteristically plastic or even fluid. A large part of the tundra is poorly drained

and consists of bog and hummocky marsh-land, making the soils similar in some respects to the glacial marsh and bog soils found in middle latitudes, many of which are now drained and cultivated. Large areas of the tundra cannot be drained, however, and thus are unsuited to tillage, supporting but a sparse natural vegetation useful only as natural pasture.

Podzolic soils The group of podzolic soils is characteristically found in those regions of the world that have broadleaf deciduous forests and humid microthermal climates. Thus they usually lie equatorward of the true podzols. As in the podzols, there is a dark surface layer of organic material 1 to 3 in. deep in the virgin podzolic soil, but because the warmer temperatures permit more bacterial action, this layer is neither so matted and soggy nor so acid as that of the podzols. Moreover, the organic material derived from a broadleaf forest contains more lime, potash, and other basic elements than does that from a needle-leaf forest, making these soils more fertile. The A horizon of the podzolic forest soil is leached but is neither so impoverished nor does it appear so bleached as in the podzol soil (Fig. 18.9). It generally is grayish-brown because of the presence of a brown hydroxide of iron and some organic matter. The quantity of organic material decreases downward, and the B horizon is commonly a lighter yellowish-brown and denser than the A horizon because the B horizon has been illuviated. As in the podzols, the C horizon is the little-changed parent material of the soil.

The podzolic forest soils generally have better structures than other forest-land soils, keep their structures better under cultivation, and respond more readily to the application of lime and organic fertilizers. The humus is better distributed in the upper soil horizons than in the podzols, because earthworms and other soil organisms thrive under the less acid conditions.

Podzolic soils occur in some of the intensively cultivated agricultural lands of the world, such as the northeastern United States, northwestern Europe, and several other regions of smaller size. These are areas of great agricultural diversity, and one of the more distinctive characteristics of the podzolic soils is their suitability for a wide variety of crops: hay and pasture, small grains and corn, vegetables, root crops, and many others.

Soils associated with podzol and podzolic soils In the areas of podzol and podzolic soils are numerous other soils that are not zonal. Some are azonal soils such as fertile river alluvium or more infertile sands and gravels, the latter resulting from accumulations such as sandy glacial outwash or from the abandoned shore deposits of temporary glacial lakes. Even more widespread are intrazonal soils resulting from poor drainage, such as the soils formed in the depressions of glaciated plains or in other marshy or boggy places.

The poorly drained soils (bog soils) are high in organic matter derived from the remains of grasses, sedges, and other marsh plants. Where underlain by clays and loams, these soils may be made productive with artificial drainage. Other poorly drained intrazonal soils (planosols) develop on extensive flat or gently sloping uplands (Fig. 18.6). Here poor drainage causes the formation of an eluviated and acid A horizon underlain by a dense pan layer.

There are also many soils with immature or imperfectly developed profiles found in areas subject to podzolic processes, especially in glaciated areas. Recent alluvial deposits and ice-scoured and stream-eroded slopes comprise large total areas of soils with abnormal or immature podzolic profiles. In the glaciated regions of North America and northern Europe there are also considerable areas of rocky ground containing what is called a lithosol, a stony, azonal soil.

Latosolic soils Not as much is known about the character and distribution of the various soils of the tropical areas as about the soils of the middle latitudes. It is apparent that the vegetative cover has more internal variety; the soils also show great variety, ranging from darker grassland soils to forest-land soils showing latosolic development.

The term latosol is applied to those soils in which high temperatures and abundant precipitation are the dominant soil-forming controls. Weathering commonly extends to considerable depths, and the chemical activity is intense. This sometimes so modifies the parent materials that there may be little similarity between the chemical nature of the soil and that of the inorganic mass within which it has formed (Fig. 18.10). The profiles are unusually deep, sometimes extending downward more than 10 ft, and the horizons are poorly differentiated. The soils are low in silica, have a relatively high clay content, and are high in the oxides of iron and aluminum, making most of them reddish or yellowish. In some there has developed a material called laterite, a claylike material especially rich in the oxides of iron and aluminum that develops into hardpans or crusts. Being highly leached, latosols are generally infertile, and they are not usually capable of sustained cropping without heavy fertilization. Many, however, are granular and very porous and are, therefore, capable of being tilled immediately after heavy rains;

FIG. 18.10 Profile of yellowish red latosol formed from a coarse-grained metamorphic bedrock parent material (gneiss) northwest of Rio de Janeiro, Brazil. Latosol profiles are typically deep and commonly do not have as much horizon differentiation as podzols. There is some darkening of the thick A horizon by organic matter. Plant roots extend to depths below 5 ft in this soil.
(Roy W. Simonson, U.S. Soil Conservation Service.)

some are highly resistant to erosion but subject to drought.

At first glance it seems remarkable that the generally infertile latosols should be able to support such abundant natural vegetation as tropical rainforest and yet be so unproductive of other kinds of plants. This no doubt results from the close interrelation between the natural forest vegetation and the soil. Woody vegetation is mostly carbohydrate (cellulose) and the deep roots of the trees bring to the surface at least small amounts of mineral nutrient elements from underlying sources. When the portion above ground dies and decays, some of these elements are returned to the surface soils, thus providing a small continuous supply so long as the forest exists. When this cyclic movement of mineral nutrients is interrupted by clearing and cultivation, the nutrients are quickly depleted.

Latosols are not well suited to shallow-rooted protein crops that draw heavily on soil fertility in the surface layers. They support crops that utilize the intense tropical sunlight and abundant rains for the production and storage of cellulose, starches, sugars, fats, and other carbohydrates. Those tropical latosolic soils that support grass are commonly more deeply weathered and less fertile than the corresponding middle-latitude soils. Like many other tropical soils they are likely to be reddish.

There are many intrazonal and azonal soils included in the tropical areas. For example, there are those intrazonal soils resulting from poor drainage and those with an unusually limy parent material. In the azonal category belong the thin, stony, immature soils of steep slopes, the porous sands without profile development, the recent deposits of volcanic ash, and, especially, the recent deposits of floodplains and deltas. The rate of alluvial accumulation is often too rapid to permit the development of mature profile characteristics, yet in many instances tropical alluvial soils are, where adequately drained, more productive agriculturally than the more mature latosols with which they are associated.

Podzolic-latosolic soils Even though the podzolic-latosolic soils are the dominant zonal soils in only a few general areas (Plate 6), they do occur in areas of considerable agricultural importance, such as the southeastern United States and China. As a result of latosolic processes the upper horizons are composed of considerably weathered, brownish clays and loams, while on the other hand, as a result of podzolic processes the thin upper horizon of moderate organic content is underlain by a leached zone above the thick, acid, latosolic B horizon of red or yellow material.

The fertility rating of these soils is not high, but with fertilization and careful management they are productive. Under cultivation the colors of the red and yellow subsoils usually predominate, because cropping quickly uses the small reserve of organic matter, and tillage tends to intermingle the A and B horizons. Podzolic-latosolic soils are especially subject to the loss of the upper horizon through rapid erosion.

SOILS OF THE SUBHUMID LANDS

Chernozemic soils Previously it was pointed out that there is considerable correlation between the occurrence of humid climates and forests, on the one hand, and between subhumid climates and grasslands, on the other. It is not possible, however, to draw a clearly defined boundary line dividing the dry from the humid lands that will also coincide with a line separating forest and grasslands. Nevertheless, limited soil moisture and grass vegetation produces soils that are very different from those that develop under conditions of more soil moisture and forest vegetation.

In subhumid regions, where there is enough moisture to support luxuriant grass, the periodic growth and death of part of the root system introduces organic matter *into* the soil and hence results in a regular automatic incorporation of a large organic fraction at depths of several inches to three

or four feet. Because these chernozemic soils are less leached than any of the soils previously considered, they are correspondingly higher in available calcium, magnesium, and other soil bases and nutrient elements; thus they are more fertile than soils developed under more humid conditions. The horizon characteristics in the profiles of the soils of subhumid areas are not so sharp as in the soils of humid lands in the middle and higher latitudes.

The zonal soil known as prairie is found in the more humid margins of the chernozemic areas, occurring widely in the United States, Russia, and South America. This soil has formed in a sufficiently humid climate so that leaching has lowered the supply of available bases to the point where the soil reaction is neutral or even slightly acid. The upper horizons have a fine granular structure and are very dark brown. Both these qualities are derived from abundant and deep accumulations of organic matter originating in the thick-grass sod. The typical mature soil is found on rolling interfluves where the natural vegetation of prairie grasses was best established. Because of its quality and climatic location, prairie soil is among the most productive of soils. In the United States it developed mainly in regions where the parent material is older glacial drift along with considerable quantities of loess to add to its fertility. The rich Corn Belt chernozemic soils of central Illinois, Iowa, and Missouri are mostly prairie soils. On steep slopes, especially along the margins of streams, fingers of woodland originally projected into the grass prairies. On such sites podzolic soils developed.

The zonal soil known as chernozem (a Russian word meaning black earth), from which the general category is named, is particularly fertile. In the middle latitudes, it formed in association with shorter prairie and steppe grasses and under sufficiently low precipitation (about 20 in. in the United States) that an abundance of lime and alkaline minerals remains. In fact, in chernozems and the soils of drier regions, calcium carbonate accumulates in a definite zone; the drier the region the nearer to the surface the horizon of lime accumulation will be. The A horizon has a high organic content, is black or very dark brown (Fig. 18.11), and has a

FIG. 18.11   Profile of a chernozem formed from glacial till in South Dakota. The A horizon extends to a depth of a little over a foot, while the B horizon extends to a depth of nearly 2½ feet. The white spots in the B and C horizons are carbonate accumulations that commonly occur in dry-land soils. *(Roy W. Simonson, U.S. Soil Conservation Service.)*

granular, porous structure. Upon tillage it crumbles into a fine seedbed with a large capacity for retaining capillary water. Both organic and fertility reserves are high. In general there is no better soil than chernozem for grains and other extensive high-protein field crops that draw heavily upon soil fertility.

In regions of subhumid tropical grasslands there are also some dark-colored soils classed as chernozemic, but these contain less abundant organic matter because long-continued high temperatures hasten decomposition, even under subhumid conditions. Thus the tropical chernozemics are clayey, plastic, and less favorable for tillage. Some chernozemic soils, such as the black soils of central India, are derived from the weathering of basic igneous rocks; they owe their color and fertility to the unusual mineral content of the parent material.

Chernozemic-desertic soils   In a traverse from the less arid to the more arid sections of subhumid lands a change occurs in the character of the soils. The chernozemic-desertic soils of the drier sections are affected by the decreased precipitation in several ways. The soils have developed under a grass vegetation less luxuriant and deep-rooted than that in the chernozemic zone, and the grass cover provides a less abundant supply of organic material. The humus is intermingled with a powdery surface soil that lies above a subsoil of a somewhat coarse and lumpy structure. The slight precipitation and the high rate of evaporation of soil moisture also results in a horizon of accumulated lime or other alkaline substances relatively near the surface (1 to 2 ft), and in some localities the lime is so abundant that it forms a pan layer in the soil. Brown or reddish-brown is the prevailing color.

In general, chernozemic-desertic soils are easily tilled, and are well adapted to cultivation, if irrigated. The fact that these soils are predominantly used for livestock grazing rather than cultivation is caused by the deficiency of precipitation rather than by the deficiencies of the soils.

Desertic soils Because they develop under sparse vegetation, usually widely spaced shrubs, desertic soils are low in organic content, making the lighter colors predominate, with the reds, browns, yellows, and grays of weathered rock minerals widely exposed (Fig. 18.12). The characteristic colors are occasionally lightened by the accumulation of whitish alkaline substances near or upon the soil surface. Although desertic soils are characteristically low in nitrogen, they are likely to contain considerable supplies of other nutrient elements.

It is to be expected that the larger parts of the great deserts contain no mature soils. Instead, there are patches of bare rock, expanses of desert gravels covered with the pebbles remaining after deflation, tracts of dune sand, and areas of immature soil resulting from the recent and rapid growth of alluvial fans. Alluvial soils are the most widely cultivated in arid lands partly because their situations allow them to be more easily irrigated. But parent materials in deserts often contain so many decomposed rock fragments that they may be well supplied with soluble minerals, and if abundant water is available for irrigation they may be made agriculturally productive.

MOUNTAIN AND ALLUVIAL SOILS

In the discussion of the plan of classifying and regionalizing the diversity of the earth's soil cover, two basically nonzonal categories were included: alluvial soils and the soils of areas of high local relief. Little characterization can be applied to the soils of high-local-relief areas because of the complexities introduced by variations in slope and climate which in turn induce great variety in vegetative cover. In any case, the soils of these areas are not widely used. From the point of view of human use alluvial soils are far more important.

As a class, alluvial soils probably support a larger proportion of the world's population than any other single kind of soil. However, it is difficult or impossible to generalize to any great extent about these azonal soils be-

FIG. 18.12 Profile of a desertic soil. A sierozem (near-desert soil) formed on alluvial deposits in Nevada. Although the regolith is deep, horizon differentiation is low. *(Roy W. Simonson, U.S. Soil Conservation Service.)*

cause the specific characteristics of an alluvial soil body are largely those typical of the regolith in the area where the specific alluvial parent material originated. Consequently, the textures may range from sands through silts to clays; the colors may range from the light hues of the desertic soils to the dark shades of the chernozemic soils; and the soils may be more or less rich in plant nutrients. However, all are generally free of stones and are easily cultivated.

Most of the great soil categories previously described also include alluvial soils associated with the mature zonal soils, and in many instances the alluvium constitutes the most prized lands. Not all alluvial soils are productive, however, because they may be too wet or too dry, they may occur where the growing season is too short, or they may be subjected to frequent flooding. In those Far Eastern areas where rice is grown in alluvial paddy lands, the alluvial soils are probably more generally utilized than elsewhere in the world. Most of Japan's productive land, for example, is alluvial but in units too small to be shown on the world map. Almost all of Egypt's dense agricultural population subsists on the production from alluvial soils. On the other hand, the tropical alluvial soils of some parts of central Africa are at present little used, but in this case one reason for not using the soils is that the lands are infested with the tsetse fly.

SOIL EROSION

Even though erosion is a normal process, it can be greatly accelerated when unnatural soil conditions are created by tilling and grazing the land. Erosion results in the loss of the finer fractions and the upper horizons of mature soils at a much faster rate than normal development processes can replace them, thus destroying the natural relationship among the soil components (fertility, texture and structure, organic content, water, and air). Because the application of ever-increasing amounts of bulk-producing, artificially derived chemicals to stimulate plant growth is a costly method of countering the effects of erosion, the most modern practice is to cultivate the land in ways that reduce the losses by erosion to a minimum.

Not all kinds of soil are equally subject to destructive erosion. Some soils, such as some latosols or eluviated sandy soils, might perhaps benefit by a faster removal of surface soil, thus exposing the less weathered minerals and less leached layers underneath. But these soils, because of their high porosity, are among those least subject to rapid erosion. On the other hand, some of the dark-colored soils that have considerable organic accumulations in the upper horizons, are highly subject to erosion, as are certain of the forest soils, such as many of those in the podzolic-latosolic category.

Causes and kinds of erosion   Soil erosion occurs primarily as a result of raindrop impact, washing by running water, and blowing winds. The principal means whereby tillage and grazing may accelerate the normal rate of erosion are the loosening of the soil by cultivation and the removal of the protective cover of vegetation. The rate at which a soil may be eroded depends upon the textural and structural conditions of the soil, the conditions of climate, particularly the number of intense rainstorms per year, and the degree of land slope. The extent to which soil erosion has progressed in the United States is shown in Fig. 18.13.

One of the most widespread and least noticed kinds of erosion on tilled land is the

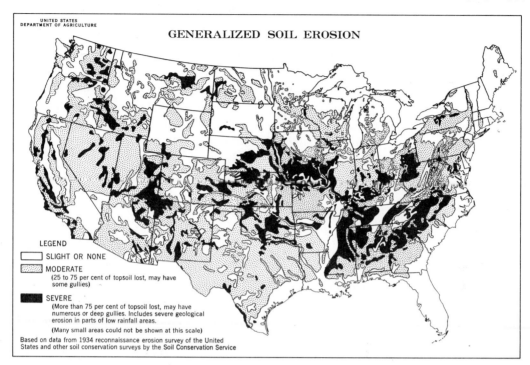

FIG. 18.13 Generalized distribution of the extent of soil erosion by wind and water in the United States. *(From a map by U.S. Soil Conservation Service.)*

sheet wash that occurs during rainstorms and results in the removal of a uniform thin fraction of the soil. This is particularly harmful because it removes the finer and more nutritionally useful of the soil particles first, some in solution and some in suspension, resulting in fertility erosion. In some kinds of soil, especially in compact clays and silts underlain by looser materials, gullying may become deep. This process, if left unchecked, can destroy both topsoil and subsoil beyond all hope of repair. The damage may spread from the eroded upland soil to the adjacent lowland soils, which can be ruined by being buried under accumulations of the coarser and less fertile alluvial products of the erosion.

In subhumid plains great damage may result from wind erosion on surfaces laid bare by plowing or by overgrazing of livestock. The powdery soil exposed on the bare surfaces may be removed to a depth of several inches by a single windstorm.

Conservation It certainly is not possible to stop losses by wind and water erosion entirely; these have gone on since the world began. However, it is possible to reduce the rate of destructive erosion brought about by careless human disturbances of the natural balance of the soil components. A program of planned soil conservation would include (1) the return to permanent forest or permanent grass of those lands in which erosion has progressed so far as to destroy the value of the land for tillage, and (2) the protection, through proper tillage and management, of those areas best suited for crop production so that they may continue to be productive. Among the recommended methods of protection are (*a*) the construction of dams or obstructions to erosion in gullies already formed; (*b*) the plowing and tilling of land in strips along contour levels so that furrows will be arranged at right angles to the land slope, thus reducing the rate of sheet wash; and (*c*) the adoption of cropping practices that provide the most nearly continuous protective vegetative cover. Above all, the consciousness of everyone must be awakened to the need for soil protection and the disastrous consequences to the world's rapidly increasing population that may arise from the needless waste of this fundamental source of nutrition.

SUGGESTED READING

Albrecht, W. A.: "Soil Fertility and Biotic Geography," *Geographical Review,* vol. 47, 1957, pp. 87–105.

Hole, F. D.: "Suggested Terminology for Describing Soils as Three-dimensional Bodies," *Proceedings of the Soil Science Society of America,* vol. 17, 1953, pp. 131–135.

Simonson, Roy W.: "Changing Place of Soils in Agricultural Production," *Scientific Monthly,* vol. 81, 1955, pp. 173–182.

Stallings, J. H.: *Soil Conservation,* Prentice-Hall, Inc., Englewood Cliffs, N. J., 1957.

U.S. Department of Agriculture: "Soils and Men," *Yearbook of Agriculture,* 1938.

U.S. Department of Agriculture: "Soil," *Yearbook of Agriculture,* 1957.

    Simonson, R. W., "What Soils Are," pp. 17–29.

    Russell, M. B., "Physical Properties," pp. 31–38.

    Richards, L. A., and S. J. Richards, "Soil Moisture," pp. 49–60.

    Allaway, W. H., "pH, Soil Acidity, and Plant Growth," pp. 67–79.

    Dean, L. A., "Plant Nutrition and Soil Fertility," pp. 81–85.

    Broadbent, F. E., "Organic Matter," pp. 151–157.

    Clark, F. E. "Living Organisms in the Soil," pp. 157–165.

Winters, E., and Roy W. Simonson; "The Subsoil," *Advances in Agronomy,* vol. 3, 1951, pp. 31–45.

CHAPTER 19

Mineral

resources

Minerals as resources In addition to the many phenomena at the surface of the earth that directly contribute to man's existence as a living organism, there occur, deeper in the shell of the earth, many substances that man has learned to use to his material advantage. These are those elements and their compounds, either inorganic or organic in origin, that are loosely classed as mineral resources, or more simply, minerals. They are employed in a variety of ways: as substances from which to fashion tools and other useful objects, as sources of energy, as materials for road building, and so on, almost without end. At man's present stage of devel-

opment the list of mineral resources is long, and it continues to grow each year at an increasing rate as he learns at an increasing rate to use these substances he finds in the earth.

To divide the mineral resources according to the use to which each is put would not be completely satisfactory, for many of them serve a variety of needs. Thus the entire class of minerals consists of three major categories only partly based on use: (*a*) those used primarily as *fuels,* i.e., as sources of energy, (*b*) those used primarily because they are *metallic,* and (*c*) nonmetallic minerals not used primarily as fuels.

Many minerals are relatively abundant but widely dispersed in the earth's crust and regolith, occurring in relatively small quantities in any one locality. To collect a mineral from this dispersed state is costly, and it is justified only when the specific value of the mineral is extraordinarily high. Consequently, man is usually interested only in those places of occurrence where the mineral content has somehow become sufficiently concentrated to form what is called a deposit. Thus the geography of mineral deposits, that is, the facts of their distribution and of related phenomena is an item of considerable concern.

Few people realize how rapidly the dependence of civilization upon mineral resources has grown in recent decades—how different the present is, in this respect, from even the recent past. Since the beginning of the twentieth century more minerals have been extracted from the earth's outer crust than in all previous history. Yet it may be asserted that the *known* supply is actually increasing. This apparent paradox lies in two facts: (*a*) As already suggested, a resource does not just exist, but in a very real sense is created by man. For example, coal and the radioactive minerals have existed much longer than man has; yet they became resources only when man learned to use them. (*b*) Man's scientific understanding and technical skill, like his capacity to utilize minerals, are increasing at an increasing rate. Consequently, he is both continually finding new supplies and able to use more efficiently those of which he now knows.

THE MINERAL FUELS

Mineral sources of energy   Of all the things that make life today different from life in the past, perhaps none is so significant as man's use of the large supplies of energy available to him in the solid earth. The power sources he has tapped, up to the present, are primarily coal, petroleum, and natural gas, and all three come from the solid earth. Of course, man uses many other sources of power, ranging from falling water to wood, but he depends primarily upon the mineral fuels. Although the time when solar and other forms of nuclear energy will supplant the mineral fuels seems to be coming steadily closer, the use of mineral fuels is still increasing and will, no doubt, for some time to come.

Through growth processes, some of the sun's energy is "built into" the tissues of all living plants and animals. Then, in the normal course of events, this energy is liberated after death as a consequence of decomposition processes. For example, heat is often liberated when oxygen combines chemically with decomposing substances. But if the complete decomposition of an organic material is prevented, it becomes a potential source of usable quantities of heat that can be obtained by inducing combustion later. The use of firewood is an example of the use of such a source of energy involving only a short delay. Coal, petroleum, and natural gas are sources of such energy that have been stored a long time. At certain times in the geologic past, conditions seem to have retarded decomposition of organic forms, and simultaneously to have allowed vast amounts of them to accumulate and be transformed into coal, petroleum, and gas.

The occurrence of deposits of these materials, called "fossil" fuels, required the interaction of a large number of physical phenomena, and as a result considerable parts of the earth are deficient in deposits of these substances, and other regions have large supplies of one or even all three.

COAL

Origin of coal Coal is sedimentary rock derived largely from the unoxidized remains of plant tissues. The carbon-bearing tissues were preserved from ordinary decomposition by their submergence in swamp waters and their subsequent burial and compaction by layers of clays, sands, and limes; and the burial ultimately made these beds of organic material members of a series of horizontal sedimentary rocks. From this sedimentary origin, two points of significance about coal beds and their coal may be inferred. First, the original attitude of swamp accumulations being nearly horizontal, as may be observed in modern swamps, many coal beds still are essentially horizontal, a condition that simplifies the problem of mining. Second, since individual swamps seldom have covered vast areas, single beds of coal are not of great extent.

In addition, some coal beds show evidence of diastrophic disturbance after their creation, and this commonly has involved a more complete metamorphism that has changed the ratios among the various constituents (carbon, gases, water, ash, etc.), a change that markedly affects their utility.

Although most coal beds are relatively small, the same is not necessarily true of coal fields, or areas of coal beds. In some areas conditions favorable to coal formation must have existed widely and for long periods. In these regions large and small swamps flourished, dried up, and their organic accumulations were buried by earthy sediments at the same time that other swamps were coming into existence nearby. If subsidence of an entire area took place, newer swamps may have formed above the remains of the older but separated from them by layers of inorganic sediments. In some coal fields the beds are widely distributed in area and in vertical sequence.

Since coal occurs among other rock layers, it is possible, by studying the general rock structure, to determine the probable extent of a coal field or region and, by means of test borings, to discover the number and relative thicknesses of the coal beds in its various parts. Thus geologists can approximate with fair accuracy the potential supply (reserve) in a given field, a given country, and even in the world.

Classes of coal Classes of coal differ greatly from region to region and sometimes even within the same field, and only four of the more significant will be mentioned here. All coal was initially similar to the first class, which is peat, the partially preserved, crumbled, and blackened organic remains that may be seen in present-day swamps and bogs. The other forms of coal represent successive stages in the transformation of peat that results from compression and the loss of water and gases (Fig. 19.1). Thus a second class, somewhat more compact than peat, is the crumbly brown coal called lignite. Further transformation—additional losses of volatile constituents and corresponding increases in the relative content of fixed carbon —produces a "soft" black class of coal called

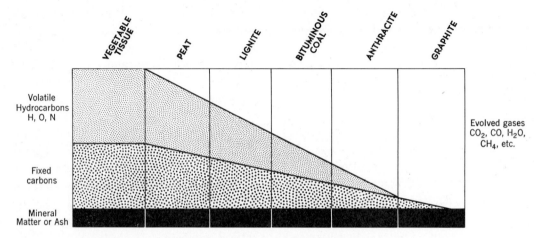

FIG. 19.1   Stages in the metamorphosis of vegetable material into coal of various types. *(After Newberry.)*

bituminous. There is an almost endless list of slightly different grades of bituminous coal, the most widely used class. Further compression still, often associated with warping and faulting, and sometimes heating produces the class of "hard" coal called anthracite, which is mostly carbon.

One of the most significant distinctions among the various bituminous coals is based upon suitability for the manufacture of coke to be used in the blast-furnace extraction of the metal iron from its ore, the only means of recovering iron in large quantities used at present. Coke for use in the blast furnace is mainly the hard carbon that remains after the volatile constituents have been driven off and is prepared by roasting bituminous coal in special ovens. But the metallurgical requirements of coke are so stringent that only a small proportion of the world's bituminous deposits can be used to produce it. Consequently, the areas where iron can be produced economically are seriously restricted.

Coal is mined in many ways, depending upon the structural and situational relation of the beds to the earth's surface to which

the coal must be brought. In some areas the coal seams (beds) occur so close to the surface that they may be mined in open pits after the removal of only a few feet of the covering earth or rock known as overburden (Fig. 19.2). In others the beds may be reached only by mine shafts of great depth. In some localities the seams have become easily accessible as a result of the exposure, by degradation, of outcrops of coal among the other rocks of valley walls (Fig. 19.3). In regions of more complicated rock structure, coal beds once horizontal may have been variously deformed, and therefore present different degrees of accessibility (Fig. 19.4).

COAL REGIONS OF THE WORLD

There is a vast amount of still-unmined coal in the world: present estimates of the total minable reserve, which are probably of the right order of magnitude, total several trillion tons, enough for many hundreds of years at the present rate of use. But the reserve is very unevenly distributed among the land areas (Fig. 19.5); and because coal is the principal source of power in manufactural

FIG. 19.2 Giant furrows turned by power shovels in the process of strip mining in southern Illinois. The 4-ft-thick bed of coal exposed in the bottom of the trench will be mined out before the next furrow is turned.

industry and in the production of electricity, as well as necessary for the smelting of iron, the location of these major deposits in relation to the world centers of heavy manufacture, present and future, is a matter of critical importance.

Three general features of its distribution are geographically significant: (*a*) almost all the known minable reserve lies in the Northern Hemisphere; (*b*) this reserve is about evenly divided between North America and Eurasia; and (*c*) more than four-fifths of the total is estimated to lie within the boundaries of only three nations: the United States (approximately two-fifths of the total), the

U.S.S.R. (approximately one-third), and Communist China (approximately one-tenth).[1] A considerable proportion of the rest of the Northern Hemisphere reserve (approximately one-eighth of the total) occurs in the several countries of western and central Europe. It should be noted that the continent of Europe, not including the U.S.S.R., ranks first in coal production, slightly ahead of both the United States and the U.S.S.R.

Thus the known coal reserves are relatively concentrated within a few national areas; but

[1] E. Willard Miller, "World Patterns and Trends in Energy Consumption," *Journal of Geography*, vol. 58, 1959, pp. 269–279.

FIG. 19.3　A stratum of bituminous coal out-cropping, with other horizontal sedimentary strata, in a road cut on a West Virginia hillside.

quite the opposite is true of usable deposits. There are many scattered over the earth that contain amounts significant to the local areas where they occur. For example, Japan, with only about 0.2 per cent of the world's reserve, extracts about 50 million tons annually to support an extensive development of heavy industry. At least 35 countries each produce a million or more tons of coal annually.

North America　North America is credited with the greatest of all coal reserves —an unmined store recently appraised at about 40 per cent of the total estimated supply of the world. The North American coals, moreover, include representatives of every class from high-grade anthracite to the lowest grades of lignite. The several fields are shown in Fig. 19.6. Certain general areas of the continent are without significant coal de-

FIG. 19.4　Several surficial and structural relationships of coal. (*a*) shows a stream-dissected hill-land area, such as in the western Pennsylvania fields; (*b*) a highly folded and faulted area, such as in the Pennsylvania anthracite area; (*c*) an area underlain by a gentle synclinal or basin structure, such as in southern Illinois; and (*d*) an area where erosion has removed some of the coal beds, the rest occurring on the flanks of the upland, such as on either side of the Pennine upland in England.

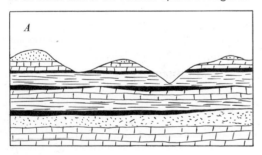

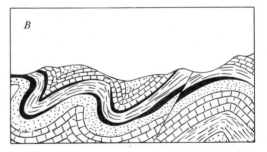

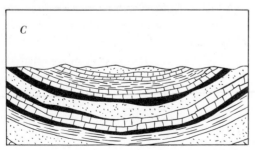

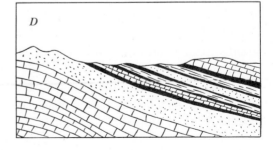

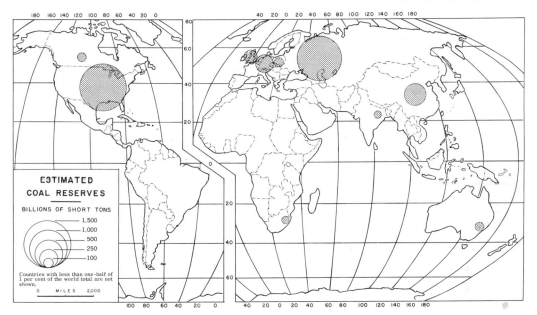

FIG. 19.5 General representation of the world distribution of estimated coal reserves. The sizes of the circles are in proportion to the reserves believed to lie within the boundaries of national areas. Countries possessing less than one-half of one per cent of the world total are not included.
(After Miller and others.)

posits, namely the ancient rocks of the Canadian Shield and the Appalachian Piedmont, the western sections of the cordilleran region, and the relatively recent sedimentary rocks of the Atlantic and Gulf Coastal margins. The two major producing areas are the Appalachian Province and the eastern region of the Interior Province.

The Appalachian Province Much the most important among the coal fields of the continent is that of the Appalachian hill region. It is comprised of two principal subdivisions: (*a*) a large section of little-folded rocks with numerous beds of bituminous coal that extends from northwestern Pennsylvania through Ohio, West Virginia, Kentucky, and Tennessee, into northwestern Alabama, and (*b*) a small, highly folded section containing anthracite in the Ridge and Valley region of northeastern Pennsylvania.

The bituminous section includes numerous workable beds of coal of good quality, some of which are of the character required for the manufacture of blast-furnace coke. The deposits are largely found within the limits of the dissected Appalachian hill country, and they are noted for the ease with which they are mined. The coal beds, traversed by innumerable deeply incised stream valleys, are often exposed along the valley walls (Fig. 19.4). The abundance, accessibility, and high quality of these bituminous coals give the Appalachian field first importance in America and perhaps in the world. More than three-fourths of the coal output of the continent is obtained from this field, including most of the coal used in the eastern and northeastern industrial districts, as well as most of the American export coal.

The anthracite occurs on the eastern

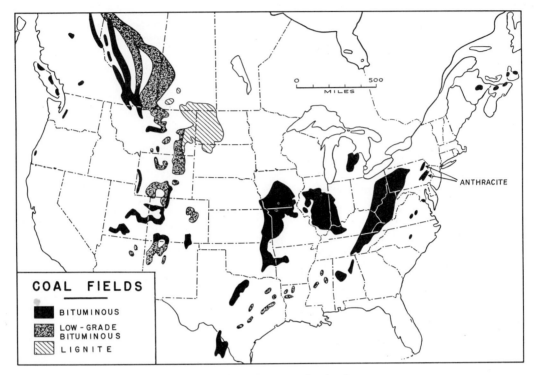

FIG. 19.6   The principal coal deposits of North America, showing the distribution of major classes of coals.

margins of the Appalachian hill region in an area that has been subjected to extreme folding, which means much greater cost and difficulty of mining. Anthracite mining has been steadily declining, and now provides less than 5 per cent of the nation's coal production.

The Interior Province Like the Appalachian bituminous section, the Interior Province is abundantly provided with coal deposits, and again the coal generally is bituminous, but not of coking quality. The several areas of the Province are known, respectively, as (*a*) the eastern region (Illinois, Indiana, and Kentucky), (*b*) the northern region (Michigan), (*c*) the western region (Iowa, Missouri, Kansas, Oklahoma, and Arkansas), and (*d*) the southwestern region (Texas). Of these, the eastern region is by far the greatest pro-

ducer. In the eastern and northern regions the rocks have broad synclinal (saucerlike) structures, and in the former, the coal beds of the middle portion are so deeply buried under younger rocks that they are difficult to reach. Therefore, mining is practiced mainly about the margins of the field.

Other areas The Rocky Mountain province is made up of many fields spread from southern Montana to New Mexico, and includes abundant deposits in Wyoming, Colorado, and Utah. Coal of all grades occurs, but most of it is bituminous quality.

The Great Plains province includes areas extending from Wyoming and the Dakotas into southern Alberta and Saskatchewan. In its eastern sections the coal is lignite, but in the western sections the coal is higher quality.

The Great Plains province ranks far below the eastern fields in production. Even the small fields in the Canadian Maritime Provinces produce more coal than the Canadian Great Plains province.

The Pacific Coast fields are made up of a few deposits, namely, those of Alaska, Vancouver Island, and the Puget Sound region. The Alaskan deposits have more future than present value.

Coal is not abundant in eastern Canada either. It is a matter of great concern to Canada that its most populous and industrially developed region, which lies between Lake Huron and the city of Quebec, is practically devoid of coal. The best and most used

deposits, including some coking coal, are found near Sydney, on the northern coast of Nova Scotia. These supply a local iron and steel industry.

Central and western Europe The area comprising central and western Europe contains numerous coal deposits that extend in a relatively narrow zone from Great Britain eastward across the Low Countries and Germany into Poland and Czechoslovakia (Fig. 19.7). As previously stated, central and western Europe ranks first in the world in coal production if the output of all its countries is totaled and compared with the outputs of other major coal-producing areas. In total coal reserves this area ranks third

FIG. 19.7   The major coal deposits of central and western Europe.

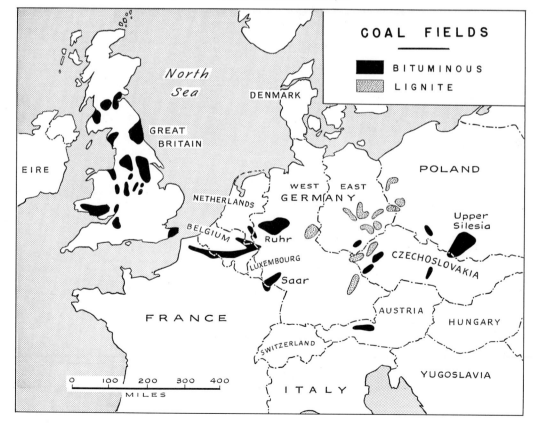

among the continents; but even though most of its supply is bituminous and thus generally high-grade, it is likely that the total European bituminous resource is little more than one-half as great as that available in North America. In addition, North America has nearly seventy-five times as much lower-grade coal.

The principal European coal deposits are so distributed that they fall within the boundaries of several European countries, the industrial advancement of which may be attributed in part to the availability of these sources of fuel. The leading nations in both production and proved reserves of good-quality coal are Germany, the United Kingdom, and Poland. Czechoslovakia, the Low Countries, France, and Spain are all second-rank producers, far below the first three named. An indication of the wide availability of coal in Europe is the fact that coal is produced in more than 20 countries. Yet only the United Kingdom and Germany have large deposits of the coking-quality coal required for the smelting of iron ore.

Great Britain   British coal fields occur in numerous regions in England, Scotland, and Wales, and only two parts of the island are more than a few miles removed from one or more of these fields, which contain mostly bituminous coal (Fig. 19.7). Associated with each of the major British coal fields is an industrial district; and some of the fields, especially those of south Wales, are close to the sea and well situated for the export of coal. Also, the quality of British coal is generally high. However, the remaining beds are becoming increasingly difficult to mine, greatly increasing the cost of production.

Continental fields   The coal fields of western continental Europe are numerous,

but none covers as much area as the greater of the fields in North America. The more important fields and most of the better grades of coal lie in an east-west belt through the center of the continent. The ancient crystalline rocks of Scandinavia and Finland to the north of that belt and the much disturbed rocks of the mountain systems and of the Mediterranean Sea Basin to the south of it include either no coal or only small and unimportant fields. The various fields include coals of many types, among them the low grades of coal and even peat which are much more used in continental Europe than in Great Britain or the United States.

The western end of this important and productive zone extends from northern France across central Belgium and into Germany, its most productive portion lying in the Ruhr River Valley, just east of the Rhine. This field is of particular importance because it has long been the center of the heavy iron and steel industries of Germany and because it contains a reserve of coking coal reputed to be larger than any other in continental Europe. Nearby is the coal field of the politically famous Saar region. The eastern end of the central European coal belt, the major deposits of which lie in East Germany and especially in Poland and adjacent portions of Czechoslovakia, is also highly productive.

The leading individual coal producers are West Germany in the western section and East Germany and Poland in the eastern section of this European area. Their combined output rivals those of the United States and the U.S.S.R.

The U.S.S.R.   The coal fields of Soviet Russia are numerous and widely distributed, but most of the large reserve of good-grade

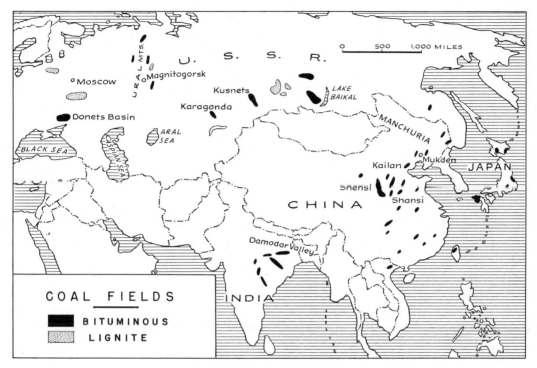

FIG. 19.8   The major coal deposits of the U.S.S.R., eastern and southern Asia.

coal is in Siberia (Fig. 19.8). The total production is approximately equal to that of the United States.

Neither of the great industrial regions in and about Moscow and Leningrad is adjacent to local supplies of good coal, although there is lignite near Leningrad, and the Moscow region includes a large area with coals of subbituminous and lignite grades. Rather, the Donets River Basin in southern European Russia is first in industrial importance: it supplies the heavy industry of the southern region, and some is shipped to the Moscow industrial center. This greatly folded area yields some anthracite and much bituminous coal, being valued especially for its coking coal, which is not generally abundant in the U.S.S.R.

The Kuznetsk Basin of southern central Siberia is second in importance at present. It is the source of fuel for a growing industrial district, and some of its coal (supplemented from Karaganda) moves more than 1,400 miles west to the iron and steel center of Magnitogorsk in the southern Ural Mountain region. The Kuznetsk region is estimated to be tremendously rich in high-quality reserves; indeed, it is thought to be second only to the Appalachian coal fields in the United States. The Karaganda field, located midway between the Kuznetsk and Ural areas, is third in importance.

There are smaller coal fields on the flanks of the Ural Mountains, in the region west of Lake Baikal, and far to the east in Siberia. In the isolated forest areas of northern Siberia

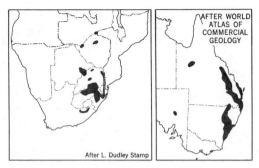

FIG. 19.9 The principal coal fields of southern Africa and Australia.

are extensive coal deposits whose boundaries and reserves are imperfectly known.

Eastern and southern Asia   In eastern and southern Asia there are widely distributed deposits of coal, with Communist China seeming to have by far the greatest amount, although estimates are perhaps based upon insufficient evidence (Fig. 19.8). Coal is found in many parts of China, but the greatest deposits are in north China and Manchuria. The provinces of Shansi and Shensi in north China seem to have the largest reserves of good quality. The coal fields of Manchuria support a considerable industrial development and are especially valuable because they contain good coking coal. As Communist China continues to grow industrially, coal production will also rise. Even currently, China is no doubt the fifth largest producer after the United States, the U.S.S.R., Germany, and Great Britain.

Other Asiatic countries that have important coal supplies are India and Japan. Those of India, located in the northeastern part of the Deccan Plateau about 150 miles inland west of Calcutta, are now being much used in the iron and steel industries of the same region. The reserve of coal is large, but the supply of coking coal is limited. Unfortunately for industrial Japan, the reserve of coal in that country is relatively small and scattered, and many of the beds are badly faulted. The most productive field is that in northern Kyushu.

South America, Africa, and Australia Hardly 3 per cent of the world's coal reserves is contained in South America, Africa, and Australia together. This small amount is unevenly distributed with Africa and Australia having the most and being about equally endowed; South America has very little.

The major field in Australia is near the east coast of New South Wales, a principal center of population (Fig. 19.9). Because of its abundance, good quality, and accessibility, Australian coal is the leading reserve in the Southern Hemisphere, but the total reserve is not comparable with that of the larger fields of the Northern Hemisphere.

The African coal reserve is not quite so large as that of Australia, but the present production meets the requirements of South Africa. The deposits are located in the southeastern part of the continent, mostly in the Union of South Africa (Fig. 19.9).

South America has the misfortune to be, of all the continents, least well endowed with coal. But there are a few small bituminous deposits in the Andes of Colombia and Peru and on the coast of central Chile, and there is some low-grade coal in southern Brazil.

PETROLEUM AND NATURAL GAS

The mineral fuels petroleum and natural gas, though relatively recent additions to man's energy resources, are important ones. Petroleum is a liquid that can be transported easily, in or out of pipes; the energy available from it is greater than that available from coal; and a large variety of lubricants and other useful compounds is available from it as well. Just the cleanliness, compactness, and convenience of petroleum as a fuel and the fact that new machines are continually being devised for using the products derived from it have made petroleum a critical item in the resource inventories of modern nations. Natural gas, a lighter hydrocarbon usually associated with petroleum, is fast becoming a major source of energy. It, too, is easily transported in pipes.

Structural associations Petroleum, natural gas, and asphalt, another substance related to petroleum, are presumably of organic origin, but they have been so long included in the rocks they are found in that no trace of any organic antecedents is clearly discernible. These hydrocarbons, which probably originated from small marine organisms whose remains were somehow prevented from complete decomposition, are only found in sedimentary rocks. Oil-and-gas-bearing rocks occur in a considerable variety of structural associations of different geologic ages. Like coal, however, the rocks are not found among ancient crystalline rocks of pre-Paleozoic age.

Easily obtainable oil and gas saturate the pore spaces of permeable rocks, especially sandstones and limestones, just as the pore spaces are filled elsewhere by ground water. Structures containing petroleum are commonly overlain by others saturated with water. This tends to place the oil under pressure and concentrates it in limited deposits, called pools, in some form of structural pocket or trap from which the oil and gas cannot escape. The most numerous of these are the tops of anticlines that are capped by shales or other impervious rocks which prevent the oil and gas from floating upward and escaping. Many other kinds of traps occur into which the petroleum has migrated

from surrounding areas because of the pressure exerted by the denser ground water.

Oil and gas are obtained by drilling through the impervious capping rocks (Fig. 19.10). When the petroleum is under considerable pressure it may be forced upward violently, but in other cases, and even eventually from such gushers, the oil must be raised by pumping. Moreover, since the oil is contained in the small pore spaces in the pervious rock, much of it exists as a film of oil clinging to the rock particles, and not all of it can be recovered by pumping. Even with the most improved methods a considerable portion of the original oil remains in the ground when the expenditure for pumping becomes unprofitable.

There is less significant difference among varieties of petroleum than among coals. Most petroleum contains a variety of hydrocarbons that may be partially separated by distillation and then compounded in almost any combination desired.

PETROLEUM REGIONS OF THE WORLD

Because of the nature of its occurrence, it is more difficult to estimate the quantity of producible reserves of oil that still exist than reserves of coal. Recent estimates indicate the amount remaining in the earth as perhaps 1,250 billion barrels, not counting large amounts in shales and tar sands.[2] As with coal, almost all of this is concentrated in the Northern Hemisphere, and the United States and the U.S.S.R. are well endowed, but there the similarity ends. The Middle East has perhaps half the world's reserve, while Europe has very little. Also, concentration of oil is much greater than that of coal. Even though

[2] E. Willard Miller, "World Patterns and Trends in Energy Consumption," *Journal of Geography*, vol. 58, 1959, pp. 269–279.

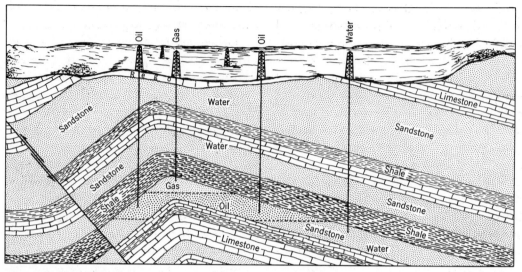

FIG. 19.10 One of many types of geologic structures in which petroleum is entrapped. Note the relation between the locations of several wells and the nature of their products. Some such anticlinal structures are concealed by overlying strata.

the major reserves of coal are concentrated in a few areas, there are numerous deposits, throughout the world, that can more or less adequately supply nonindustrial needs, as previously noted. This is not nearly so true of petroleum. Indeed, two circles with radii of a little less than 2,000 miles and with centers approximately at 35°N Lat and 50°E Long in the Eastern Hemisphere and at 20°N Lat and 85°W Long in the Western Hemisphere would outline areas that probably contain some three-quarters of the world's known reserves.

As a consequence, trade in petroleum is far more important than trade in coal, and the relative locations of producing areas and consuming areas are items of extreme geographical significance.

Western hemisphere The United States is endowed with several regions in which petroleum and gas occur in great volume, and the production and consumption of these

fuels in the United States far exceed those of any other country. In recent times productive deposits have also been discovered in Canada, and the regions bordering the Caribbean are likewise important producers of petroleum, especially for export to less favored areas. Each of these regions includes a number of subdivisions. Some of the included structures contain both oil and gas, some yield oil but not much gas, and others yield gas alone. The several regions are shown in Fig. 19.11.

Mid-continent, Gulf Coast, and California The mid-continent region includes several widely scattered fields including hundreds of pools in Kansas, Oklahoma, central and western Texas, southeastern New Mexico, southern Arkansas, and northern Louisiana. This region has been producing for many years. Many of its deposits have been exhausted, but new ones have been discovered, and the practice of deeper drilling has reached oil in lower and older rocks. Gas is abundant in this region also, and pipelines now carry it to industrial consumers far to the north and east.

The Gulf Coast region includes numerous pools found in many locations in the rocks of eastern Texas, Louisiana, and Mississippi. In some areas the deposits are associated with a large number of salt domes, or mounds underlain by rock salt. The deposits also extend out into the continental shelf, and considerable offshore development is taking place, although the cost of such recovery is, of course, much greater than on land.

The mid-continent and Gulf Coast regions have long been the most productive in the United States and contain its greatest proven reserves, with the Gulf Coast region estimated to have the largest proportion of the nation's total reserves.

They are followed by the California region, which includes oil and gas fields in a belt that extends from the environs of Los Angeles northward. The California region is also highly productive; as a state California ranks second only to Texas in importance.

Other regions of the United States The Rocky Mountain region is comprised of many

FIG. 19.11 The principal oil-and-gas-producing regions of the Western Hemisphere.

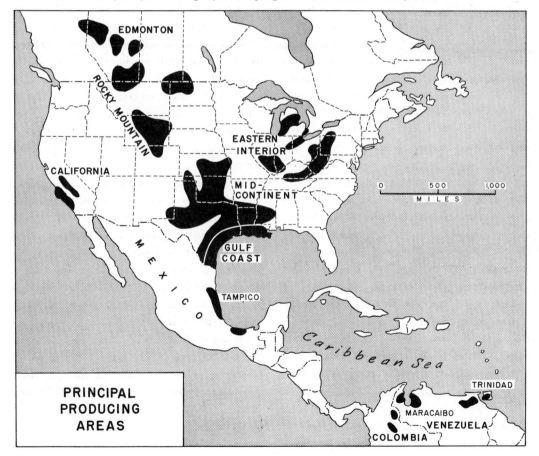

EDMONTON

ROCKY MOUNTAIN

CALIFORNIA

EASTERN INTERIOR

MID-CONTINENT

0   500   1,000

MILES

GULF COAST

M E X I C O

TAMPICO

Caribbean Sea

TRINIDAD

MARACAIBO

VENEZUELA

COLOMBIA

PRINCIPAL PRODUCING AREAS

fields distributed over a large area which is mainly in Wyoming, although it extends northward into Montana, south into Colorado, and eastward into North Dakota. Production is increasing in this area, but it is far behind that of the above regions. The eastern interior region includes several fields of minor importance located in Ohio, Indiana, Illinois, and Michigan. The greatest producer here is the field located in southeastern Illinois and adjacent Indiana.

The first oil and gas field to be developed on a modern scale was in the Allegheny region of Pennsylvania, and it was for many years the most productive area in the world; but it has now declined to minor significance. The petroleum has long been noted for its superior quality as a source of lubricating oils.

The question of how long the United States can maintain its present abundant petroleum production is not capable of assured answer. A feverish search continues for new pools and for new structures in all areas where the occurrence of petroleum is a possibility. Tens of thousands of new wells are drilled annually, and the proven reserves of the country have been increasing a little each year. But for several years the United States' imports of petroleum and its products have exceeded exports, and the demand continues to increase rapidly. The need for conservative practices in the production and use of these essential products is evident.

Canada   Until recently oil production in Canada was restricted to small amounts produced in Ontario in the section north of Lake Erie, in southern Alberta, and in the Mackenzie River Basin west of Great Bear Lake. But with discoveries in the vicinity of Edmonton in central Alberta, Canadian production and reserves have increased. Recent estimates indicate that Canadian reserves and

production are ahead of Indonesia and Mexico and exceeded only by the United States, Venezuela, the U.S.S.R., and the Middle Eastern countries. There is, moreover, every reason to believe that Canadian status in the world oil situation will continue to rise. Most of the production occurs in Alberta, with some in British Columbia to the northwest and in Saskatchewan and Manitoba to the southeast (Fig. 19.11).

The Caribbean   Included in the Caribbean region are several areas of considerable importance. Chief among them is that located in northern South America, mainly in the Maracaibo and Orinoco River Basins of Venezuela but including smaller areas in Colombia and the island of Trinidad (Fig. 19.11). Venezuela has perhaps 6 to 8 per cent of the world's known reserves, and has regularly ranked next after the United States among the countries of the world in production. A second productive area, located in eastern Mexico, near Tampico and Tuxpan, yielded abundantly early in the present century, but it has now passed the peak of its productivity.

South America beyond the Caribbean borders gives some evidence of widespread occurrence of petroleum, but only Argentina and Peru have significant production.

Eastern Hemisphere   Because of the extreme fragmentation of the oil-producing areas in the Eastern Hemisphere by national boundaries, the casual observer may not realize that the major producing deposits there are as localized as those of the Western Hemisphere. Although some oil and gas is known in many localities in Europe, Asia, Africa, and Australia, the region of large present output is confined to an area centered in the Middle East and extending north into the U.S.S.R. (Fig. 19.12). The only other

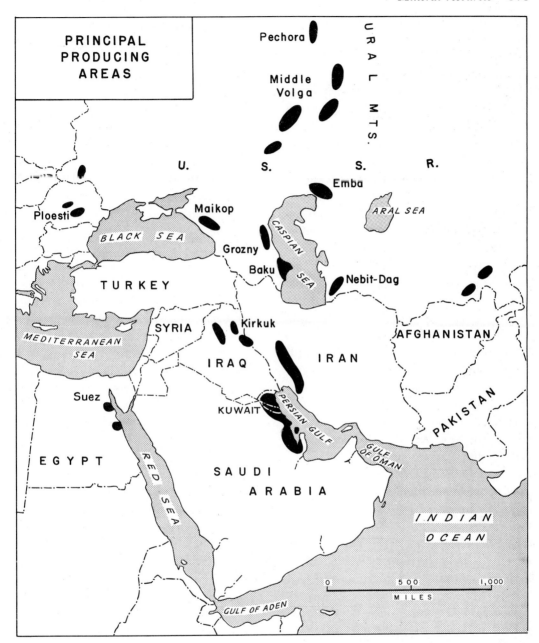

FIG. 19.12 The principal oil-and-gas-producing regions of the Eastern Hemisphere.

area that produces a significant amount is Indonesia, and its production is less than 5 per cent of the hemisphere's total.

Middle East Several facts related to the great importance of oil in the Middle East contribute to the explanation of why so many problems of world politics and economic strategy originate in or near this part of Asia.

The petroleum deposits there are located in several political subdivisions near the Persian Gulf, mainly in Saudi Arabia, Iran, Iraq, and Kuwait (Fig. 19.12). Moreover these areas, taken together, produce about two-thirds as much oil as the United States, most of which is destined for export to the great consuming area of Europe. Finally, the proven reserves of the region are perhaps half the world's known supply, as previously stated.

U.S.S.R., Europe, and others   The U.S.S.R. has been rapidly increasing its petroleum and natural gas production. It now rivals Venezuela as a petroleum producer second to the United States; and although the output of the U.S.S.R. is perhaps one-third that of the United States, its potential reserve seems to be larger.[3] The major producing areas of the U.S.S.R. are adjacent to the Ural and Caucasus Mountains and the Caspian Sea. Of several fields in this region those near the Middle Volga River and west of the Ural Mountains, Baku (at the eastern extremity of the Caucasus Mountains), Grozny (north of the Caucasus), and Turkistan are the most productive.

Europe, outside the U.S.S.R., is one of the great petroleum-consuming areas, but within its area it produces less than 3 per cent of the world's total. The leading production is still in the Ploesti area of Romania in southeastern Europe; there is much smaller, but locally significant, production in West Germany, Austria, France, and the Netherlands.

Eastern and southeastern Asia contain widely scattered deposits from Sakhalin southward, the most important being in the Indonesian region, especially Sumatra, British Borneo, and New Guinea.

Petroleum has long been produced in Egypt, and is now being produced in the

[3] *ibid.*

western part of north Africa in Algeria and the Sahara, but southern Africa, like Australia, has no known deposits of significance.

OTHER MINERAL FUELS

Although liquid petroleum, coal, and natural gas are the most widely used mineral fuels today, they are not the only mineral sources of energy upon which man may draw. For example, the petroleum that exists in oil shales and tar sands is already being used. Yet these sources are expensive because the material must be quarried or mined and then treated before the crude oil it holds can be obtained. Moreover, no very reliable estimate of the total potential energy available from these sources has yet been made. It is known that the supplies are large, perhaps considerably more than those of liquid petroleum. Nonetheless, nearly three-fourths of the remaining supply of energy obtainable from fossil fuels is in the form of coal.

Because of the rapidly increasing production and consumption rates of the fossil fuels, other mineral sources, such as the nuclear energy from uranium and thorium are already being developed; and the total energy potentially available from these sources is enormously greater than that from the remaining fossil fuels. Consequently, it appears more accurate to predict that the future of mineral sources of energy will be different from the past than to say it will be dim.

THE METALLIC MINERALS

Metals and modern civilization Among the many elements available in the earth's crust are some—such as iron, copper, or aluminum—that are called metallic. Man learned early that the use of these metallic elements was greatly advantageous in many ways, and the development of civilization and the course of human events have been strongly influenced by variations in the occurrence of metallic resources from place to place and by the differing abilities of people to put these endowments to use.

The early use of metals was largely confined to such forms as utensils, weapons, tools, and sewers. Since the Industrial Revolution, however, the employment of metals has increased a thousandfold. Modern blast furnaces produce in a day now more iron than was produced in a year 200 years ago; and the power-driven machines that are the major use of metals today made man a mobile being and have increased his productivity and efficiency beyond the wildest expectations of even 100 years ago. The changes wrought by the use of metals are indeed staggering.

Metals are sometimes used in the pure state, as, for example, copper or gold, but usually they are mixed to produce an alloy that has more desirable characteristics. Bronze, a mixture of copper and tin, and brass, a mixture of copper and zinc, are examples of alloys with which man has long been familiar. But by far the most important alloys are the steels, made by mixing other metals with iron, without which modern high-speed metal-working machines and efficient technologic processes would be impossible.

A few metals that are used for a variety of purposes and in large quantities, such as copper, aluminum, and, especially, iron, may be thought of as fundamental resources. Thus, so much iron is required, and it is of such comparatively low specific value, that the possession of a domestic supply of iron ore is considered—along with a supply of coal or petroleum—a matter of major economic importance by the great nations. Other metals, such as chromium or tungsten, are used in relatively small quantities, and although they may be economically important to a particular region, they can hardly be called basic mineral resources. The limited quantity required, coupled with high specific value, enable these and similar metals to move freely in the channels of international trade, unless tariffs and restrictive trade regulations are imposed to prevent it. In a sense, the whole world draws upon the same sources of supply of these metals.

Physical associations of metallic minerals An *ore* is a deposit of a metallic mineral (or one of its chemical compounds) sufficiently concentrated so that it is profitable to use it. Some metals, such as copper, occasionally occur in the native state. But more often the metallic elements are found in chemical combination with other elements, in such forms as sulphides, sulphates, oxides, or carbonates, from which they must be set free by processes of reduction called smelting. Usually the desirable minerals are also intermingled with some quantity of unwanted rock material, called gangue, from which they must be separated by mechanical means.

The local concentration of metallic minerals is a result of the workings of a variety of natural processes that can be grouped in three general categories: (*a*) igneous activity, (*b*) weathering, and (*c*) sedimentation. Compounds of chromium, nickel, copper, lead, zinc, and tin are examples of metals commonly found in association with crystalline igneous rock masses. They may become concentrated within the mass itself during its cooling and crystallization, or they may have intruded or have been chemically precipitated from circulating ground waters in the rock zone adjacent to the cooling mass.

Weathering processes, the second category, produce concentrations of metallic ores in several ways: (*a*) The decomposition of rock masses in the normal course of events may involve a desirable chemical change, for example, in the transformation of the unusable silicate of aluminum to the usable ore of aluminum, a hydrous oxide called bauxite. (*b*) Undesirable components may be simply removed by leaching, thereby concentrating the remainder, for example, as when the removal of a large portion of the silica from an iron formation concentrates the iron oxide. (*c*) A mineral may be leached from one zone and precipitated in a more usable form at a lower level, an example of which is the transformation of the insoluble sulphide of copper into the soluble sulphate.

Finally, in the alluvial process useful minerals are transported by running water, and because of their relative weight may become concentrated as placer deposits in the present or former beds of streams. For example, a majority of the world's tin supply comes from placer deposits.

In general, no matter how the ultimate concentration of a usable ore came about, it began in the majority of instances by the segregation of elements that occurs as a result of heat and pressure in rock masses. It is not surprising, therefore, that ores containing metallic minerals are commonly associated with regions of igneous activity or where the processes of metamorphism have been accompanied by great pressure and the development of heat. Although there are some notable exceptions, it is broadly true that the great areas of tectonically undisturbed sedimentary rocks are poor in the ores of metals—an exactly opposite relationship from that regarding the occurrence of the mineral fuels.

IRON

Iron is usually found in some chemical combination, the more important ones being the oxides named hematite, magnetite, and limonite, and the carbonate named siderite. The oxides are particularly abundant, and they are scattered widely but thinly through a large part of the regolith and give its common red, brown, and yellow colors to it, but ordinary regolith has not enough iron per unit volume to make it an ore, that is, to give it the at least 30 to 35 per cent of the metal most ores of iron must contain under present economic conditions. Iron-bearing minerals, such as hematite and magnetite, contain as much as 70 per cent of iron, but deposits seldom consist solely of these minerals; instead the iron content of a mass is reduced by the occurrence of associated gangue minerals, especially silica.

Iron deposits of the world   Iron is more abundant than any other metallic mineral except aluminum, and iron deposits occur widely, so that no large area of the earth is far removed from iron-ore supplies. The supply is sufficient for many years to come. Among the outstanding deposits, measured by their present contributions to the world's iron industries, are those of the United States, Canada, Venezuela, the western European countries, the U.S.S.R., and India. There are many other places where deposits of potential future significance occur. But since at present iron must be separated from the ore by the use of coke, it is important to consider in what parts of the world these two ingredients are found close together.

The distribution of the world's populated plains is such that they contribute to the commercial supremacy of the areas tributary to the North Atlantic Basin which is the only region in which abundant deposits of iron ore and coking coal are known to be closely associated. This area includes the eastern United States, the countries of northwestern Europe, and the U.S.S.R. In them are the present world centers of heavy iron and steel manufacture, as well as many other industries that depend on cheap iron and steel. Some of the world's greatest reserves of iron ore are in Brazil and India, but Brazil has almost no coking coal, and India has only a limited supply. China apparently has large reserves of excellent coal but no known supply of ore of comparable importance. With respect to the basic raw materials for iron and steel manufacture the endowment of the United States has indeed been fortunate.

Western Hemisphere In the Western Hemisphere there are several regions of unusual present and potential future iron-ore production. Outstanding are those associated with the crystalline rocks of the Canadian Shield, both in the United States and Canada.

United States: Lake Superior district The United States has the most renowned iron deposits, those of the Lake Superior district (Fig. 19.13). These ores are mostly hematite of high quality, and those mined until recent years were very rich, the average iron content being 50 per cent or over. They were concentrated by ground-water action, and some of the deposits were so near the surface that they could be easily mined by power shovel (Fig. 19.14). The Lake Superior district has been the most productive iron-ore deposit in the world, and this region has supplied the bulk of the ore used in the steel industry of the United States. But the reserves of easily mined, high-quality ore are limited, and although they are not about to be depleted, an

alternative ore, taconite, is now being used.

Taconite is the parent iron formation in the Lake Superior district, an iron-bearing silica rock, from which in some areas the richer ores were derived through the removal of silica by leaching. Because its iron content is only about 25 per cent, such low-grade ore is not suitable for direct shipment. Instead, the taconite must be beneficiated, that is, artificially concentrated. It is first quarried, then crushed and processed into a concentrate containing some 60 per cent iron.

The relation of the Lake Superior ores to regions of manufacture and market is fortunate. The Great Lakes, with the canals connecting Lakes Superior and Huron, provide a deep waterway almost from the mine to the very margin of the Appalachian coal field and the heart of the American industrial region. Iron deposits are found elsewhere in the United States than in the Lake Superior district, but the reserves are limited. The most used deposit is in Alabama, where iron is mined in the same district with the coal and limestone required in the smelting (Fig. 19.15).

Iron ore moves so cheaply by water that large supplies of foreign ores move to meet abundant coal upon the eastern seaboard of the United States for smelting there. Most of these continually growing imports come from other North or South American sources, chiefly from Venezuela and Canada, which together supply more than three-quarters of the total.

Canada and Latin America Canada includes the larger part of the Canadian Shield, but until recently it was not known to contain such large and easily mined ore deposits as those in the Lake Superior district of the United States. Now, considerable deposits

FIG. 19.13 The major Western Hemisphere iron deposits. The insets show the locations of those in the Lake Superior and Labrador districts.

are being mined in the western Ontario region in districts northwest and northeast of Lake Superior. A most important and productive recently discovered ore deposit lies in the Knob Lake-Schefferville district in the eastern part of the shield, in the boundary area between Quebec and Labrador some 360 miles

from the north shore of the Gulf of Saint Lawrence (Fig. 19.13). This seems to be one of the world's great reserves; much of the ore is hematite with an iron content exceeding 60 per cent, and open-pit mining is practiced.

Venezuela supplies a large share of the iron-ore imports of the United States. The deposits

FIG. 19.14 Mining ore in an open pit in northern Minnesota. Open-pit
ore of high quality is no longer abundant in the Lake Superior district.
(Oliver Iron Mining Company.)

of high-grade ore are located near the lower
Orinoco River, so that the ore is easily
moved by water to the smelting centers of
the eastern United States.

Other Latin American deposits are located
in Brazil, Chile, Peru, Mexico, and Cuba.
The Brazilian deposits lie some 200 miles
north of Rio de Janeiro in the crystalline
rocks of the Brazilian plateau. They contain
iron minerals of the highest quality—some
hematite, some magnetite—and they rank
near the top of the world's great and rich reserves of iron ore. Their utilization is just
beginning.

Eastern Hemisphere Throughout the
Eastern Hemisphere are many known iron
deposits, many of which now produce
abundantly for local consumption (Fig.

FIG. 19.15 Distribution of essential minerals
in the Birmingham, Alabama, industrial region.

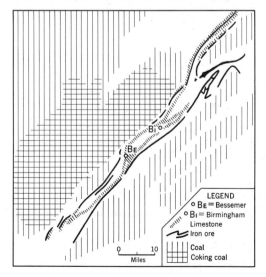

LEGEND
B_E = Bessemer
B_I = Birmingham
Limestone
Iron ore
Coal
Coking coal

0   10
Miles

19.16). But only a few appear to rank among the major world reserves.

Western Europe The iron industries of western Europe depend primarily upon European sources of ore. As in North America, the greatest centers of iron manufacture are located in or close to the principal coal fields; but only in a few places are the ore and coal found together, and one or the other must usually be transported. Although some of the countries contain both iron ore and coking coal, the numerous boundaries of western Europe have politically fragmented some of the more important deposits, and much of the ore, especially the high-grade ore, must move in international trade to reach the principal smelting centers. The large iron resources are in France and

Sweden. Sweden has less iron than France, but the iron is superior in quality. Other important ore deposits are in England, Germany, and Spain. Those of Germany and England provide low-grade ore for local processing, but those of the northern part of Spain, a country of little coal, provide ore for export, especially to England.

The iron ores of France include the largest single iron reserve in western Europe and one of the large ones of the world. They are found in the northeastern part of the country in the province of Lorraine, and extend across the boundary into Luxembourg and slightly into Belgium (Fig. 19.17). The Lorraine ores are mainly limonite, a hydrous oxide of iron, and are of relatively low quality, averaging only about 25 to 35 per cent in iron content.

FIG. 19.16 The major Eastern Hemisphere iron deposits.

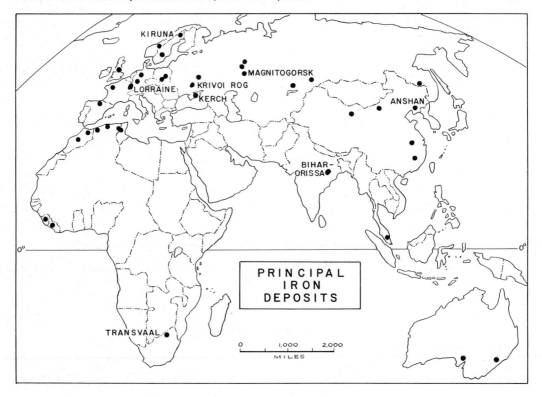

However, they lie near the German, Belgian, and French coal fields and the great industrial market of Europe.

The iron ores of Great Britain have been greatly depleted. The remaining ores are scattered, of different kinds, and mainly of low grade. It has long been the practice of British smelters to supplement the domestic supply with imported ores. Nevertheless, Britain has a supply of domestic low-grade ores sufficient for many years. They are closely associated with supplies of coal and limestone.

The iron ores of Sweden are noted for their high quality. They are mainly magnetite and average 55 to 65 per cent iron. High-quality ore is obtained in central Sweden, but the largest deposits are situated in the crystalline rocks of the far northern part of the country in the Kiruna district. Since there is almost no coal and but relatively little iron manufacture in Sweden, much of the ore is exported to other European countries.

U.S.S.R. and others   The iron ores of the U.S.S.R. include large reserves, the most important of which are found in three localities. These are Krivoi Rog in the southern Ukraine, the Kerch Peninsula in the Crimea, and Magnitogorsk, near the southern end of the Ural Mountains. The Krivoi Rog deposit is the richest and normally the most productive. It is located about 300 miles west of the Donets coal basin, and thus contributes to the Ukrainian region of heavy industry. The ores at Magnitogorsk are used in association with the coal from several small deposits farther north in the Ural region, but especially with the coal of the distant Kuznetsk and Karaganda fields in Siberia. Smaller iron-ore deposits in Siberia, such as that at Gornaya Shoriya south of the Kuznetsk coal field, are becoming more important in the growing industries of the eastern U.S.S.R.

FIG. 19.17   Location of the great Lorraine iron-ore field of France in relation to nearby coal fields.

The iron ores of India constitute the only major deposit elsewhere in the Eastern Hemisphere. It lies adjacent to the principal coal field of the country in the Deccan Plateau about 150 miles west of Calcutta.

Throughout the other areas of Africa, Asia, and Australia, iron-ore deposits are known to exist in many places. Some of them now produce in sufficient quantity to provide for local industry, as for example do those of southern Australia, southern Africa, and Manchuria. Also, it is probable, since iron is generally widespread, that in localities as yet imperfectly explored other, and perhaps more significant, resources will be found.

OTHER METALLIC MINERALS

THE FERROALLOYS

For the fabrication of finished products, the modern industrial world does not use much iron in the state in which it comes from the blast furnace. Instead, iron is compounded with various other metals and nonmetals to make steels, which are, as already stated, the most important alloys. Many of these ferroalloying elements—including such metals as nickel or tungsten and the nonmetals, carbon and silicon—are used to make the desirable mixtures, but the two in greatest demand are manganese and chromium.

The mixing of these materials with iron imparts special qualities to the steel—renders it stainless, or makes it hard or tough, or gives it the ability to hold a cutting edge at high temperatures, and so on. These properties are so important that the major alloying metals are in great demand, although they are not needed in large quantities. The one most used, in terms of quantity, is manganese, which is used in the manufacture of all steel; about 13 lb of manganese is used in making each ton of steel in the United States. Next to manganese in terms of quantity used are chromium and nickel, in that order.

More than 70 nations produce ores of the alloying elements, and generalizations concerning the rank of the producers and distribution of the product are difficult. The major known deposits of manganese are in the U.S.S.R., which has in the southern Ukraine and in Georgia the world's largest known reserves. Other major producers are India, the Union of South Africa, Ghana, Brazil, and Morocco. The largest reserves of chromium are in southern Africa, Turkey, the U.S.S.R., and the Philippines. Canada is the world's greatest nickel producer.

Although the United States produces a greater number of alloying elements than any other nation, and leads in the production of several, virtually all its supplies of the most used three—manganese, chromium, and nickel—must be imported.

IMPORTANT NONFERROUS METALS

The list of metals other than iron used in the modern arts and industries is very long, and even summary descriptions of the uses and regions of occurrence of all cannot be included in this book. So comment will be restricted to a few that illustrate some of the many complexities of the geography of minerals.

A great variety of earth conditions is favorable to the occurrence and discovery of the ores of metals, but it is worth repeating that the principal world regions of mineralization are those where crystalline rocks are at or near the surface or where there have been recent crustal disturbances or igneous activity. Even this general rule has notable exceptions—an apparent one being the deposits of lead and zinc ores associated with sedimentary rocks. Examples of these are the lead and zinc deposits of southwestern Missouri, southwestern Wisconsin, and adjacent Illinois, and those of Belgium and Poland. Another exception of great importance is the occurrence of the ore of aluminum, bauxite.

Aluminum Aluminum, an even more abundant element than iron, is a common and widely distributed constituent of the regolith. On the other hand, only in relatively few places are there rich deposits of the ore. Varieties of bauxite are of different origins, but it seems clear that some are derived from sedimentary clays that have been changed through long-continued leaching by ground water. Others are known to have been derived by a process of natural beneficiation of igneous rocks that originally were low in iron and silica; of such origin are the limited deposits of the Ouachita Mountain region of Arkansas.

Major deposits of bauxite are known to

exist in many parts of the world: northern Australia, British Guiana, Brazil, Ghana, Surinam, Jamaica, the East Indian region, China, and the U.S.S.R. Large reserves also exist in Hungary, Yugoslavia, and France, and they provide abundantly for European consumption. The United States, on the other hand, must import much of the ore it uses.

Copper Second to iron in amount produced, copper is quite the opposite of iron and aluminum in its occurrence: whereas the other two are widespread in the crust of the earth, copper is not. But the occurrence of copper ore conforms to the generalization repeated earlier; namely, it is found in regions of crystalline rock or in areas of recent tectonic activity. Because copper is the basis of the modern electrical world it is much sought after, and a deposit yielding as little as 1 per cent of the metal is considered a usable ore.

The largest known reserves are located in three general regions, western North America, western South America, and south central Africa, in that order; among them they account for some three-quarters of the known copper resource. None of the great industrial nations, except perhaps the U.S.S.R., is self-sufficient in copper production.

In North America, which produces approximately a third of the world's copper, the copper reserves are located primarily in the western cordilleran sections of the United States and Canada. Other known deposits are in the Canadian Shield area of northern United States and southern Canada. South American copper, in the cordilleran region of that continent also, is concentrated in Chile and southern Peru, the former having perhaps the greatest single known deposit. In Africa copper is located in the Katanga Province of the southern Congo and in adjacent Northern Rhodesia. Copper reserves elsewhere in the world are small, although those of the U.S.S.R. are estimated to be perhaps one-fourth as great as those of North America.

SOURCE REGIONS OF METALLIC MINERALS

A survey of metallic minerals can at best mention only a few of the many used today in modern industry, so it is impossible to treat in detail here the major known areas of their present and potential supply. However, some of these areas and the bases of their world importance are noted below.

The Canadian Shield The Canadian Shield is highly productive of metallic minerals and has large possibilities for future discoveries. From its ancient crystalline rocks are obtained not only rich iron ores but a wealth of other metals. These include most of the world's supply of nickel and large amounts of gold, silver, cobalt, copper, uranium, and others. Important discoveries are made in this extensive region each year, and the exploitation of mineral resources is one of the principal industries that has attracted people there.

The American cordilleran region The American cordilleran region, from Alaska to Cape Horn, is also an area noted for the abundance and variety of its mineral products. At least half the world's copper is found here in deposits as far separated as Chile, Peru, Arizona, Montana, and Alaska. Gold, silver, lead, and zinc are sufficiently abundant that Mexico, the United States, and Canada hold high rank in the production of each of them. The Andean countries of South America are important producers of platinum, tin, and tungsten, and have an appreciable output of other metals. It was the gold of this region that gave impetus to its conquest by Spain.

Central and southern Africa and other

regions   In central and southern Africa the crystalline rocks include several productive mineral regions. Within that vast area are The Rand, the world's leading gold-producing district, and such important centers in the production of copper as those of the Katanga in Northern Rhodesia and the adjacent Congo. There are also districts producing chromium, manganese, and uranium, and important localities from which most of the world's diamonds are mined.

Other mineral regions of world renown may only be mentioned. Among them are the following: (*a*) Areas of igneous and crystalline metamorphic rocks in southern and western Australia which have yielded gold, silver, lead, zinc, and minor quantities of other metals. (*b*) The crystalline rocks of the highlands of eastern South America, in Brazil and the Guianas. In addition to deposits of iron ore and bauxite, these highlands yield important quantities of manganese, gold, and precious stones. They are known also to contain deposits of several other metals which are as yet little developed. (*c*) A large region of crystalline rocks in eastern Asia. They extend from Korea on the south to the shores of the Sea of Okhotsk on the north, and thence westward in southern Siberia. From this region is obtained a large part of the gold that makes the U.S.S.R. one of the leading producers of that metal. The region contains large areas that are as yet little explored geologically. (*d*) The highlands of southeastern Asia. From them are now obtained the larger part of the world's tin, tungsten, and several other metals. (*e*) The cordilleran region of southern Europe and the Mediterranean borderlands. In it are included important centers in the production of several metals. (*f*) The Ural region of the U.S.S.R.

It may once again be observed that the world's principal centers of actual and potential production of the metallic minerals are those associated with igneous or crystalline rocks, in contrast to those regions which are comprised mainly of sedimentary rocks. Despite the fact that the regions of sedimentary rocks contain the world's supplies of mineral fuels and certain of the ores of iron, aluminum, lead, and zinc, they are, in general, poor in the ores of other metallic minerals.

THE NONMETALLIC MINERALS

Modern use of nonmetals   Man has used the nonmetallic minerals of the earth's crust longer than he has used either the metallic minerals or the mineral fuels. He very early learned to fashion implements and utensils from stones and appreciated the value of rock in the construction of many things. Rock is still widely used today, but in markedly different ways and in vastly greater quantity.

Some nonmetallic minerals are used in their natural states, while others pass through processes of industrial manufacture and appear as components in goods having hundreds of uses. Rocks, sands, clays, salts, abrasives, fertilizers, gems, and many others make up the long list. Most of them are found in a variety of grades. Nonmetallic minerals are essential qualities of the natural equipment of regions, and no limited portion of the earth contains all of them; indeed, there are few regions, if any, that contain all of even the most essential.

Because of the great number of these substances and the variety of their occurrences, many cannot be discussed in this brief treatment. Only those considered relatively essential and those required in great quantity— such as the compounds and elements used in large amounts by the chemical industries and the rock, sands, limes, and clays used in the construction and manufacturing industries— can be included.

Salt and its sources   Salt, sodium chloride, is one of the common rock minerals, and it is widely used in great volume as a food, a food preservative, and a basic raw material from which industry derives a number of the useful compounds of sodium and chlorine. Owing to its solubility in water, it is not abundant in the zone of free ground-water circulation in humid climates, but inexhaustible supplies are available for human use from the following sources: (*a*) the sea, which contains 2⅔ lb of salt for every 100 lb of water; (*b*) natural brines, which are the waters of ancient seas that saturate deeply buried sedimentary rocks cut off from ground-water circulation; (*c*) deposits of rock salt, called evaporites, which probably resulted from the evaporation of water in the arms of ancient seas or in former arid interior drainage basins (these deposits now are sedimentary rocks deep underground, where they are protected by other sediments from the solvent action of ground water); and (*d*) the present limited surface incrustation of salt in interior drainage basins in dry climates. Salt is found in so many places that few parts of the world are without some local supply.

For industrial uses salt is obtained largely by mining rock salt or by the pumping of brines, either natural brines or those produced by pumping water down to bodies of rock salt. The industrial regions of North America are supplied from abundant reserves. Thick beds of rock salt underlie large areas in central and western New York, northeastern Ohio, southeastern Michigan, and peninsular Ontario. Other large reserves are found in the buried salt domes of the Louisiana and Texas Gulf Coast, in deposits in central Kansas, and at various places in the southwestern states.

The industrial centers elsewhere in the world likewise are well provided with salt. There are large deposits in western England, central Germany, Austria, and the southern U.S.S.R.

Sulphur   Sulphur, especially in the form of sulphuric acid, has many uses in modern industry. It is variously used in connection with the manufacture of steel, oil, paper, rayon, rubber, and explosives, and in other chemical industries. It has long been obtained from pyrite (a mineral containing iron and sulphur) and from deposits associated with recent volcanic activity, and is mined from these sources in Italy, Spain, Japan, and Chile. In the United States the principal deposits occur in the Louisiana and Texas Gulf Coast area. There native sulphur is recovered by means of wells through which superheated steam is pumped underground to the sulphur beds, causing molten sulphur to be returned to the surface. Alternatively, industrial sulphur is recovered from oil-refinery operations, and is a by-product of the smelting of certain mineral ores in which the metals are chemically combined with sulphur. Such are certain ores of iron, copper, and zinc.

Mineral fertilizers   Continuous cropping and accelerated erosion remove the elements of soil fertility faster than they can be

FUNDAMENTALS OF PHYSICAL GEOGRAPHY

388

resupplied by natural processes in the soil. The most needed nutrients, moreover— calcium, nitrogen, potash, and phosphorus— are among those especially susceptible to depletion. The volume of agricultural production can be increased markedly in areas of initial or induced low soil fertility, however, by adding these elements, especially the last three. For each of the four, there are known mineral deposits which are drawn upon for the manufacture of fertilizers.

Calcium Calcium, in the form of calcium carbonate, is readily available in the limestones of many regions. The other three are much less abundant, and notable deposits of them are considered to be resources of great importance.

Nitrogen Nitrogen is the most abundant element in the atmosphere, but it is largely unavailable to plants in the gaseous form: it must be combined to form a soluble nitrogen compound. Most natural inorganic nitrogen compounds are soluble in water and so are quickly lost when water seeps downward in the soil. The great need for nitrogen compounds for fertilizer (and for industrial use) led to the discovery of ways of producing such compounds from the nitrogen in the atmosphere. This is now accomplished in a number of ways, and synthetic nitrogen production has practically superceded its production from natural sources. Until recently, however, the principal source was mineral deposits in arid lands, chiefly those in the Atacama Desert in northern Chile which are accumulations from ages of seepage and surface evaporation.

Potash Potash[4] is obtained in small

quantities from the ashes of wood, seaweed, and other substances, but the principal commercial sources are deposits of complex minerals. Large deposits are located in western Europe, mainly in central Germany and in Alsace in northeastern France, where, until recently, the greater part of the world's supply has been obtained from mines 1,000 ft or more beneath the surface of the earth. Deposits of potash minerals are known to exist in many areas; in the United States there is a very large reserve in New Mexico.

Phosphorus Phosphorus is an indispensable constituent of all living cells, the principal mineral sources of which occur as calcium phosphates, mainly in rock form. This rock is believed to have been formed from the alteration of limestone by the chemical action of ground water which had first passed through ancient accumulations of bird and fish remains.

Valuable beds of phosphate rock usually occur as local pockets in limestone strata, and useful deposits exist in several parts of the world. The principal sources for Europe are located near the Mediterranean Coast of Africa in Tunisia, Algeria, and Morocco. The United States is largely supplied from extensive beds in western Florida and central Tennessee. Other great reserves are known to exist in the Northern Rocky Mountain region of the United States, in the U.S.S.R., and in some of the islands of the Pacific Ocean.

Sand, lime, gypsum, and clay Sand is used in vast quantities in construction as an ingredient of concrete, mortar, and plaster. Also it is the chief raw material in the manufacture of glass, and it shares with clay and calcium compounds a place of great importance as a raw material of industry generally.

---

[4] Potash is a term generally used to refer to simple potassium-bearing compounds, such as potassium carbonate (lye), potassium hydroxide, or potassium oxide.

Lime (calcium carbonate that has been calcined, i.e., heated to drive off the carbon dioxide) and clay are required in the manufacture of cement; gypsum (calcium sulphate) is widely used in plaster materials; and clay is basic to the brick, tile, and pottery industries.

These substances are of common occurrence. There are, for example, river sands, beach sands, wind-blown sands, sands in glacial deposits, and pure sandstones. There are unconsolidated marls, soft chalks, and other limestones as source materials from which lime may be obtained. Deposits of gypsum and anhydrite (anhydrous calcium sulphate) are relatively common. There are river clays, marine clays, residual clays, and shale rocks. Indeed, not many regions are without one or more of these minerals.

However, qualities differ, and needs for particular grades of these minerals often cannot be supplied locally or even regionally. Glacial-lake clays are good enough for the manufacture of ordinary brick and tile, but other uses have more particular requirements. Pottery clay especially must be pure and burn white in the kiln. It is usually found in residual deposits where it has weathered from coarsely crystalline feldspars. Good grades of glass sand, free from iron and clay, may be sought hundreds of miles from the centers of glass manufacture. Therefore, some regions gain advantage from particular natural endowments suited to particular requirements. Some, indeed, have achieved international fame through their products. Such are the regions of pottery clays in southern England, northern France, or Bavaria.

Crude rock   Many kinds of crude rock are used in large quantities in architectural and engineering structures; and some form' of cut stone, crushed rock, or gravels of stream or glacial origin that will serve these purposes is found in many parts of the earth. Thus it may seem that rock, in this broad sense, is one of the universal items of regional equipment, like the air. That, however, is not true. Some regions are endowed with large quantities or with rock of unusual quality; others have none at all.

Indeed, a few regions of considerable size are practically devoid of any kind of rock. Among these are the great deltas of the world, where silt covers hundreds of square miles and rock is buried to great depths. Much larger still are certain plains of older alluvium or regions of deep loess accumulation. Among these are the loess-and-alluvium-covered Pampa of Argentina and similar areas in the American Corn Belt, where older glacial drift and loess cover the rock strata deeply. In these regions are localities that do not even have any crude rock or gravel with which to surface roads.

Where crude rock does exist, it seldom moves far from its place of origin unless it has some particular quality to recommend it to a wider market, because crude rock is heavy and of low value. Regions in which rocks of special quality abound, however, have a valuable resource, especially if they also are near a large market for stone. Such a region is New England. There, in a region of igneous intrusion and metamorphosed sediments, beautiful and massive granites, slates of parallel cleavage, and excellent marbles all are produced near a good market. The even-textured and easily worked gray limestones of southern Indiana have a national market, and some other stones of unique quality, such as the statuary marble of Italy, have practically world-wide markets.

SUGGESTED READING

Leet, L. Don, and Sheldon Judson: *Physical Geology*, Prentice-Hall, Inc., Englewood Cliffs, N. J., 1958, chap. 20.

Miller, E. Willard: "Mineral Regionalism of the Canadian Shield," *Canadian Geographer*, no. 13, 1959, pp. 17–30.

———: "World Patterns and Trends in Energy Consumption," *Journal of Geography*, vol. 58, 1959, pp. 269–279.

Pratt, Wallace E., and Dorothy Good: *World Geography of Petroleum*, American Geographical Society and Princeton University Press, New York, 1950.

Riley, C. M.: *Our Mineral Resources*, John Wiley & Sons, Inc., New York, 1959.

Smith, J. Russell, M. Ogdon Phillips, and Thomas R. Smith: *Industrial and Commercial Geography*, 4th ed., Henry Holt and Company, Inc., New York, 1955.

Van Royen, W., and Oliver Bowles: "The Mineral Resources of the World," *Atlas of the World's Resources*, vol. 2, Prentice-Hall, Inc., Englewood Cliffs, N.J., 1952.

Zimmerman, E. W.: *World Resources and Industries*, rev. ed., Harper & Brothers, New York, 1951.

A selected list of United States topographic quadrangles

The topographic quadrangles indicated below have been selected from those published by the United States Geological Survey because they illustrate in map form certain of the land-surface types discussed in the text. Some of the types discussed, ice-scoured plains, for example, are not clearly illustrated in any of the quadrangles now published and are therefore omitted from the list.

Because of the great progress made during the last two decades in accuracy of representation, recently published sheets have been selected wherever possible. To provide uniformity and to afford adequate-sized samples of the terrain, the selection has been largely confined to sheets on the scales of 1 : 62,500 or 1 : 63,360. Scales other than those are noted where chosen. In some instances two or three quadrangles are required to show adequately the terrain type in question. Such quadrangles are listed as a series.

In recent years the Geological Survey has begun issuing a number of sheets in shaded relief as well as in contour editions. Because of the excellence of these maps and their clarity of terrain representation, they are especially valuable for teaching purposes. Quadrangles for which shaded-relief editions are available are marked with an asterisk in the list below.

All the quadrangles listed may be obtained from the United States Geological Survey, Washington 25, D.C.

PLAINS

STREAM-ERODED PLAINS

YOUTHFUL

Binger, Okla. (dendritic dissection)
Carlinville, Ill. (dendritic dissection)
Florence West, S.C. (upland swamps)
Sandon, Kan. (flat; dissected edge)

MATURE

Marlow, Okla. (early mature)
Oxford, N.C. (mid mature)
Chatham, La. (late-mid mature)
Wiergate, Tex.–La. (late mature)

PLAINS WITH CUESTAS

Fredonia, Kan. (two well-marked escarpments)
Epes, Ala. (ragged escarpment)
Denmark and New Albany, Miss. (eroded, low)
Fond du Lac, Wis. (clean, glaciated escarpment)

WATER-LAID PLAINS

FLOODPLAINS

Clarksdale, Miss. (meander scars)
Davis Island, Miss.–La. (meanders, cutoffs, scars)

Fairbanks C-1 and Fairbanks D-1, Alaska (meanders, cutoffs, braided channels)
Augusta, Mo. (narrow floodplain, bluffs)

ALLUVIAL TERRACES

Wabasha, Minn. (well-defined low terraces)
*Ennis, Mont. (high terraces)

DELTAS

Hahnville, La. (inner part large delta)
East Delta, La. (margin large delta)
Mount Vernon, Wash. (small delta)
Bouldin Island and Isleton, Calif. (diked delta lands)

ALLUVIAL FANS; PIEDMONT ALLUVIAL PLAINS

*Ennis, Mont. (well-defined fan)
Santaquin, Utah (several small fans)
Cucamonga and San Bernardino, Calif. (piedmont alluvial plain)
Unionville, Nev. (pied. alluvial plain; many fan heads)

LAKE PLAINS

Grand Forks, N.D. (flat)
Wheaton, Minn. (beach ridges)
Merrill, Mich. (slightly dissected)
Perrinton, Mich. (margin and outlet)

COASTAL PLAINS

Limerick, Ga. (low, swampy)
Lake Drummond, Va.–N.C. (broad swamp)
Nixonville, S.C. (swampy; low terrace)
White Lake, N.C. (terrace, upland swamps)

GLACIALLY MODIFIED PLAINS

TILL PLAINS

Gilman, Wis. (undulating; swampy; small moraines)
Perry, Ia. (smooth; well-drained)

Lastrup, Minn. (undulating)

Beaver Dam, Wis. (drumlins)

MARGINAL MORAINES

Vergas and Pelican Rapids, Minn. (broad rough moraine)

Noonan, N.Dak. (broad moraine)

Alma, Mich. (narrow and low; lake plain)

Arrowsmith, Ill. (smooth, clayey moraine)

OUTWASH SURFACES

Three Rivers, Mich. (with moraine)

Schoolcraft, Mich. (pitted; with moraine)

Delavan and Manito, Ill. (broad; terraces; sand hills)

Saponac, Me. (esker)

PLAINS AFFECTED BY UNDERGROUND SOLUTION

Interlachen, Fla. (large sinks, lakes)

*Mammoth Cave, Ky. (sinkholes on plains and in hills)

Glendale, Fla. (swampy depressions, surface streams)

Holt, Fla. (solution valleys, springs)

PLAINS AFFECTED BY WIND

WIND-BLOWN SAND

*Ashby, Neb. (clumped sand hills)

Crescent Lake, Neb. (low sand hills)

Ogilby, Calif. (strip of live dunes)

Holland, Mich. (large coastal dunes)

LOESS SURFACES

Utica, Neb. (smooth depositional surface; dissected edges)

St. Francis, Kan. (depositional surface; much dissection)

Broken Bow SW, Neb. (1:24,000) (sharply dissected)

HILLS AND MOUNTAINS

STREAM-ERODED; LITTLE STRUCTURAL CONTROL

*Dutchman Butte, Ore. (high relief; mature)

Round Spring, Mo. (moderate relief; mature)

Sparta, Wis. (moderate relief; late mature)

Cuny Table West, S.Dak. (1:24,000) (badlands)

STREAM-ERODED; STRUCTURAL CONTROL EVIDENT

*Orbisonia, Pa. (smooth monoclinal ridges)

*Waldron, Ark. (irregular monoclinal ridges)

*Maverick Spring, Wyo. (1:24,000) (eroded structural dome)

Navajo Mountain, Utah–Ariz. (laccolith; joint control of erosion)

FAULT SCARPS

Hurricane, Utah (relatively undissected scarp)

Mount Whitney, Calif. (1:125,000) (high dissected scarp)

Mount Tom, Calif. (high dissected scarp)

Logan, Utah (1:125,000) (high straight scarp)

MODIFIED BY CONTINENTAL GLACIATION

*Old Speck Mountain, Me. (smoothed slopes)

*Monadnock, N.H. (smoothed knobs; ponds; swamps)

*Ithaca West, N.Y. (1:24,000) (smooth slopes; lake)

West Point, N.Y. (smoothed forms; lakes; water gap)

MOUNTAIN VALLEY GLACIERS

Cordova C-3 and Cordova C-4, Alaska (large glaciers; medial moraines)

Seldonia D-1 and Seldonia D-2, Alaska (ice field and many ice tongues)

Mount Rainier, Wash. (1:125,000) (radial system on volcanic cone)

Fremont Peak, Wyo. (largest system in U.S. Rockies)

MOUNTAINS MODIFIED BY VALLEY
GLACIATION

Mount Goddard and Mount Tom, Calif.
(cirques, troughs; moraines; hornlike peaks)

*Holden, Wash. (troughs; small cirques; small
glaciers)

*Holy Cross, Colo. (cirques; troughs; moraine
loop)

Glacier National Park, Mont. (1:125,000)
(cirques; troughs; sharp peaks and ridges;
lakes)

VOLCANIC CONES

Lassen Volcanic National Park, Calif. (cones;
flows)

Amboy Crater, Calif. (cinder cone; flow)

*Umnak, Alaska (1:250,000) (huge caldera;
glaciated cones)

TABLELANDS

UPLANDS AND VALLEYS

Hatch Point, Utah (broad upland; cliffs;
canyons)

*Portage, Mont. (low; narrow valleys)

Grand Canyon National Park, Ariz. (2 sheets)
(great canyon)

Mouth of Dark Canyon, Utah (several canyons)

ESCARPMENTS AND OUTLIERS

Boot Mesa and Agathla Peak, Ariz. (escarpment
and many outliers)

The Spur, Utah (escarpment and outliers)

*Anvil Points, Colo. (1:24,000) (high, dis-
sected escarpment)

Promontory Butte, Ariz. (high, dissected escarpment)

PLAINS WITH HILLS
OR MOUNTAINS

EROSIONAL VARIETIES

*Warm Springs, Ga. (residual ridges; rolling
plain)

Greenville, S.C. (residual mountain; rolling
plain)

Saponac, Me. (residual mountains; glaciated)

Cooperton, Okla. (exhumed granite knobs)

TECTONICALLY PRODUCED VARIETIES

*Antelope Peak, Ariz. (isolated peaks; pedi-
ments)

Sonoma Range, Nev. (1:125,000) (basin and
range)

*Bray, Calif. (volcanic cones on plains)

Ship Rock, N.M. (volcanic neck; dikes)

COASTAL FEATURES

ESTUARIES AND BAYS

Kilmarnock, Va. (branching estuaries; bottom
contours)

Empire and Coos Bay, Ore. (large estuary)

Foley and Ft. Barrancas, Ala.–Fla. (large
branching estuary)

Boothbay, Me. (drowned glaciated coast)

FIORDS (all sheets have bottom contours)

Kodiak B-6 and Kodiak C-6, Alaska (basins;
sills; moraines)

Seldovia B-2 and Seldovia C-2, Alaska (branching)

Blying Sound D-8, Alaska (large; sill; glaciers)

SEA CLIFFS AND TERRACES

Orick, Calif. (cliffs; bay bars; beach)

Pt. Reyes, Calif. (high cliffs; rocky islets)

Suffolk and Smithfield, Va. (3 terrace levels)

Limerick, Hinesville, and Glennville, Ga. (3
terrace levels)

BEACHES AND BARS

Edgartown, Mass. (1:31,680) (bay bars; hook)

Eureka, Calif. (large bay bar; inlet)

Toms River, N.J. (offshore bar; inlets)

Potrero Cortado, Tex. (broad, duned offshore
bar)

Index

Map Section

AVERAGE ANNUAL PRECIPITATION

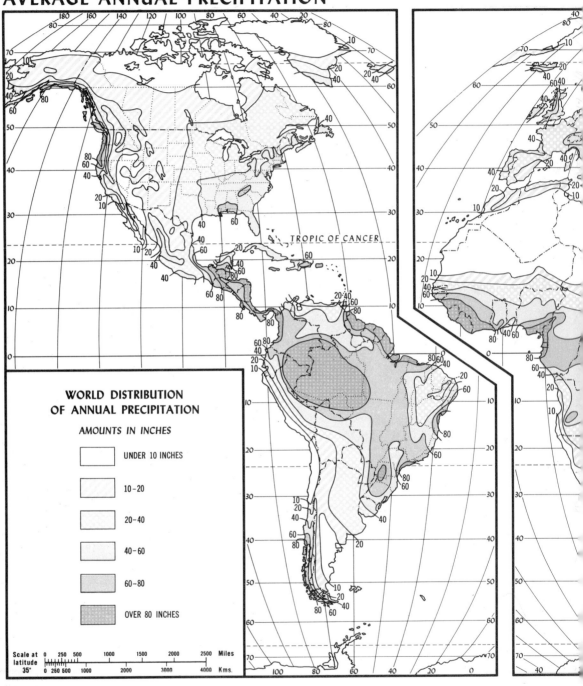

TROPIC OF CANCER

**WORLD DISTRIBUTION
OF ANNUAL PRECIPITATION**

AMOUNTS IN INCHES

- UNDER 10 INCHES
- 10 – 20
- 20 – 40
- 40 – 60
- 60 – 80
- OVER 80 INCHES

Scale at latitude 35°

0 250 500 1000 1500 2000 2500 Miles

0 250 500 1000 2000 3000 4000 Kms.

1

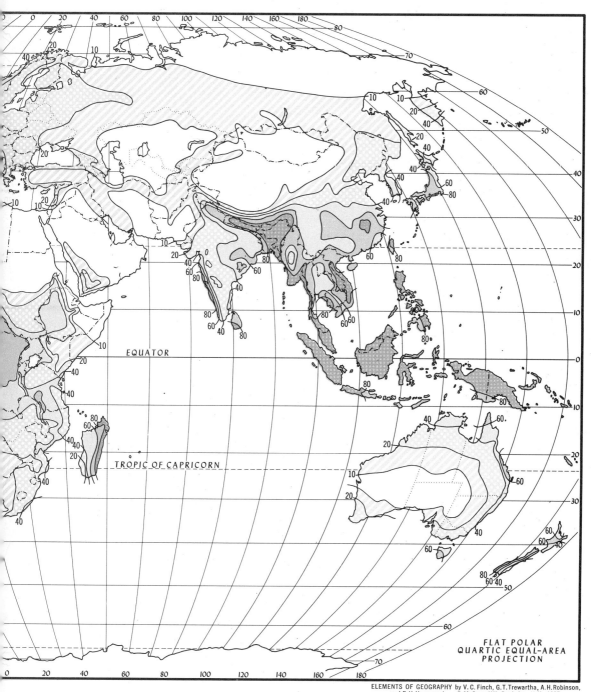

0 20 40 60 80 100 120 140 160 180

80
70
60

10 10
20
40
50
40
40
40 60
80
40 40

80
70

60
20
10
10

40
10
20 40
60 80
60
80

EQUATOR

80
80
40
60 40
80
80

80
60 60

80

40
40
20

80
60 40 40
20

TROPIC OF CAPRICORN

80
60
60
60 80
40 40
50
60

10

30

20

10

0

10

20

30

40 60
20 60
10
20

40
60

80
60 40

FLAT POLAR
QUARTIC EQUAL-AREA
PROJECTION

60

70

0 20 40 60 80 100 120 140 160 180

ELEMENTS OF GEOGRAPHY by V.C. Finch, G.T.Trewartha, A.H.Robinson,
and E.H.Hammond.   © McGraw-Hill Book Co., N.Y., 1957.

TERRAIN OF THE EARTH

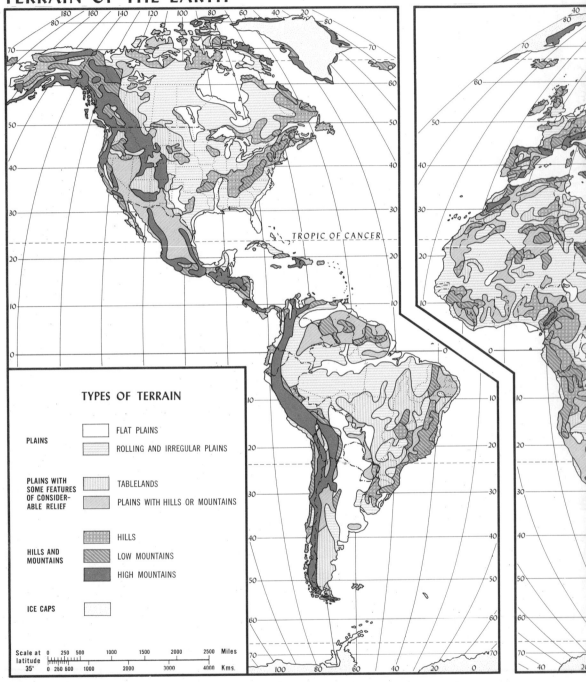

TROPIC OF CANCER

TYPES OF TERRAIN

PLAINS
- FLAT PLAINS
- ROLLING AND IRREGULAR PLAINS

PLAINS WITH SOME FEATURES OF CONSIDERABLE RELIEF
- TABLELANDS
- PLAINS WITH HILLS OR MOUNTAINS

HILLS AND MOUNTAINS
- HILLS
- LOW MOUNTAINS
- HIGH MOUNTAINS

ICE CAPS

Scale at latitude 35°
0   250 500   1000   1500   2000   2500 Miles
0 250 600 1000   2000   3000   4000 Kms.

3

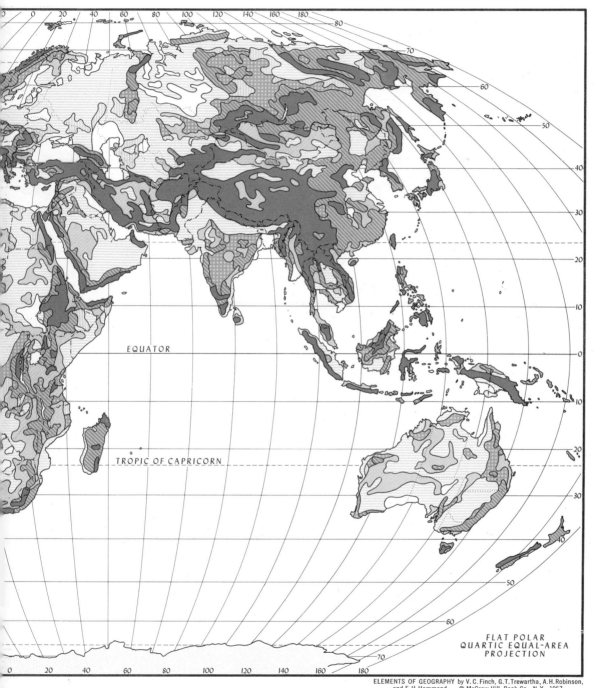

0 20 40 60 80 100 120 140 160 180

80

70

60

50

40

30

20

10

0

10

20

30

40

50

EQUATOR

TROPIC OF CAPRICORN

0 20 40 60 80 100 120 140 160 180

FLAT POLAR
QUARTIC EQUAL-AREA
PROJECTION

ELEMENTS OF GEOGRAPHY by V. C. Finch, G.T.Trewartha, A.H.Robinson,
and E.H.Hammond.   © McGraw-Hill Book Co., N.Y., 1957.

LITHIC REGIONS

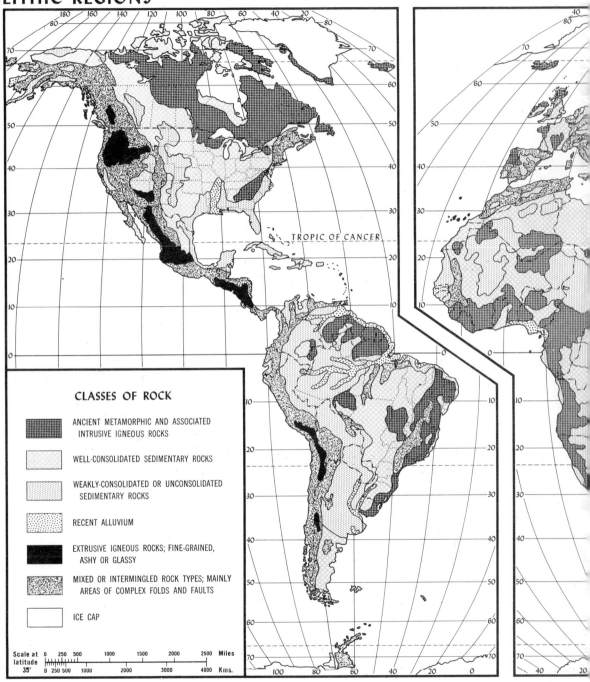

CLASSES OF ROCK

ANCIENT METAMORPHIC AND ASSOCIATED INTRUSIVE IGNEOUS ROCKS

WELL-CONSOLIDATED SEDIMENTARY ROCKS

WEAKLY-CONSOLIDATED OR UNCONSOLIDATED SEDIMENTARY ROCKS

RECENT ALLUVIUM

EXTRUSIVE IGNEOUS ROCKS; FINE-GRAINED, ASHY OR GLASSY

MIXED OR INTERMINGLED ROCK TYPES; MAINLY AREAS OF COMPLEX FOLDS AND FAULTS

ICE CAP

Scale at latitude 35°

| 0 | 250 | 500 | 1000 | 1500 | 2000 | 2500 | Miles |
| 0 | 250 | 500 | 1000 | 2000 | 3000 | 4000 | Kms. |

TROPIC OF CANCER

4

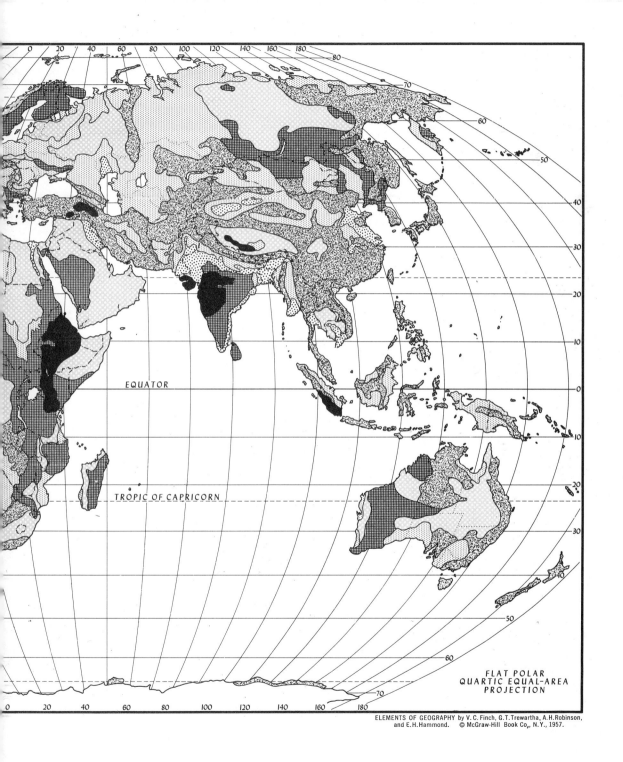

0 20 40 60 80 100 120 140 160 180

80

70

60

50

40

30

20

10

EQUATOR

0

TROPIC OF CAPRICORN

10

20

30

50

60

70

FLAT POLAR
QUARTIC EQUAL-AREA
PROJECTION

0 20 40 60 80 100 120 140 160 180

ELEMENTS OF GEOGRAPHY by V.C. Finch, G.T. Trewartha, A.H. Robinson, and E.H. Hammond.   © McGraw-Hill Book Co,, N.Y., 1957.

NATURAL VEGETATION

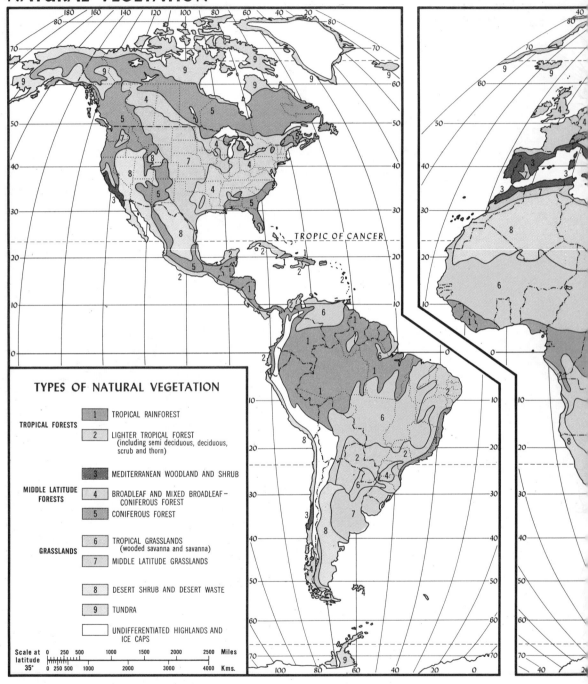

TROPIC OF CANCER

TYPES OF NATURAL VEGETATION

TROPICAL FORESTS

| 1 | TROPICAL RAINFOREST |
| 2 | LIGHTER TROPICAL FOREST (including semi deciduous, deciduous, scrub and thorn) |

MIDDLE LATITUDE FORESTS

3	MEDITERRANEAN WOODLAND AND SHRUB
4	BROADLEAF AND MIXED BROADLEAF– CONIFEROUS FOREST
5	CONIFEROUS FOREST

GRASSLANDS

6	TROPICAL GRASSLANDS (wooded savanna and savanna)
7	MIDDLE LATITUDE GRASSLANDS
8	DESERT SHRUB AND DESERT WASTE
9	TUNDRA
	UNDIFFERENTIATED HIGHLANDS AND ICE CAPS

Scale at latitude 35°

| 0 | 250 | 500 | 1000 | 1500 | 2000 | 2500 | Miles |
| 0 | 250 500 | 1000 | 2000 | 3000 | 4000 | Kms. |

5

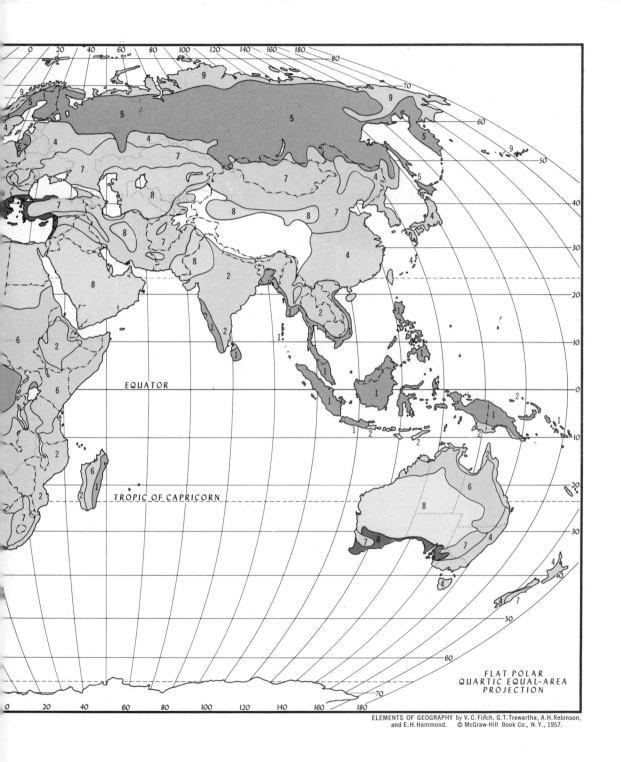

EQUATOR

TROPIC OF CAPRICORN

FLAT POLAR
QUARTIC EQUAL-AREA
PROJECTION

ELEMENTS OF GEOGRAPHY by V.C. Finch, G.T. Trewartha, A.H. Robinson,
and E.H. Hammond.   © McGraw-Hill Book Co., N.Y., 1957.

DISTRIBUTION OF SOILS

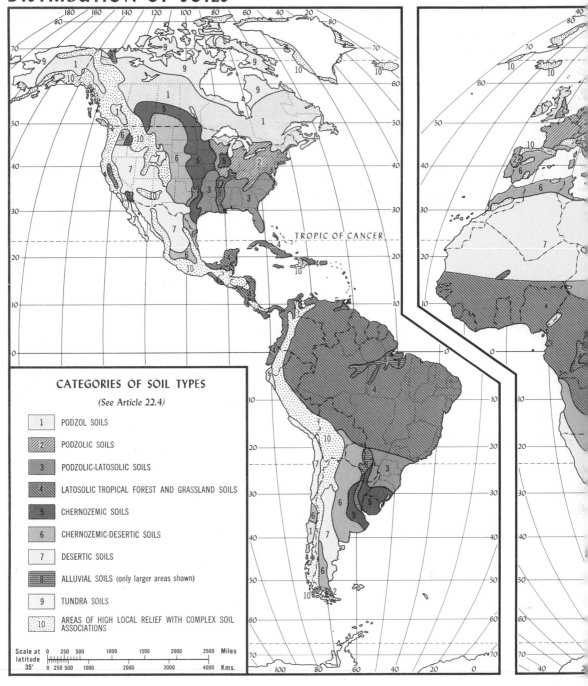

CATEGORIES OF SOIL TYPES

(See Article 22.4)

1	PODZOL SOILS
2	PODZOLIC SOILS
3	PODZOLIC-LATOSOLIC SOILS
4	LATOSOLIC TROPICAL FOREST AND GRASSLAND SOILS
5	CHERNOZEMIC SOILS
6	CHERNOZEMIC-DESERTIC SOILS
7	DESERTIC SOILS
8	ALLUVIAL SOILS (only larger areas shown)
9	TUNDRA SOILS
10	AREAS OF HIGH LOCAL RELIEF WITH COMPLEX SOIL ASSOCIATIONS

Scale at latitude 35°

Miles: 0 250 500 1000 1500 2000 2500

Kms.: 0 250 500 1000 2000 3000 4000

TROPIC OF CANCER

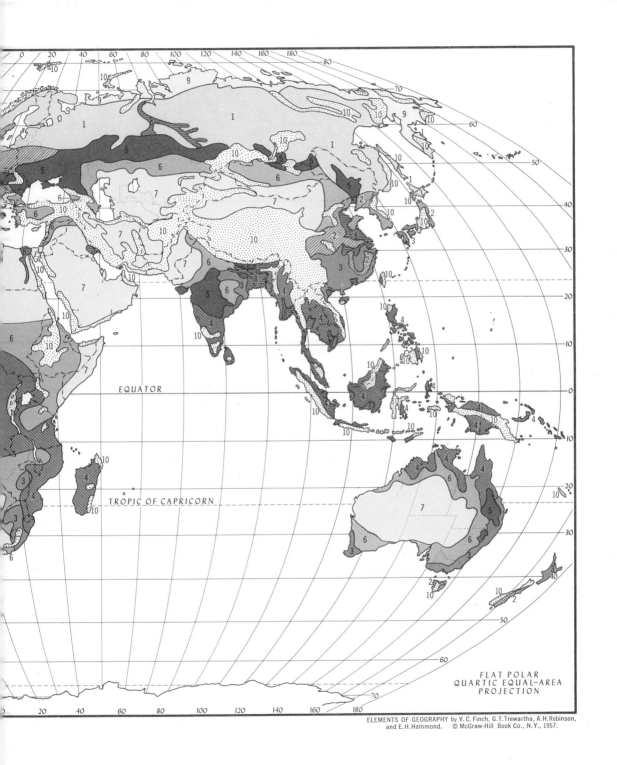

EQUATOR

TROPIC OF CAPRICORN

FLAT POLAR
QUARTIC EQUAL–AREA
PROJECTION

ELEMENTS OF GEOGRAPHY by V.C. Finch, G.T.Trewartha, A.H.Robinson,
and E.H.Hammond.   © McGraw-Hill Book Co., N.Y., 1957.

DISTRIBUTION OF POPULATION

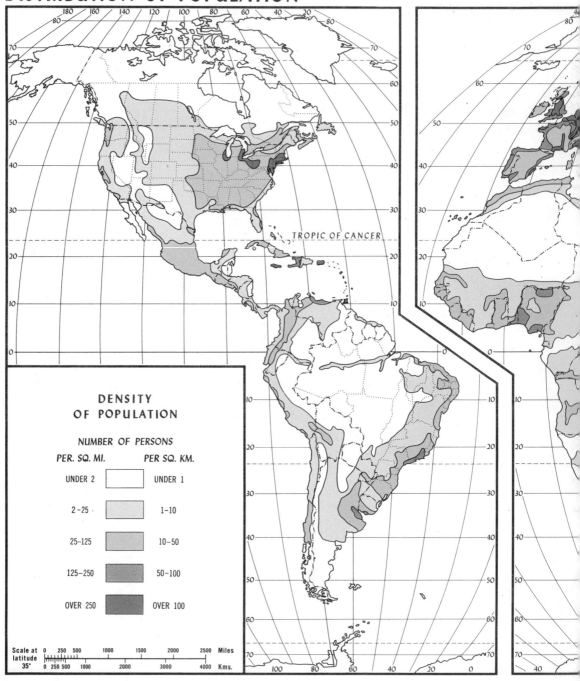

DENSITY OF POPULATION

NUMBER OF PERSONS

PER. SQ. MI.		PER SQ. KM.
UNDER 2		UNDER 1
2–25		1–10
25–125		10–50
125–250		50–100
OVER 250		OVER 100

TROPIC OF CANCER

Scale at latitude 35°

| 0 | 250 | 500 | 1000 | 1500 | 2000 | 2500 | Miles |
| 0 | 250 500 | | 1000 | 2000 | 3000 | 4000 | Kms. |

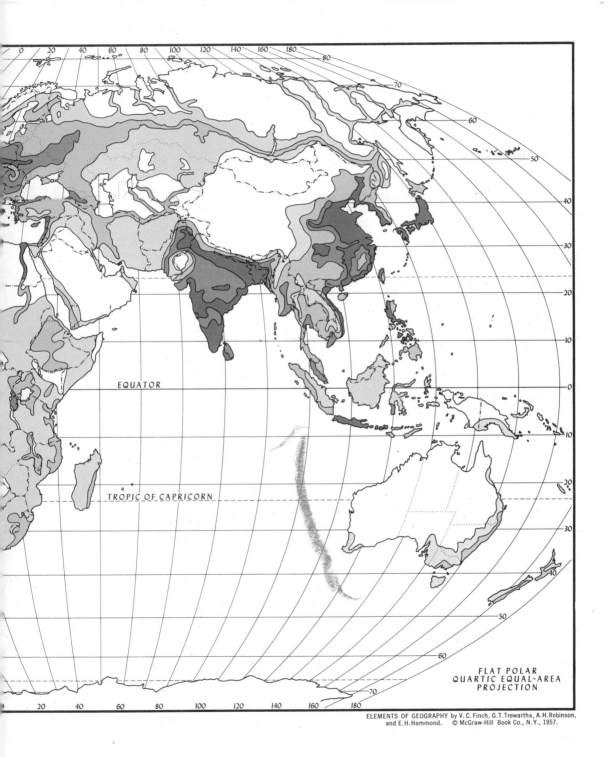

EQUATOR

TROPIC OF CAPRICORN

FLAT POLAR
QUARTIC EQUAL-AREA
PROJECTION

ELEMENTS OF GEOGRAPHY by V.C. Finch, G.T. Trewartha, A.H. Robinson, and E.H. Hammond.   © McGraw-Hill Book Co., N.Y., 1957.

AGRICULTURAL TYPES AND REGIONS

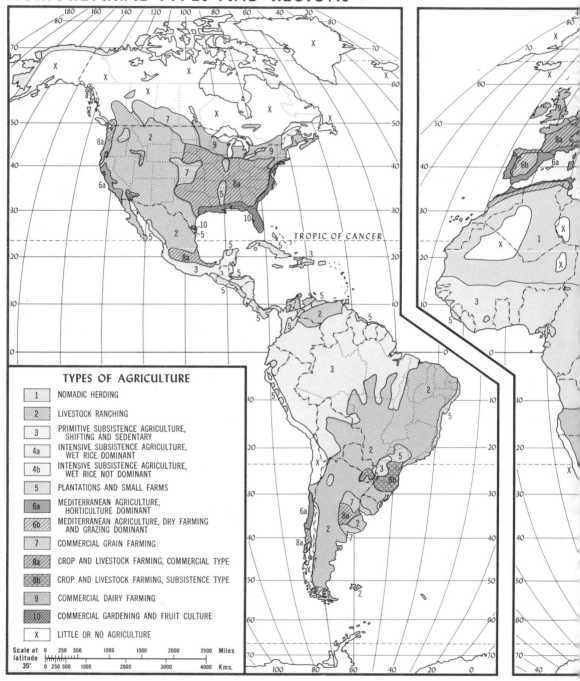

TROPIC OF CANCER

TYPES OF AGRICULTURE

1	NOMADIC HERDING
2	LIVESTOCK RANCHING
3	PRIMITIVE SUBSISTENCE AGRICULTURE, SHIFTING AND SEDENTARY
4a	INTENSIVE SUBSISTENCE AGRICULTURE, WET RICE DOMINANT
4b	INTENSIVE SUBSISTENCE AGRICULTURE, WET RICE NOT DOMINANT
5	PLANTATIONS AND SMALL FARMS
6a	MEDITERRANEAN AGRICULTURE, HORTICULTURE DOMINANT
6b	MEDITERRANEAN AGRICULTURE, DRY FARMING AND GRAZING DOMINANT
7	COMMERCIAL GRAIN FARMING
8a	CROP AND LIVESTOCK FARMING, COMMERCIAL TYPE
8b	CROP AND LIVESTOCK FARMING, SUBSISTENCE TYPE
9	COMMERCIAL DAIRY FARMING
10	COMMERCIAL GARDENING AND FRUIT CULTURE
X	LITTLE OR NO AGRICULTURE

Scale at latitude 35°

| 0 | 250 | 500 | 1000 | 1500 | 2000 | 2500 | Miles |
| 0 | 250 | 500 | 1000 | 2000 | 3000 | 4000 | Kms. |